20 June 2003

To

Bi

You

Best wishes,

Jeff Kent

The Mysterious Double Sunset

Jeff Kent

Witan Books

Jeff Kent was born in 1951 and educated at Hanley High School in Stoke-on-Trent. He gained a second-class honours degree in International Relations from London University in 1973 and has lectured at several colleges in North Staffordshire.

He is a prolific writer on a variety of subjects and has previously published nine books: *The Rise And Fall Of Rock*; *Principles Of Open Learning*; *The Last Poet: The Story Of Eric Burdon*; *Back To Where We Once Belonged!: Port Vale Promotion Chronicle 1988-1989*; *The Valiants' Years: The Story Of Port Vale*; *Port Vale Tales*; *The Port Vale Record 1879-1993*; *Port Vale Personalities: A Biographical Dictionary of Players, Officials and Supporters* and *The Potteries Derbies*.

Jeff was the editor of and the main contributor to *The Mercia Manifesto: A Blueprint For The Future Inspired By The Past* and *A Draft Constitution For Mercia*, which were produced by The Mercia Movement in 1997 and 2001 respectively. He also edited Denis Dawson's autobiography, *Port Vale Grass Roots: From Supporter To Groundsman And Back Again* and was the historical adviser to the Port Vale video histories, *Up The Vale!: The Story of Port Vale FC* and *The Millennium Documentary*.

He was a pioneer of Green music, has performed benefit concerts for several environmental and humanitarian organisations and has released four albums: *Tales from the Land of the Afterglow, Parts 1 & 2*; *Port Vale Forever* and *Only One World*. Consequently, his biography has gained entry into the *International Who's Who In Music Volume Two: Popular Music*.

Jeff was the convener of the Confederation for Regional England from 1999 to 2000 and has been the co-ordinator of The Mercia Movement since its formation in 1993. In addition, he became the convener of the Mercian Constitutional Convention, which was established in 2001 to help determine the future of the English Midlands.

Witan Creations
2001 Main Catalogue

WTN 001 *Butcher's Tale/ Annie, With The Dancing Eyes* – Jeff Kent & The Witan (animal rights protest single), 1981 - £1.50 including p & p.

WTN 002 *The Rise And Fall Of Rock* – Jeff Kent (484-page critical Rock music history, 56 photographs), 1983 - £7 including p & p.

WTN 024 *Port Vale Forever* – Jeff Kent (10-track first ever football club album, with songbook), 1992 - £5 including p & p.

WTN 025 *The Port Vale Record 1879-1993* – Jeff Kent (292-page statistical compilation, 60 photographs), 1993 - £14.10 including p & p.

WTN 027 *The Mercia Manifesto: A Blueprint For The Future Inspired By The Past* – The Mercia Movement (128-page radical political manifesto), 1997 - £7.80 including p & p.

WTN 028 *The Man Who Sank The Titanic?: The Life And Times Of Captain Edward J. Smith* – Gary Cooper (180-page biography of the merchant navy's most controversial captain, 70 photographs), 1998 - £13.10 including p & p.

WTN 029 *The Potteries Derbies* – Jeff Kent (208-page history of the clashes between Stoke City and Port Vale, 57 photographs), 1998 - £14.10 including p & p.

WTN 030 *Only One World* – Jeff Kent (13-track environmental concept CD), 2000 - £7.75 including p & p.

WTN 032 *A Draft Constitution For Mercia* – The Mercia Movement (20-page draft constitution for an independent Midlands), 2001 - £1.50 including p & p.

The Mysterious Double Sunset

First published in December 2001 by Witan Books, Cherry Tree House, 8 Nelson Crescent, Cotes Heath, via Stafford, ST21 6ST, England. Tel. (01782) 791673.

WTN 033

ISBN 0 9529152 5 1

A CIP record for this book is available from the British Library.

Design and cover concept: Jeff Kent.
Cover artwork: Ken Longmore.
Editorial adviser: Rosalind Kent.
Main research: Jeff Kent, Roy Parker, Kevin Kilburn, Professor Richard Stephenson and Cyril Kent.
Printed and bound by: PKA Print & Design, 5 & 7 Dunning Street, Tunstall, Stoke-on-Trent, ST6 5AP. Tel. (01782) 575280.

Dedicated to the memory of Paul Doherty (1947-1997)

ACKNOWLEDGEMENTS

I should like to express my thanks to the following people and organisations for their invaluable assistance, not credited elsewhere, in the production of this book: Bernice Allman, Ashbourne Library, Ian Bailey, Harry Ball, John Band, Reg Barks, Chris Barlow, Richard Baynes, Brenda Beniston, Roy Beniston, Elizabeth Ann Biddulph, Harold Bode, Jean Bode, Tony Bode, Bob Booth, Cathy Braddock, The British Library, Chris Brown, Linda Brown, Joe Buchdahl, Colin Burgess, Buxton Library, Cardiff Central Library, Geoff Channon, Lesley Channon, Peter Chimes, Rosalind Chimes, Tim Cockin, Congleton History Society, Congleton Library, John Cooper, Rob Cotterill, Graham Cranfield, David Dodd, Chris Doherty, Linda Doherty, Paul Doherty, Tim Duffin, Paul Farrington, Frank J. Gent, Frank Grayson, Peter Graystone, David Gregory, Julie Grime, Carl Hambleton, Susan Hamilton, Hanley Library, Cath Hayes, Dr James L. Hilton, Philip Holland, Phil Jackson, Anne Jepson, Keele University Library, Mick Keeling, Jackie King, Samantha Lawton, Leek Library, *Leek Post & Times*, Ken Longmore, Ray Lovatt, Macclesfield Library, Steve McQuade, Gerald Mee, Robert Milner, Doug Moller, Dr Patrick Moore, Cherry Moss, Asher Mupasi, Dorothy Newall, Newcastle-under-Lyme Library, Reverend Matthew Parker, Doug Pickford, Nigel Pickford, Ray Poole, Ros Prince, Dave Randle, Michael Raven, William Salt Library, Phil Savage, *The Sentinel*, Mike Shaw, Andrew Shipley, Linda Skellam, Tony Smith, Stafford Library, Staffordshire Record Office, Allan Staples, Susan Taylor, Cathryn Walton, Chris Wardle, Doreen Watts, Nigel Webberley, Robert Webberley, Albert Williams, Wendy Willshaw and Barry Woodcock.

ILLUSTRATION CREDITS

Illustrations were kindly supplied by the following:
Gerald Mee – front cover, 10 (i.); Chris Doherty – back cover, 2, 14 - 19, 22 - 26; Jeff Kent – 1, 6, 20, 21; Kevin Kilburn – 3-5; Leek Library 7, 8; Leek Town Council – 9; John Cunningham – 10 (ii.); Harold Bode – 11; Roy Parker – 12, 13; *The Sentinel* – 27; Geoff Channon – 28.

Contents

Preface

When the *Evening Sentinel* came through the letter box on Wednesday 21 June 1972, I eagerly picked it up and immediately turned to the back page to see whether Port Vale, whom I avidly supported, had signed any new players. They hadn't and I was rather disappointed at the lack of news. With nothing better to do, I browsed the rest of the newspaper, without any expectations of finding anything particularly interesting. However, on page five was an article which was to change my life.

My eye caught a stirring headline, which read: 'LEEK SUNSET SPECTACULAR IF WEATHER CLEARS.' Excited by this, I quickly investigated the report beneath, which stated that, 'It happens only at Leek on the longest day of the year when the sun first sinks down behind the top of The Cloud and then reappears to set again on the horizon.' My emotions were by then on fire and I set off soon afterwards in my dilapidated Mini to experience this incredible phenomenon.

Although a sizable number of people gathered for the occasion in St Edward's churchyard that evening, the supposedly spectacular event did not occur, but there was no shortage of explanations offered by various members of the assembled crowd to account for, apparently, a series of recent failures. This was a situation that became very familiar to me as I made a vain pilgrimage to the churchyard on the summer solstice seventeen times during the following nineteen years. I still believed in the double sunset despite these endless failures, but, in mid-June 1990, I began to think about investigating the mysterious nonevent, with a view to publishing my findings.

The fundamental snag was that no-one I spoke to presented any convincing ideas as to why the phenomenon had not been witnessed for so long and, as I had never seen it myself, I found it difficult to explain why it no longer seemed to occur. I made yet another apparently disappointing visit to the churchyard on 20 June 1990, when any prospect of a double sunset was ruined by a bank of cloud on the horizon, but, surprisingly, that evening marked the turning point in my connection to this enigmatic event.

I found myself in conversation with an unusual-looking small man, who had long white hair and a grey beard. His name was Roy Parker and he claimed not only to have seen the double sunset, but also to have photographed it from Lowe Hill, on the outskirts of the town, on 29 June the previous year! He had discovered gold, but revealed its whereabouts in a rather nonchalant manner. Three nights later, thanks to Roy, I saw my first double sunset and, emotionally charged by seventeen years of consistent disappointments, my excitement was absolutely uncontained!

The experience of finally seeing the event for myself, combined with Roy's enthusiasm for the phenomenon, rapidly turned my traditional spiritual quest into a real investigation of the double sunset, its history and its occurrence, with the aim of removing it from the realm of myth and legend, into which it had descended, and restoring it to the real world built upon actual fact and data. The project had now been fully formulated and born.

With great enthusiasm, Roy and I investigated the double sunset events at an increasing number of locations through a lengthening period of the year and our understanding of the phenomenon consequently grew accordingly. Although our recorded data rapidly expanded into a considerable dossier, our observations were, of course, weather dependent and the elements frequently left us frustrated. Days of double sunset hunting therefore turned into weeks, then months and finally years, before sufficient information was finally accumulated to enable a, hopefully, definitive account of the phenomenon to be written and published.

Contrary to our wildest expectations, double sunsets proved to be both commonplace and occurring from more than one location at a time, so Roy and I eventually decided to conduct independent investigations in order to cover the ground more quickly. Consequently, my pursuit of the project became essentially solitary, although my interest in it never waned.

In 1996, I acquired a new companion on some of my visits to double sunset viewing points when Chris Doherty, who had photographed a solar eclipse in the South China Sea, eagerly joined me in order to capture on film vital sequences of the occurrence at key times of the year. As might be imagined, these were extremely difficult to obtain, requiring near perfect weather conditions and exactly the right film exposure, which was gradually deduced. Subsequently, Chris took a series of splendid photographs of the phenomenon, a selection of which is printed in this book.

After the bulk of the necessary observations had been successfully undertaken, my research took me to a whole series of libraries in Staffordshire and Cheshire where I studied the available local newspaper archives, invariably kept on microfilm, as well as all the texts I could find that had even the vaguest connection to the phenomenon and a series of relevant maps. I also conducted interviews with a variety of people who either claimed to have seen a double sunset or had information to offer regarding its occurrence. In addition, I discovered that Kevin Kilburn, the secretary of the North West Group of Astronomical Societies, was independently researching the phenomenon and his work and publications fortunately enabled this book to emphasise the astro-geometry of the occurrence considerably more than I had originally envisaged. Furthermore, I acquired a scientific adviser in Professor Richard Stephenson of the University of Durham, on the recommendation of the famous astronomer, Dr Patrick Moore, and it was my extremely good fortune that he enthusiastically contributed his skills to the production of this book. Finally, my father, Cyril Kent, assisted in the project research as usual, whilst my wife, Rosalind, scrutinised the completed text with her normal rigour.

I hope that this book will prove to be both informative and readable and I would be indebted to anyone who notifies me of any errors that it contains or any important details that are absent (for example, relating to other double sunsets), which I can consider for a future edition.

Jeff Kent,
Cotes Heath,
October 2001.

1 The Double Sunset Astronomy

In northeast Staffordshire is situated the small town of Leek. Although unspectacular in size, it has an impressive setting, especially if approached from the southwest on the A 53 from Newcastle-under-Lyme and Stoke-on-Trent. From the brow of Ladderedge, a glorious view unfolds, with Leek nestled in a hollow below and the stark Millstone Grit outcrops of Ramshaw Rocks, Hen Cloud and The Roaches dominating the landscape beyond. Towards the north of the town can be seen the outline of the tower of The Parish Church of Saint Edward the Confessor.

The church stands at an elevated point (approximately 198 metres above sea level), which retains a largely open aspect to the north and northwest, with little interference from buildings. On a reasonably clear day, a fairly typical Millstone Grit Pennine hill, with a shallow dip slope and a steep scarp slope, can be seen from the churchyard, 6½ miles to the northwest. This is The Cloud, which, it is generally believed, aptly took its name from the Anglo-Saxon word *clud*, meaning *a rock*. Indeed, it is an eminent feature of the landscape, especially when viewed from the west and east, and rises sharply from the lowlands of Cheshire. Almost immediately to the north of The Cloud's 343.77 metre summit, the land falls away rapidly towards the Cheshire Plain and it is this happy topographical accident that enables Leek's mysterious double sunset to occur.

The Cloud is well, but not perfectly, shaped to produce this extraordinary phenomenon when it interacts with the setting sun on the summer solstice, as traditionally viewed from St Edward's churchyard and its vicinity. The hill dips gently to the south, which enables the whole of the sun to disappear before the steeper, north-facing slope allows part of the disc to re-emerge. This north-south bias of The Cloud therefore enables the setting sun to intersect its northern edge to produce the midsummer occurrence. In addition, as observed from Leek, the hill is of a sufficient size in relation to that of the sun for the phenomenon to be clearly viewable, although the churchyard is rather distant and therefore not ideally placed. However, despite the existence of myths to the contrary, the coincidence of the geometric angles of the setting sun and the contours of The Cloud from this observation position at this time of year do not allow the sun to re-emerge fully after its initial disappearance.

The double sunset is an unusual and exciting, but certainly not unique, phenomenon, which has long been visible or theoretically visible from St Edward's churchyard, although it has not been witnessed from this location in recent years. The lack of contemporary successful sightings has considerably dulled the public memory as to precisely what transpires during the event, so much so that nowadays many more mythical and highly erroneous descriptions of the occurrence are in circulation than accurate versions of the phenomenon. Even more prevalent are a series of completely mistaken ideas, which are projected, without hard facts to support them, as explanations to account for the recent non-observation of double sunsets from the churchyard. Therefore, it is imperative to give a graphic description of the double sunset as it should be seen, at least theoretically, from St Edward's churchyard on the summer solstice, currently 21 June, on which date it has been reliably witnessed.

From the churchyard, The Cloud is visible as a relatively small, but distinctive, feature on the landscape, appearing to be more remote than it actually is. It rises beyond the intervening ground as a ridge and an escarpment running broadly northwards. To the south or left of The Cloud's summit, the slope of the ridge is relatively gentle, but to the north or right of its peak, the ground falls away rapidly, so that the lower part of the scarp slope is obscured from view. As seen from the northeastern corner of the upper churchyard on a clear solstitial evening, the sun begins to set on the dip slope of The Cloud, just to the south or left of the summit, and disappears before it reaches the sharp face of Cloud End, with the whole of the disc becoming hidden by the hill. A small portion of the sun later reappears from the north or right of the scarp slope and is visible for a short period before setting for the second and final time on the horizon.

Even though the available evidence shows that the double sunset has not been observed from this location since 1977, it still happens every summer solstice from its whereabouts and/or its immediate vicinity. However, this situation is neither static nor permanent. In the distant past, the phenomenon did not occur from the vantage point of what eventually became St Edward's upper churchyard and it may well already have ceased to exist once more from that precise location. Therefore, the Leek double sunset is a transient phenomenon within geological time, but it is also an event in constant transition, even though it may not seem so from an individual human perspective.

The astro-geometry of the occurrence was little understood until an article entitled, *Dr Plot and the Amazing Double Sunset*, was published in volume 40 of the Royal Astronomical Society's *Astronomy & Geophysics* journal in February 1999. Its author, the experienced amateur astronomer, Kevin Kilburn, had acted as the president of Manchester Astronomical Society from 1978 to 1981 and 1983 to 1984 and had long been fascinated by the geometry of the solar system. However, in his feature, he applied his talents more specifically to Leek's astro-geographical phenomenon. Nevertheless, despite Kevin's very best efforts through his article and since, it might well be argued that many, if not most, aspects of the phenomenon remain barely comprehended, especially in lay circles. Irrespective of that, his document was one of the most significant reports ever produced on the double sunset and broke new ground.

The most important aspect of Kevin's pioneering work was a series of diagrams, which illustrated the interaction of the setting sun and The Cloud as observed from the site of St Edward's Church on the summer solstice in four separate years: 2700 B.C., 500 B.C., 2000 A.D. and 2500 A.D. Intriguingly, these depictions showed quite radically different outcomes, which were explained in the article:

'In August 1998 I began my own investigations from an astrogeometrical point of view . . .

I used Ordnance Survey data to determine the geographical relationship of the Cloud . . . as seen from the church . . . I computed elevations and azimuths and used them to construct a horizon profile . . .

I used astronomical software, tested for accuracy against documented historical observations, to "measure" sunsets back to prehistoric times and forwards into the future. Overlaying the precomputed track of the setting Sun onto the horizon profile allowed me to study the changing geometry of Leek sunsets, over a period of several thousand years, and to estimate when the phenomenon started and, indeed, when it will cease to be visible from the church.

In 2700 BC the setting Sun clipped the tip of the Cloud at the solstice before setting just north of the hill. The occulted sunset would then have been seen twice each year, before and again after the solstice. It would have occurred first as the sunset crept northwards along the horizon to the solstitial azimuth and then as it slid southwards. For a day or two either side of the solstice itself, the Sun would appear to set at the same point on the horizon, the summer standstill. By counting and averaging the few days between the two occultation periods, even poor weather would not have badly affected the prediction of the solstice.

These occultation periods became closer in time until, since about 500 BC, they have essentially coincided with the summer standstill . . . It is now almost coincident with the hill, and poor weather can make or break the chance of seeing the double sunset. It should be noted that since the mid-17th century, reduction of the obliquity of the ecliptic has essentially compensated for the truncation of the Cloud by quarrying – a nice coincidence for local observers.

Over the centuries the inexorably slow southward movement of the solstitial sunset will continue. Eventually, after about AD 2500, the Sun will not reappear beyond the hill having once set upon the summit. The double sunset will cease to be visible from Leek churchyard for more than 10 000 years.'

In summary, the diagrams show the sun almost overshooting The Cloud in 2700 B.C.; not quite entirely disappearing behind the hill in 500 B.C.; setting and re-emerging today and completely failing to reappear in 2500 A.D. It is important to note that the depiction for 2000 A.D. illustrates Kevin's calculation of what a spectator standing by the church, with a clear view of The Cloud, should see around sunset on the summer solstice.

However, although these carefully constructed diagrams represented the best that astro-geometry had yet offered to the public regarding the phenomenon, they are by no means infallible. For example, in the article, Kevin stated that the church was 208 metres above sea level, which figure he used for his calculations, whereas its actual height is approximately 198 metres. This difference is important and means that the outline of the hill in his diagrams is slightly lower than it should be. Therefore, the plotted profile of The Cloud needs to be raised accordingly, which has the effect of reducing the proportion of the sun reappearing in 2700 B.C., 500 B.C. and 2000 A.D. Indeed, as the amount of solar re-emergence is already so small on the diagram of the last date, redrawing the profile will produce a noticeable change, with even less of the sun reappearing.

Furthermore, other evidence presented in this book suggests that the double sunset may no longer be observable from the upper churchyard at all, even when The Cloud can clearly be seen on the horizon. It is well possible that the viewing window of the phenomenon has shifted on to the path running from the upper churchyard around the southeastern corner of the lower churchyard and along its eastern boundary. In addition, as Kevin came to realise, the church (and, even more so, the churchyard) covers too large an area to be regarded as a complete observational zone of the exact events depicted in his diagrams. Even at a distance of 6½ miles from The Cloud, minor alterations in the spectator's viewing position can lead to dramatically different results. Furthermore, as I argue later, I believe that Kevin's diagrams greatly exaggerate the impact of quarrying on the hill, as seen from Leek. It is my opinion that the summit of The Cloud remained at approximately the same height throughout the ages and that the profile of the hill was less angular than the first two plans depict.

It is most important to the understanding of the double sunset phenomenon to consider the factors and forces which led Kevin to construct his impressive diagrams in the first place. The occurrence is not a fixed event and this is primarily because we do not live in a static universe, but a dynamic one, which is forever changing.

As is common knowledge, the length of daylight varies everywhere in the United Kingdom according to the seasons. Romantic images abound in England of long summer evenings spent drinking in the beer garden of a canal-side pub and equally atmospheric ones of rare white Christmases spent huddling around a log fire with the curtains drawn to keep out the long, dark night. The reason for the variation in the length of day and night is that the earth is tilted on its axis, but is always inclined in the same direction. During the planet's annual orbit around the sun, the position of the tilt relative to the sun varies according to the precise point in the cycle and, as a result, different places in the world experience different amounts of daylight through the varying stages of the earth's journey.

According to this, the summer solstice (or longest day) currently occurs in the northern hemisphere on 21 June, when it is at its most tilted towards the sun, and the winter solstice (or shortest day) on 21 or 22 December when the reverse is true. In the southern hemisphere, the opposite situation applies. This in turn enables, at least theoretically, the double sunset to occur from the churchyard on and around the summer solstice when the sun reaches its maximum point north in relation to the earth in the annual cycle, which broadly conforms with the position of The Cloud on the horizon. After the solstice, the sun moves increasingly south along the back of the hill until it reaches its midwinter position before returning northwards once more and yet again raising hopes of a churchyard double sunset.

However, this has not always been the case because the angle of tilt of the earth's axis is not fixed and has varied over the last million years or so between approximately 22.07° and 24.44°. This change in the obliquity of the ecliptic is primarily caused by the perturbations of the other planets in the solar system, especially Jupiter because of its immense size. As a consequence, the earth's axis rolls gradually from its minimum angle of tilt to its maximum and back again over an average period of around 40,500 years.

The precise angle of tilt of the earth's axis in relation to the sun is of vital importance with regard to the double sunset phenomenon because it determines exactly where the sun sets on the horizon. The current tilt is approximately 23.439° and at this angle the double sunset occurs on the summer solstice as seen from the whereabouts of the northeastern corner of St Edward's upper churchyard. However, as Kevin's diagrams indicate, because the angle is constantly changing, even though extremely slowly, the position of the setting sun is also inexorably altering. In 2700 B.C., the angle was inclined at 23.998° and approximately produced the effect shown on the first of Kevin's diagrams. The tilt was angled at 23.757° in 500 B.C. to give the situation depicted on the second diagram, whilst the earth's axis will rotate at 23.374° in 2500 A.D. to create the position illustrated in his final drawing. Thus, as observed from this fixed point in the churchyard, the sostitial sunset has crept southwards along the northwestern horizon since 2700 B.C. and is continuing to do so.

The overall impact of the changing tilt of the earth's axis is to alter very gradually the viewing position of the observers of the double sunset gathered on the north wall of the upper churchyard. Kevin has calculated that the observation zone of the phenomenon is moving eastwards along the wall at a rate of about fourteen feet per century and therefore, in order to continue seeing the occurrence on the summer solstice, the spectators have no option except to keep pace with this astro-geographical spatial movement.

To show the relentless effects of time on the viewing window of the double sunset from the churchyard on the longest day, in March 2000 Kevin produced a plan of the area based on three separate observation dates and explained its implications as follows:

'Let's examine the geometry of the *reappearance* in more detail . . . the northern aspect of the hill is not vertical, it is largely concave and a line drawn across this hollow closely parallels the setting sun angle. By definition, to reappear, the sun must first disappear within this concavity. The depth of this concavity dictates the time span during which the disappearance-reappearance phenomenon can be observed from any fixed observation point within an observing 'window' in which the double sunset is clearly visible.

The depth of the concavity is about 6 arcminutes (360 arcseconds) and the obliquity is reducing by 47.7 arcseconds per century at right angles to it. So the double sunset lasts for about 750 years from any given place in the churchyard (360/47.7 centuries). Standing within this 'window' and looking towards the sunset and hill, the sun only just disappears and immediately reappears from the window's leading NE edge and from the SW trailing edge, the sun disappears and only a speck of reappearance is visible. At 10.5 km from the hill, the 'window' is about 35 metres (110 ft) wide and, owing to the changing obliquity of the ecliptic, has scanned slowly north-eastwards across the churchyard since the Iron Age. The trailing edge is now approaching the NE boundary wall and only a sliver of sun reappears.

In 1681, or thereabouts, the slim reappearance seen from the Doctor's [sic] Corner in 1975 would have been visible about 10.5 metres (34 ft) away, on a line towards the church. At that time, anywhere NE of this position would have shown rather more of the sun protruding against the hill profile than can theoretically be seen now.'

Kevin's plan specifically shows his projection of the entire observation window in the vicinity of the upper churchyard for 1 A.D., contained within two parallel northwest-southeast lines. The trailing edges of the viewing zones of 1681 and 1975 are depicted as further straight lines running in the same direction, with only part of their observation windows marked to the northeast. However, the real beauty of the map is that it allows the person studying it to project the viewing zones of all dates between 1 A.D. and 1975 and even beyond, simply by laying a ruler at right angles to the northwest-southeast window boundary lines and calculating what was, is or will be observed, when and from where. For example, the distance on the plan between the trailing edges of the viewing windows for 1 A.D. and 1681 is 176 millimetres, so, by halving that measurement, the trailing boundary of the observational zone of 841 A.D. can be plotted as a northwest-southeast line equidistant between and parallel to the two aforementioned lines. Thus the trailing edge of the viewing window of 841 cuts through the western end of the current church and just clips its south porch.

The precise methods which Kevin used to come to his conclusions were described in a letter sent to me on 7 May 2000:

'The problem in defining the limitations of the geometry of the Leek Double Sunset, as seen traditionally from the churchyard, is this: The reappearance is no longer visible, even from the Dr.'s [sic] Corner, so it is necessary to calculate what could be seen, trees permitting, and then try to extrapolate this calculation both backwards and forwards, hundreds of years, in time.

In 1998 I used Ordnance Survey maps and an astronomy computer program, '*Dance of the Planets*', (ARC Science Simulations Software, Denver, Colorado) to show that the solstitial double sunset has been visible from the churchyard since the Iron Age . . .

From the churchyard the hill is tiny, less than three-quarters of a degree high and comparable to the sun's diameter. It has been necessary to study this geometry in great detail. For verification purposes, a slide of the 1999 sunset of 20th June taken from midway along the church wall, showing the sun setting onto the hill, was projected onto graph paper and outlined in pencil. The azimuth and elevation of the trig. point on the Cloud, clearly visible on the photo, was calculated on a Microsoft Excel spreadsheet, from grid references taken from Ordnance Survey maps of the hill and church and taking into account the offset necessary to convert Grid N to True N and allowing for earth curvature and nominal atmospheric refraction.

Having only one reasonably accurate azimuth/elevation position, that of the trig. point on Bosley Cloud, the hill profile was calibrated further using an image of the lunar eclipse of 29th November, 1993, taken with the same 400mm lens. The apparent diameter of the moon was accurately known and gave a scale in two dimensions of 135mm = 0.505 degrees. Onto this was then overlaid the pre-calculated setting sun position, to compare actual observations with theoretical calculation. Recent attempts, to determine geographic positions using a Magellan GPS, global positioning system, proved to be very inferior to Ordnance Survey data, even when using up to ten satellites, but did allow some useful infilling of data points on the horizon profile. Even allowing for the de-restriction of GPS accuracy limitations on 1st May, 2000, GPS elevation positions are still not sufficiently accurate for these calculations.

But astro-geometry is now extremely predictable and sunset tracks were calculated to four decimal places for several specific years; 1999, 1681 (when Dr. Plot went to Leek) and for AD 1, using the on-line GROK Solar Calculator, at http://www.gcstudio.com/cgibin/sunpage. These were plotted onto the hill profile graphs.

From an estimate of the depth of the concavity of the northern slope of the hill, in which the elusive reappearance takes place and from the now known 47.7 arc-second/century reduction, moving at right angles to this depression, it was possible to determine that the reappearance could be seen from any given place in the churchyard within a 'window', about 34m (110ft) wide, which has scanned north-eastwards across the churchyard during the past 2500 years.

With this basic understanding of the geometry of the double sunset, it is possible to calculate, with reasonable accuracy, what was seen from any position within the churchyard at any time during the past two and a half thousand years.

Using data from the GROK Solar Calculator and the geometry taken from Ordnance Survey data, and from the 47.7 arc-second/century reduction in the obliquity of the ecliptic, it has been possible to calculate the progression of the 'window' across the churchyard. The hill is 10.5 km away from the church and the horizontal regression of the solstitial sunset is about 90 arc-seconds per century. This is the included angle of a long, thin triangle with the hill at its apex. From the churchyard the shadow of the hill, at a right angle to the sunset, moves NE by 3.66m/century (10 feet).

These calculations, still subject to refinement, show why the Leek double sunset has been visible from the church for so many centuries but also show why the phenomenon is now coming to an end.'

Despite, or even perhaps as a consequence of, the complexity of his research method, Kevin's conclusions as expressed in his map remain open to criticism, especially because observations of the double sunset on the summer solstice in 1977 suggest that the phenomenon had by then overshot the upper churchyard altogether. At present, this is not categorically confirmed, but, should it prove to be the case, it will mean that the trailing boundary line of at least the 1975 window was drawn somewhat too far southwest and will need to be readjusted accordingly. Indeed, it seems that this may well require to be done because the apparent discrepancy between the map and the 1977 report is most likely accounted for by the fact that Kevin believes his data to be positionally accurate only to within three or four metres.

On 11 April 2000, Kevin sent me three further diagrams depicting the interaction of the setting sun and The Cloud, entitled, *Leek Sunset showing the effect of changes in the Obliquity of the Ecliptic From St. Edward's churchyard*. The three dates on which the phenomenon was examined (2500 B.C., 1975 A.D. and 2200 A.D.) were entirely different ones from the four that he had considered in his *Astronomy & Geophysics* article, but there appeared to be little disparity between the solstitial effects of the two groups of diagrams and thus the events of the seven presented dates combined to produce a harmonised pattern.

Nevertheless, the three new diagrams contained an obvious and significant flaw in that the shape of The Cloud was different in each and, when applied, this would clearly have a notable impact on what could be observed during the sunsets in question. Kevin explained the reason for these varying profiles in a letter to me, dated 22 March 2001:

'The different Cloud shapes stem from my original Autumn 1998 calculations which were based on Ordnance Survey positions 'modified' to look similar to the 1738 profile and the present one. I now realise that the 1738 sketches in the Gentleman's Magazine were grossly exaggerated. The hill was never as pointed as it is shown there. The present profile is much as it has been in historical times. The idea that the demolition of Bully Thrumble [a significant landscape feature formerly on The Cloud] changed the profile drastically is, I believe, unsubstantiated.'

Therefore, the variation between the outline of The Cloud as portrayed in 2500 B.C. and 1975 A.D. was the result of Kevin's original interpretation of the impact of the quarrying of the hill during modern history. Clearly, this position is no longer adhered to by Kevin and, indeed, it is argued later in this book that it is far from conclusive that the shape of The Cloud, as seen from Leek, was considerably altered by these excavations. Furthermore, quarrying could not be held responsible for the discrepancies visible in Kevin's hill profiles for 1975 and 2200, which showed the latter as containing a significantly shallower scarp slope.

The uncertainty surrounding the accuracy of Kevin's conclusions has unfortunately been exacerbated by the research undertaken on the subject at my request by Professor F. Richard Stephenson of the University of Durham, who was specifically recommended to me as an expert on astro-geography by the legendary astronomer, Dr Patrick Moore. Part of Richard's brief was to give me a second opinion on Kevin's calculations and conclusions. On 15 September 2000, he sent me a letter discussing his findings, along with an amended copy of Kevin's diagrams, *Leek Sunset showing the effect of changes in the Obliquity of the Ecliptic From St. Edward's churchyard*. Richard had the following to say:

'I have plotted on the enclosed chart, in green, the path of the Sun's centre. The scale on the chart is 1 deg = 26.5 mm. Taking the solar semi-diameter as 0.26 deg (= 6.9 mm), I have marked in red on the enclosed diagram the path of the upper and lower solar limbs. Even allowing for the slight change in refraction with decreasing altitude, the curvature of these lines is virtually negligible [unlike those in Kevin's plans, which were slightly, but noticeably, curved]. You will see that I disagree somewhat with Mr Kilburn's calculations – but not by very much. In particular, less of the Sun would be visible after the first sunset in 1975 . . .

I have assumed the hill profile on the chart to be accurate. However, I estimated the angle of elevation of the Cloud from the church as 0.68 deg – equivalent to a height of 18 mm on the chart. This is significantly lower than that marked by Mr Kilburn (21 mm or 0.79 deg), and could materially affect the double sunset.'

Although the visual quality of Richard's diagrams was insufficient to allow them to be printed in this book, that pertaining to 1975 had important implications. It showed the sun setting slightly further south from the summit of The Cloud than was the case in Kevin's corresponding plan. Not only did this mean that significantly less of the disc would reappear from this specific viewing point after the initial sunset, but also that the observation window would be a little to the northeast of that suggested by Kevin. This is particularly instructive because that is exactly what the recorded evidence of the 1977 midsummer occurrence had indicated.

In addition, on 30 March 2001, Richard sent me a letter which included refined calculations, based on the height of the church being reduced from the 208 metres used by Kevin to 198 metres, as determined from the Ordnance Survey 1:1250 map, SJ9856. His conclusion was that the outline of The Cloud in Kevin's diagrams should be raised by a millimetre, which has the effect of reducing still further the degree of solar re-emergence in 1975 to the extent of raising the question as to whether it would be seen at all. Also, in a further communication, despatched on 11 April 2001, Richard expressed his concern that the profile of the hill on the three charts was 'very smooth' and pointed out that 'any rough features' on the outline of The Cloud might well affect the sun's reappearance. Although the hill is a small feature as observed from the churchyard, subtle differences in the landscape introduced or ignored by Kevin could actually have a decisive effect as to whether part of the sun would re-emerge or not in the 1975 diagram because the proportion depicted is so small to begin with.

Finally, on 23 May 2001, Richard made the key point that the diagrams only represent the position from the northeastern corner of the upper churchyard and not the whole of it, as is implied by the title of the drawings. The vital importance of his comment is well illustrated by the impact of spatial change on the leading and trailing edges of the viewing zone of the double sunset, where the slightest positional movement of the observer can make or break his chances of seeing the phenomenon. Therefore, even the most minor error in calculating the precise location of an occurrence can mean the difference between witnessing a double sunset and observing no solar re-emergence at all. Consequently, in astro-geographical forecasting, a miss really can be as good as a mile.

Nevertheless, the reader should not allow the imperfections contained in Kevin's pioneering work on the double sunset to divert attention from the numerous fascinating aspects of the phenomenon which have been revealed as a result of his bold ventures into uncharted territory. Kevin has in effect acted as an explorer opening the path for contemporary scientific study of the midsummer occurrence and in doing so has inevitably made mistakes, which in themselves have led to further profitable discussion and research on the subject.

It is noteworthy that both Kevin and Richard were well aware of the potential impact of refraction upon the double sunset and took it into account when producing their various calculations. Nevertheless, although I accept the scientific relevance of refraction with regard to the phenomenon, I did not notice any resulting variation in the occurrences which I painstakingly observed from identical locations on the same days in different years. Consequently, this suggests that the varying effects of refraction on the double sunset are sufficient to be mathematically computed, but are generally too insignificant to be detectable with the naked eye.

Although the changing tilt of the earth's axis has a crucial impact on the double sunset over time, there is a second, though less significant, phenomenon which affects the occurrence and that is the precession of the equinoxes. Unlike the former process, which decides where the solstitial sunset occurs, the precession of the equinoxes determines the date on which that sunset takes place. This phenomenon was discovered in the second century B.C. by the Greek astronomer, Hipparchus, who realised its important implications for the calendar and calculated the solar year accordingly. This precession results from the gravitational pull of the sun and the moon on the earth's equatorial bulge, which causes the axis to wobble slowly rather like a spinning top. The outcome is that the axis precesses by just over 50 arc-seconds per year and, consequently, the equinoxes occur gradually earlier as time passes. A full cycle takes 25,695 years to complete, at the end of which the equinoxes return to the same position that they were in, relative to the stars, at the beginning of the process. The cycle then starts all over again.

The precession of the equinoxes proved an increasing headache under the Julian calendar, which was implemented by the Romans on 1 January 45 B.C. and eventually became adopted in England. The problem was that the average length of the calendar year was 365¼ days, which was over eleven minutes longer than the tropical or solar year and led to the retrogression of the date of the summer solstice by an average of one day every 128 years. Consequently, midsummer, which had fallen on 24 June in Britain in 45 B.C., had retrograded to 10 June by 1752 A.D.! Even worse, by persisting in using the Julian calendar, England found itself well out of synchronisation with most of the rest of Europe, which had switched to the more accurate Gregorian calendar. Consequently, Parliament finally decided that the country had to conform, so that eleven days were lost from the year 1752 and the summer solstice was celebrated on 21 June the following year. However, the Gregorian calendar year itself is not identical with the tropical year, being just under half a minute too long, so that midsummer is now retrograding by a day every 3,300 years approximately. Clearly, this effect is extremely slight and is currently overwhelmed in its significance by the impact on the date of the summer solstice caused through the modern use of leap years. Thus, although the longest day has most commonly occurred on 21 June since 1752, in 1975 it fell on 22 June, whilst in 2008 it will just creep into 20 June. However, the degree of variation is still currently sufficient for the Leek midsummer double sunset observers to need to be vigilant as to which date each June represents the summer solstice, the traditional viewing evening.

Nevertheless, under the present Gregorian calendar, the precession of the equinoxes will have no noticeable impact on the double sunset spectators for around 3,000 years. Also, despite the important long-term effects of the changing tilt of the earth's axis on the phenomenon, it is extremely doubtful whether a devoted viewer of the midsummer occurrence from the churchyard would notice the slightest impact of this process in a whole lifetime. Perhaps a most discerning and meticulously-minded individual would recall or elicit from his diary that his original observation position had moved slightly northeastwards or eastwards over an extremely long period of time. However, to the ordinary spectator, the solstitial event, or lack of it, would seem forever the same. No doubt since the distant past, weather-dependent Leek double sunset observers have occasionally experienced delight at seeing the exciting phenomenon, but, more commonly, frustration at their failure to do so, irrespective of the immense astro-geographical forces at work, shaping the unrecognisable long-term future.

2 The Double Sunset Origins

It has been argued that the double sunset phenomenon was considered in ancient times to be so extraordinary that it was responsible for the very origin of the settlement at Leek. In his article, *Dr Plot and the Amazing Double Sunset*, published in the *Astronomy & Geophysics* journal, Kevin Kilburn calculated that the midsummer occurrence had first become visible from the site of the churchyard from around 500 B.C. This date is extremely convenient in fuelling the projection and circulation of popular mythical explanations of the origins of double sunset observations, according to which the phenomenon was embraced by ancient peoples.

This abstract idea has been heavily promoted by mythistorians and was in circulation well before Kevin's article was published, as is witnessed by the comments of C.K.R. Pearce, B.A., in his feature, *Early History of the Ancient Parish Church of Leek*, which was published in 1966 within the booklet, *900th Anniversary Year Saint Edward the Confessor Leek*:

'The site upon which the Church of St. Edward the Confessor stands may well have been one with religious associations long before Christianity came to this part of Staffordshire. The fact that it is from the churchyard that the strange, and, [to] primitive people, awe-inspiring phenomenon of a double sunset on 20th and 21st June can be seen is no mere coincidence. Sun worshippers would have held in great reverence a place from which their god made this strange second appearance, and there might well have been some form of pagan Temple here similar to that at Arbor Low.'

Unfortunately, Pearce's comments on the history of the church and the double sunset are pure guesswork and I have not been able to uncover a single shred of concrete evidence to support them. Although it is more than possible that the site had a pre-Christian religious function, the idea of 'primitive people' being 'awe-inspired' by this entirely natural event seems rather far-fetched. It needs to be borne in mind that people living in pre-modern society had a much greater connection to the landscape than contemporary man and usually spent most of their working lives outside. Therefore, they were considerably more in tune with their environment than the vast majority of people in England are today and it is consequently highly likely that they would have been well aware of the movements of the sun against the horizon throughout the seasons. Also, Pearce made the reckless assumption that these 'primitive people' were 'sun worshippers', who had a god which made a 'strange second appearance' on 20th and 21st June. The implication is that these entirely unspecified people were incapable of appreciating the natural causes of the phenomenon they were seeing, but this idea is demeaning to the intelligence of our predecessors.

Furthermore, the precise days of the year given by Pearce for the ancient double sunset on the site of the church are erroneous because the date of the summer solstice is not fixed and changes over time. Indeed, this situation is exacerbated because our current calendar was only adopted in 1752 and its predecessor, the Julian calendar, had already retrograded by two days from the present date of midsummer by the time that Saint Augustine arrived in England in 597 to convert the heathen Anglo-Saxons to Christianity. Finally, Pearce's strong suggestion that there was once a 'pagan Temple' on the site of the church 'similar to that at Arbor Low' was again utterly unsupported by any evidence, archaeological or otherwise, and remains without historical foundation. Indeed, this is so in spite of the fact that a considerable area surrounding the church has obviously seen a great deal of disturbance through the excavation of the ground for burials over the centuries, without the recorded discovery of any ancient artefacts.

In 1972, a further attempt to provide a human connection of great antiquity to the double sunset was made by the Reverend P.D.S. Blake, M.A., in his chapter entitled *Early History – 1066*, contained within the booklet, *Leek Parish Church Of St. Edward The Confessor: History And Guide*:

'The mysterious double sunset that is seen from the Church on the June solstice still draws crowds of curious onlookers today; it would have seemed an even more wonderful portent to Druid worshippers. Druid worship was much connected with the sun and the moon, as their great temple at Stonehenge clearly shows.'

Although Blake's opinion was 'confidently surmised', he presented not a jot of evidence to back his claim. A Druid connection to the site of St Edward's Church cannot categorically be disproven, but it can only remain an entirely unsubstantiated belief until clear facts, of which there are currently none, are produced in support of this view. Unfortunately, the one factual link that Blake did specify, namely between Druid worship being 'much connected with the sun' and 'their great temple at Stonehenge', was woefully inaccurate. In this statement, Blake clearly inferred that the Druids were the builders of Stonehenge, but they categorically were not! Stonehenge was constructed between approximately 1900 and 1600 B.C., whilst the Druids were ancient Celtic priests who arrived in Britain from around 800 B.C.! In addition, although the Druids were polytheistic, their rites were mainly practised in sacred groves, particularly comprised of oak trees, which were obviously highly unsuited to sun worship because of the abundance of foliage to obscure the sky! Consequently, although it is likely that the Celts used Stonehenge as an astronomical calendar, the available evidence indicates that the Druids were not primarily sun worshippers. In conclusion, because Blake bungled the little fact that he did produce, it is essential to treat his claims of Druid worship of the double sunset at Leek with the utmost caution.

The well-known Leek author, Harold Bode, further perpetuated the idea of the ancient link in his booklet, *Visiting Leek: Part 1 The Town Centre*, which was published in 1974:

'On the horizon is . . . Bosley Cloud. From this point, the sun can be seen to set twice on Mid-summer's night. It sinks below the head of Bosley Cloud, then re-appears to set over the Cheshire Plain. This fact would be known to our remote ancestors, and a stone circle may have marked the spot where the summer solstice could be observed.'

Unfortunately, in this extract, Harold confused Midsummer's Night, which occurs on 24 June, with the summer solstice, which is currently three days earlier, on 21 June. The double sunset, as seen from the vicinity of St Edward's churchyard, is at its optimum on the 21st, the longest day, and not the 24th. Perhaps more important than this point, which might be regarded as a technicality, is Harold's suggestion of the possible existence of a stone circle on the site at an unspecified time in history. Whilst this possibility cannot be entirely discounted, there is no known tangible evidence to indicate that a stone circle was ever actually constructed at this location and so, until some proof emerges, Harold's claim can at best only remain pure speculation. Stone circles and other human constructions can be projected to have once existed in an endless variety of places, but whether they really did or not is an entirely different issue, which can only be resolved through the painstaking efforts of experienced and highly skilled archaeologists and historians. Furthermore, as calculated from Kevin Kilburn's plan of the churchyard, the solstitial double sunset did not begin to occur from that location until about 350 B.C., which was around a millennium after the building of megaliths had ceased. Consequently, according to this, there is categorically no connection between the solstitial double sunset, as observed from the churchyard, and the building of a stone circle on the site.

In 1991, further support was given to the theory of the great antiquity of human connection to the double sunset, with the publication of *The Seventh Sword* by Andrew Collins. The author was a leading practitioner of psychic questing, a ritualistic and unscientific method of investigating mysterious phenomena, which is anathema to orthodox historians. Nevertheless, Collins has been acclaimed by the well-known local writer, Doug Pickford, as 'internationally renowned' and 'one of the most celebrated authors in his own field of Earth Mysteries or New Age Writing'.

The Seventh Sword was described on its front cover as, 'A dramatic true story of Magic, Sorcery and Supernatural Discovery in Britain today,' and the site of Leek's solstitial phenomenon played a part of some importance within its story line. Strangely, however, St Edward's churchyard was referred to throughout the book as the 'Place of the Double Setting Sun', perhaps because this made it sound more mysterious, and it was even indexed as such!

In the book, Collins outlined a story in which Mary Heath, a Victorian 'visionary', was instructed by a 'clandestine mystical fraternity' to 'establish a new group of similarly-minded individuals . . . who shared a belief . . . that following the biblical Exodus . . . sacred knowledge had been brought . . . to Britain in particular, by an enlightened colony of Egyptians . . .' Apparently, she was told 'to set up her centre of operations in Staffordshire, close to where the Moses-influenced Egyptians had first settled . . . near a place of great magical power where every year over the midsummer period, by virtue of the layout of the western horizon of hills, the sun was seen to set twice in one day. The location was known only as the Place of the Double Setting Sun.' Incredibly, Collins described this story as 'quite plausible'!

This extraordinary account was not only in complete disharmony with the vast body of acquired conventional wisdom on the ancient history of Egypt and Britain, produced by painstaking research, but also was inaccurate in its claims regarding the double sunset. For example, Kevin Kilburn has already shown that the phenomenon moves over time and so it is not true that the event occurred 'every year' in the past, even taking into account the endless clear skies assumed in Collins' tale. Also, the phrase 'over the midsummer period' is extremely vague, whilst the phenomenon does not result from the layout of the 'western horizon of hills', but from the shape of one specific ridge to the northwest of the churchyard, The Cloud. Furthermore, it is ludicrous to have stated that 'The location was known only as the Place of the Double Setting Sun.' It is obvious that, to the vast majority of people in the nineteenth century, the observation point was known as St Edward's churchyard in the town of Leek!

Nevertheless, having acquired some geographical knowledge of the area, Collins revisited the site later in his book:

'The Place of the Double Setting Sun was undoubtedly a churchyard at Leek, a mere six miles or so east of the town of Biddulph. The raised ground surrounding the church of St Edward the Confessor was known locally as the only spot in the country where the sun could be seen to set twice on one day. The event took place on the summer solstice due, it seemed, to the shape and position of a hill known as the Cloud, situated just three miles north of Biddulph Grange. Although now in a relatively built-up area, the churchyard was an ancient place of worship with the remains of stone crosses dating back to Saxon times.

An anomalous and obviously mysterious event such as a double setting sun would have been seen as particularly important by the priest magicians of the Neolithic people, who are known to have orientated their monuments towards solar or lunar events such as the equinoxes and solstices. A location from which such an occurrence could be observed would have become sacred ground, revered as a place of communion with the earth spirit. Much later this holy site would have been Christianised and a church built upon the spot.'

The only criticism that can reasonably be made of Collins' primarily factual first paragraph is that by no means everyone in Leek regarded the churchyard as a double sunset observation point unique in England. However, in the rest of his extract, myth and speculation largely replaced fact as the basis of his argument. The crux of the matter is that, as Kevin Kilburn has shown, the midsummer double sunset was not visible from the site of the churchyard in Neolithic times and therefore Collins' opinion as to the response of the 'priest magicians' to its 'sacred ground' has no validity whatsoever.

Nevertheless, in 1993, Doug Pickford presented even more speculative claims, in his book, *Magic, Myth & Memories In and Around The Peak District*:

'At Leek . . . there stands a church dedicated to St Edward the Confessor. This edifice is built atop a sandstone escarpment where there was (even as far as the official history of the Church is concerned, and that is unusual) a large stone circle. This could have been as big, if not bigger, than Arbor Low and was a site where the double sunset could be witnessed.'

As I have just stated, there is no known evidence in existence to show that the site of the church once contained a stone circle of any description and therefore it remains a complete mystery as to how Doug managed to conclude that this mythical feature was large in size. Also, 'the official history of the Church', to which he referred, was not actually such, but was in fact a publication undertaken in 1966 by two private individuals, Angus Walkden and Gerald Mee, the aforementioned *900th Anniversary Year Saint Edward the Confessor Leek*. In addition, the relevant article within this booklet, *Early History of the Ancient Parish Church of Leek*, did not state that 'a large stone circle' had existed on the site, but instead speculated that, 'there might well have been some form of pagan Temple here.' Thus it appears that Doug somewhat exaggerated the original claim. Furthermore, even if Doug's initial source had been 'the official history of the Church', this in itself would have given absolutely no indication as to whether the account was accurate or not. An official version of something simply means that it has been sanctioned or recognised by an authority. Consequently, no history of St Edward's Church can be considered sacrosanct and beyond criticism and, in any case, none of the histories contained within the various church guides currently available for research actually refer to a stone circle on the site.

Undaunted by the lack of evidence to support his arguments, Doug presented precisely the same claim in 1994 in another of his books, *Staffordshire: Its Magic & Mystery*, but took the opportunity to push it a stage further:

'I have looked before, in a previous book [*Magic, Myth & Memories In and Around The Peak District*], at the healing aspects of the water that flowed from the site of the Double sunset where a stone circle was erected and where later a Church dedicated to St Edward was built.'

Doug not only put forward his highly contentious statements about the presence of healing water and a stone circle at the site as though they were actual facts, but the sole ground on which he did so was the authority of his own previous book. That provided a remarkable circular argument whereby he quoted himself as the source of his information!

The great antiquity of human observation of the double sunset from St Edward's churchyard was also strongly argued in Doug's further book, *Earth Mysteries of the Three Shires*, which was published in 1996. Chapter eight was entitled *Sun and Moon Worship* and within it the aforementioned Andrew Collins was quoted as stating that the nearby Lud's Church, the hanging stone and the Leek double sunset 'appeared to form individual components of a much larger picture involving an intimate knowledge of geo-celestial events and a long lost ceremonial landscape of great age.' Unfortunately, no evidence whatsoever was presented to support this sweeping statement, nor, conveniently, was the specific time period of the 'long lost ceremonial landscape' actually considered! Therefore the conjectured myth was presented entirely in the absence of any of the awkward historical facts which would have challenged its validity. Nevertheless, it still provided sufficient encouragement for Doug to promote the theory that 'the whole area was not just devoted to Sun Worship as in the mystical Double Sunset visible from Leek but had Moon connections with the Lunar Standstill' and that 'this land has been one of the "holiest" there could be in the eyes of those who have gone before.' He then concluded: 'Forget Glastonbury, forget Avebury and the rest. Here, in the Mystical Middle of England, is one of the most magical and mystical sites there has ever been.' However, Doug in turn presented no hard evidence to support these extraordinary claims and thereby consigned them at best to the realms of wild conjecture.

Kevin Kilburn himself perpetuated the theory of the link of ancient peoples to Leek's double sunset in his *Astronomy & Geophysics* article, in which he stated:

'Although there is no direct evidence in the form of artefacts, because the immediate area has not been excavated, circumstantial evidence suggests that the hilltop on which [The Church of] St Edward the Confessor stands may have been in use as a Neolithic place of reverence, more than 3500 years before the church was built . . .

There is one other astronomical alignment at Leek . . . that lends weight to the idea that it was a place of organized solar observation in prehistoric times . . . The site of Cock Low has been totally obliterated but was approximately 500m west-south-west of St Edward's [church] at the present site of Spring Gardens . . .

From Cock Low the sunset never reached the Cloud, but in 2500 B.C. the midsummer sun did set above a shallow depression in the horizon between the southern end of that hill and Long Edge to its south.'

These comments in themselves did not give the full picture of precisely what Kevin was postulating, but he revealed the missing link during his talk at the Green Dragon Mysteries Society meeting in Leek on 30 June 1999: 'Between Cock Low and the churchyard is a sacred landscape because they would have seen sacred sunsets between there and The Cloud.' He also stressed the tribal nature of these events by referring to the people concerned 'getting out their ancestors' bones' to mark the occasion each year!

These points were further clarified by Kevin in a letter to me, dated 22 March 2001. He projected that the Neolithic people in the vicinity of Cock Low discovered that there was a nearby midsummer double sunset, which they began to celebrate, and so came into existence 'a slowly moving site of worship' that ended up with St Edward's Church being built when the occurrence had finally reached that location.

Unfortunately, Kevin's line of argument was entirely bereft of hard fact to back his case, as he had indeed noted himself. It is not impossible that the site of St Edward's Church was 'a Neolithic place of reverence', but there is no actual evidence to show that it was, nor does there seem to be any plausible reason to suggest why it should have been. Therefore, this opinion can at very best only be conjecture. In addition, Kevin's argument suggested that there were Neolithic people living in the vicinity, who, around 2500 B.C., became excited because the sun set 'above a shallow depression in the horizon' on the summer solstice. That is extremely unlikely. There are many relief features visible from around Leek that have far more pronounced and dramatic outlines than the aforementioned 'shallow depression', so it is very difficult to accept that these people regarded its particular solstitial sunsets as 'sacred'. Nevertheless, it is possible that the builders of Cock Low related to the 'shallow depression' as the point at which the sun set on the summer solstice and, at some stage, noticed that a midsummer double sunset occurred a quarter of a mile or more to the east-northeast of their site. However, Kevin's 'slowly moving site of worship' hypothesis is based upon the existence of an uninterrupted religion and culture in Leek spanning two millennia, which enabled an astonishingly settled and impregnable tribe to worship a relatively ordinary annual sunset and/or a nearby midsummer double sunset over the whole of that period! History suggests otherwise.

The Neolithic period lasted until around 2000 B.C. when the Bronze Age began, approximately concurrent with the arrival in Britain of a new race of people from Iberia, the Beaker folk. The newcomers had a bigger build and broader heads than their predecessors and there were significant cultural differences between the two peoples. There was another major interruption in continuity from about 800 B.C. when the Gaels, the first wave of Celtic invaders, migrated to the British Isles and they forced the existing peoples into the highlands in the west. In turn, these new settlers came under pressure from the Brythonic Celts, who appeared with formidable iron weapons from around 500 B.C. and drove all before them into the more barren regions of the country.

Consequently, the projected Neolithic Leek sunset religion would have had to have survived three momentous invasions and waves of new settlement over 1,500 years before the viewing point of the solstitial double sunset finally reached the site of the churchyard around 350 B.C.! Furthermore, for the continuity of observation of the phenomenon to have survived from then until the building of St Edward's Church, the annual occurrence would have had to have resisted the impact of the new, dominant cultures introduced in turn by the Romans (from about 71 A.D.) and the Mercian Angles (from perhaps the late sixth century). Even then, Kevin's hypothesis relies on there having been an uninterrupted view of The Cloud along the 'slowly moving site of worship', free from the interference of natural vegetation, unless the latter was progressively removed to enable the sunsets to be seen.

The enduring legend of the ancient link was further perpetuated by Elizabeth Ann Biddulph in her book, *Leek's Forgotten Centuries: It's* [sic] *Ancient History Unearthed*, which was published in 1999:

'Neolithic/Bronze/Iron Age monuments were special places where religious rites and ceremonies were carried out. It is believed by historians, that these actual monuments were used to celebrate the passing of the seasons, the changing of the fertility of the land and, more significantly in the case of the site of St. Edward's Church, '*the astronomical events which marked out the yearly cycle*'.

It is agreed by archaeologists that, there is strong evidence to suggest that these religious sites were aligned to be important at certain times of the year, such as the winter and summer solstice or where the sun or moon rose or set behind a prominent feature in the landscape.

Consider then the famous double sunset which takes place behind Bosley cloud every Midsummer and which can only be observed from the churchyard of St. Edward's Church . . .

We know Leek and much of its Moorlands had many Neolithic/ Bronze/Iron Age farming communities. Surely these early people, so closely tied to the land and the seasons for their very survival, could not have failed to observe the amazing astronomical Midsummer spectacle which still takes place every year at St. Edward's churchyard! Would that not have been the very place for our ancient Leek ancestors to celebrate the passing of the seasons, to carry out religious rituals and raise a sacred low for the burial of their dead?'

At first glance, Elizabeth's arguments regarding the site of St Edward's Church sound highly plausible, but they do not hold up in the face of two particular facts. Firstly, because of astro-geographical factors, the midsummer double sunset, as observed from Leek, cannot be seen from the same place now as it could 4,000 years ago. As Kevin Kilburn showed, the solstitial occurrence could not be viewed at the current site until at least around 500 B.C. and therefore there was definitely no connection between Neolithic and Bronze Age peoples and the churchyard phenomenon. Secondly, Elizabeth's extract reaffirmed the enduring myth that the double sunset can only be seen from the churchyard in Leek. That is categorically not so, as I shall later demonstrate, which consequently disproves the existence of a unique link between the double sunset and the church site.

However, Elizabeth was not alone in greatly exaggerating the astro-geographical importance of Leek's midsummer phenomenon. The superlatives used by the Reverend Blake, C.K.R. Pearce, Andrew Collins, Doug Pickford and Kevin Kilburn in their projections of the great antiquity of the observation of the double sunset indicate that they believed the phenomenon to be extremely rare, if not unique. However, it is not! As I will show later, not only are there many further viewing points of this particular double sunset additional to those in St Edward's churchyard, but also there are other nearby hills which produce the same phenomenon to a greater and more impressive extent. Consequently, it is likely that ancient peoples living in their vicinity were sufficiently in tune with their environment to be well aware of this and the fact that the event on the site of the church was unusual, but not rare. Indeed, the evidence suggests that the double sunset phenomenon was not the initial factor which led to human interest in and the subsequent development of the site.

Even today, Leek and its surrounding area is not blessed with the most favourable of locations, nor the most desirable of climates and certainly not the richest of soils. Its position in the Staffordshire Moorlands makes it a rather cold, wet and out of the way place to visit and its main communications artery to the north, the A 53 to Buxton, is periodically blocked by snow in the winter. The hill farmers of the area bear little or no comparison with the wealthy agribusinessmen of East Anglia and concentrate on livestock, especially hardy sheep. Indeed, these facts are testified to by the continuing low population of the region.

In ancient and prehistoric times, the Staffordshire Moorlands were an even less attractive option for human beings, with dense woodlands occupying the river valleys and bare, scrub-covered Millstone Grit and Sherwood Sandstone uplands rising beyond them. It was virtually the same unfavourable environment that was first encountered by small bands of hardy Mercian Angles, gradually following the River Churnet towards its source from its confluence with the Trent, the major highway for the migrants into the Midlands from the east coast. The eighth century *Tribal Hidage* indicated that the Staffordshire Moorlands had become occupied by two Anglian tribes, the North Mercians and the Pecsaetan, the dwellers of the Peak. Place name evidence clearly indicates that they were the earliest people who can have given Leek its name in founding what appears to have been the initial settlement close by or on the site of St Edward's Church. Additionally, it is known for certain that Leek existed before the Norman Conquest of 1066 because there is reference to its presence and value prior to that date in *Domesday Book*, which was compiled twenty years later.

The vast majority of place names in the ancient parish of Leek are of Anglo-Saxon, or, more accurately, Anglian, origin, as can be seen on the relevant Ordnance Survey maps and as is testified to by *The Victoria History Of The County Of Stafford* in its Volume VII, *Leek And The Moorlands*, which was edited by the notable historian, M.W. Greenslade, and published in 1996. Nevertheless, this detailed reference book points out an exception to the rule, noting a scattering of Old Norse sources in the hillier northern area of the parish, namely Upper Hulme, Middle Hulme, Bearda and Swythamley, although the last two mentioned have been alternatively argued as being Anglian. The Mercian settlements date from no earlier than the fifth century, whilst the Scandinavian ones originated not before the late ninth century and resulted from the Viking incursions into England.

Place names are extremely important in helping to determine the history and cultural development of specific areas and a careful study of the possible options strongly suggests that the name *Leek* itself was Germanic in origin. Evidence to this effect was presented in 1862 by John Sleigh (a barrister of the Inner Temple) in his book, *A History of the Ancient Parish of Leek, in Staffordshire*, although he strangely preferred an unconvincing alternative explanation on the advice of a colleague:

'As to the origin of the name of the town, Robert Ferguson, F.S.A., an authority of great weight on such points, inclines to the opinion that it is derived from the Cymric *lech*, a stone, which the nature of the country in its immediate neighbourhood seems to corroborate, rather than from *leak* (which is equivalent in its meaning to water, and from which are evidently derived *Leck*, a river in the Netherlands: *Lech*, another river in South Germany; and *Leuk*, in Switzerland, noted for its hot springs), or from the old Norse *lik*, Anglo-Saxon *lic*, a corpse.'

It is peculiar that Sleigh favoured the Celtic option when the Leek area is so lacking in place names of ancient British origin and so dominated by those of Germanic derivation, especially as he himself presented a stronger case for the latter. Also, there is no logic in his argument that because 'the nature of the country in its immediate vicinity' was of great similarity to that of the site of Leek itself, then Leek was specifically distinguished by a name that could have applied to anywhere round about. The whole point of place names is (and always was) that they distinguish a specific place from others in the vicinity and that is best and most commonly done by choosing a distinctive name. That is precisely the opposite of what Sleigh concluded.

In 1883, in the second edition of his book, Sleigh reaffirmed the essence of his original argument, but amended the source of the town's name from *lech* to *llêch* and thereby altered its meaning to 'a broad flat stone'. This served only to weaken his hypothesis even further, especially because the rather soft Sherwood Sandstone, on which the centre of Leek lies, is not renowned for being weathered into noteworthy broad, flat stones. Nevertheless, it was still evidence enough to indicate to him that it 'seems to point to it [Leek] as a place of sepulture after some sharp pre-historic struggle'!

For good measure, Sleigh then added in his new edition a second option, to which he also seemed partial:

'Lach in the old Keltic meant a desert place; and this derivation is favoured by the immediate vicinity of the vast tract of wild moorlands, with their "infinite distances of brown waste, rolling mists and snow-capped Roaches." '

Despite their undeniably unfavourable location, it is difficult to accept that the Staffordshire Moorlands were regarded by the Celts as being a desert, whilst The Roaches in the late nineteenth century were too low-lying to hold snow for any length of time, except in the occasional particularly severe winter. Furthermore, Sleigh offered no reasons to explain why it was Leek that was called a desert when its situation was altogether more favourable to human beings than the surrounding moorlands, whose barrenness he described. Finally, and most importantly of all, a study of dictionaries of both the Welsh and Gaelic languages reveals no word similar to *lach* meaning a *desert*. Therefore, it can be argued that Sleigh's new supposition was rather reliant on the moulding of facts to fit his hypothesis.

However, the case which he put, and then dismissed, for the Germanic origin of the name *Leek* has much to commend it. Firstly, and obviously, as the bulk of the place names in the vicinity of Leek are of Germanic derivation, there is every likelihood that the town's name originated from the same source. Secondly, the

Old Norse word *loekr* referred to a *brook*, whilst *laecc*, *laece*, lec, lecc and *lece* are Anglo-Saxon forms associated with the word *leccan* meaning *to water*. Consequently, this suggests that Leek was the site of a watercourse which was of note and therefore probably of use to the Mercian or Scandinavian people who first settled there.

In addition, Sleigh was quite right to cite evidence from the similar Germanic names of features and places in Europe in support of this particular theory. His River Leck is none other than the current River Lek, a major distributary of the mighty River Rhine; the Lech is an important headwater of the even more impressive Danube and Leuk is a notable centre on another important waterway, the Rhône. Furthermore, there are many more Germanic names of the same type to be found on the Continent, for example, Leek and Lekkerkerk in the Netherlands and Leke in Belgium. It is intriguing that the above names located in the Low Countries are very close to the coast, which faces England, because this was a region where Anglo-Saxon tribes settled prior to their migration to this country. Consequently, it provides a further argument in support of the hypothesis that the town of Leek has Germanic origins.

Finally, in areas of England where Germanic place names predominate, there are a number of them of similar construction to Leek, which have been identified by Margaret Gelling, an eminent authority on the subject, as originating from the same root, the Old Norse word *loekr*. In her book, *Place-Names in the Landscape*, which was published in 1984, she therefore determined that not only Leek stemmed from this source, but also Leake in Yorkshire; Leake Commonside, Leake Hurn's End, Old Leake and New Leake in Lincolnshire; West Leake and East Leake in Nottinghamshire and Leck in Lancashire. It is of note that all these places are located in the North of England and the North Midlands, in areas of Scandinavian settlement.

John Sleigh's other suggestion for Leek's Germanic origin, namely the sources *lik* or *lic*, must also be considered. *Lic* is indeed the Anglo-Saxon word for *corpse*, as well as *body*, and cannot be entirely discounted as the original derivation. Nevertheless, it is obvious that there is a far greater likelihood of the town being named after a watercourse or spring than a corpse. Also, as the settlement was listed in *Domesday Book* in 1086 as *Lec* (pronounced *Lek*), then *lic* is a less likely root source of the word than *laecc*, *laece*, *lec*, *lecc* and *lece*, or even *loekr*, even more so because the vast majority of place names have mundane rather than dramatic meanings. Additionally, if a word which refers to a body or a corpse is accepted as a major contender, then other equally unlikely options must be examined and the task of tracing the settlement's origin becomes immeasurably more difficult and time consuming. In other words, as the precise details surrounding the foundation of Leek are entirely unknown and almost certainly always will be, then it can only be productive to argue the case between the most likely options and not every remotely plausible possibility that may be offered.

Harry Ball, a fluent speaker of and a relative expert in Anglo-Saxon, or Old English, made a number of enlightening comments on the situation in his booklet, *Place-Names in the Moorlands*, which was published in 1990. He pointed out that the town had become known as *Leke* by the thirteenth century, which indicates a further intermediary stage in the development of the name from *Loekr*, or *Leccan*, and then *Lec* to *Leek*. Harry then mentioned Sleigh's favoured etymon of *llêch*, but gave his hypothesis short shrift because ' . . . there is no real evidence to support this suggestion, no such flat stone has ever been found for example, so it cannot now be accepted.' Harry then proceeded by expounding his own illuminating conclusions on Leek's foundation:

'A more recent suggestion however is that the name is derived from the Old Norse word "loekr" which means "a small brook". Following this interpretation the name "Leek" would have the same origin as the modern word "leak". The observation has also been made that the "leaking brook" was originally a spring which flowed from the side of the hill on which the Old Church now stands. Today this spring is covered by a well built into the churchyard wall at the corner of Church Street and Church Lane. The brook itself would have ran down the valley which contains Mill Street. Opposite the well lies St. Edwards Street which was formerly called Spout Street from a spout or a channel of water which ran down its western side presumably once fed by this same spring. These indicators do lend support to the interpretation of the name being from the Old Norse "loekr". This in turn provides further evidence for some Scandinavian or Viking settlement in the Moorlands.'

In 1995, a further publication broadly supported Harry's conclusions. In his book, *Staffordshire Place-Names*, Anthony Poulton-Smith stated:

'Many have insisted this name originates from the town's close proximity to Wales and the story goes that it provided the vegetable which was to become symbolic of that principality. Others have suggested a name from a Celtic root related to Welsh *llec* – a flagstone . . . But the origin is possibly far less complex. If we accept Domesday's listing of Lec (later Lech and Leke) it seems the Old Norse *laekr* meaning 'brook' may be the origin. This possibility is given some credence by the Saxon *lecan* (which would have the same root) meaning 'to drip or leak'.'

Clearly, Poulton-Smith did not favour the Welsh link and this hypothesis of the town's origin contains serious flaws. It is absolutely obvious that Leek is not located near to Wales and neither has it ever been famed for its production of alliaceous vegetables, whilst the Celtic stone connection has already been discussed and criticised in relation to the comments of John Sleigh in 1862 and 1883.

The strong preference of Harry Ball and Anthony Poulton-Smith for the Old Norse *loekr* as the source of Leek's name, as opposed to the Anglo-Saxon words *laecc*, *laece*, *lec*, *lecc* and *lece*, has very powerful circumstantial evidence to support it. As has already been shown, there are a number of settlement names similar to Leek, with the same derivation, in the northern half of England, a region which was heavily settled by Scandinavian peoples, who commonly used the word *loekr*. Whilst this Old Norse word was pronounced with a *k* sound, as one would expect in the name Leek, the corresponding Old English words were spoken using a modern English *ch* sound. Also, the Anglo-Saxon words *laecc*, *laece*, *lec*, *lecc* and *lece* are essentially known in connection with charter boundaries and most commonly describe landscape features rather than refer to settlement names. In addition, the majority of place names of Old English origin contain two elements, unlike Leek, which obviously has only one.

Furthermore, the equivalent Anglo-Saxon word for a *brook* was *broc* and there is a wealth of settlement names in England confirmed by Margaret Gelling as having their first element stemming from this source, for example, Brockdish,

Brockford, Brockhampton, Brockington, Brockley, Brockton, Brockweir, Brockworth, Brocton, Brogden, Brook, Brooke, Brookhampton, Brookthorpe, Brookwood, Brotton, Broughton and Broxfield. These places are located especially, but by no means entirely, in the South, in regions essentially not colonised by the Norsemen. In addition, Gelling identified 72 examples of separate place names in England whose second elements originated with the word *broc*, many of which were recorded more than once. The most pertinent amongst these numerous listed cases are Bilbrook, Gosbrook and nearby Meerbrook and Forsbrook, all of which are located in Staffordshire. This clearly confirms that the Anglo-Saxon word *broc* was used in the vicinity of Leek, which strongly suggests that the town was not named after an Old English watercourse.

Consequently, it is very difficult to dispute the conclusion that Margaret Gelling, Harry Ball and Anthony Poulton-Smith came to, that the name *Leek* is derived from the Old Norse word *loekr*. This firmly indicates that the original settlers considered the outstanding feature of the site to be a brook and not the midsummer double sunset which occurred in good weather throughout the Anglo-Saxon and Viking ages. The likely explanation for this is very simple indeed – these pioneer settlers were extremely practical people whose very survival depended on the land and they were not initially driven by romantic quests. Therefore, the choice of a productive site was of paramount importance. That at Leek was relatively fortunate, being well above the flood plain of the River Churnet, probably less densely covered by natural woodland and, of course, containing a regular supply of fresh water from the brook that flowed from it. The observation of astro-geographical phenomena was an interesting nicety that could wait until later.

In addition, if it had been the double sunset which had attracted the first settlers to the site, it seems most probable that the place name would have been based on the unusual event itself. The near fact that Leek was named after a brook indicates that the double sunset had still not been observed from the site of St Edward's churchyard at that point, unless, of course, it had been noticed, but was considered of no interest, which is not particularly likely. Prior to the arrival of the Norsemen in England, the Mercians had lived in the Staffordshire Moorlands for perhaps around 300 years and yet there is no evidence to suggest that they took an interest in the phenomenon or that the conjectured Neolithic observation tradition had been handed down to them. Neither are there any reliable grounds on which to suggest that the site of the church or the surrounding area had been occupied before the late ninth century when the Viking incursions into Mercia began in earnest.

Furthermore, it was the custom of the Anglo-Saxons and the Norsemen to establish their settlements on virgin sites and historical evidence shows little disruption of the existing habitation upon their arrival. Indeed, when the Vikings put down roots in England following their invasions, they almost invariably founded their own settlements, sometimes nearby, although entirely distinct from, those of the indigenous Anglo-Saxons, so that the two related peoples flourished thenceforth both independently and inter-dependently. Because Old English and Old Norse were very closely related languages, the Mercians and the Vikings were well able from their first point of contact to engage in conversation and to understand each other quite clearly. Therefore, it seems very reasonable to assume that had the Mercians who inhabited the Staffordshire Moorlands known of and been inspired by Leek's double sunset, any incoming heathen Norsemen would have quickly got to hear about it and taken a look at the event for themselves. However, that does not appear to have happened because the new settlement at Leek was based on and almost certainly named after a watercourse which was very near to, but not precisely on, the viewing site of the astro-geographical phenomenon.

For these reasons, it is my belief that human observation of the double sunset at Leek postdated the settlement of the site and that the people who lived there noticed the occurrence in due course because of their general awareness of their environment. Consequently, it appears highly unlikely that the first observation, and especially regular viewing, of the occurrence took place before the late ninth century at the earliest.

Although, as I have shown, the case for the Old Norse origin of the place name of Leek is extremely compelling, this in itself does not categorically prove that Norsemen were the actual founders of the settlement or the first people to witness the double sunset. The Old Norse word *loekr* probably came into general circulation in the northern half of England because Scandinavian settlement in this area was considerable and the term may well have been used by Mercians and Vikings alike in the Staffordshire Moorlands. Therefore, it can be argued that the founders of Leek were Angles who simply used an Old Norse word, which had come into their language, to describe their new settlement.

However, there is much to suggest otherwise. By the late ninth century, the Mercians had been settled in North Staffordshire for approximately 300 years and the era of Anglo-Saxon migration from the Continent had long passed. Therefore, there were extremely few if any new settlers appearing from this quarter. Although it is true that secondary settlements continued to be formed periodically in Mercia, many of the villages already had an extensive history which stretched back to the formative Anglo-Saxon period. The original pioneers had chosen their initial settlement sites as the best available and had consequently, in most cases, stuck with them.

The majority of new settlements founded in northern and eastern England between the late ninth and the mid-eleventh centuries were, not surprisingly, created by the incoming Norsemen. However, the Staffordshire Moorlands were located beyond the main zones of both the Danish settlement to the east and that of the Norwegians to the west and, as has already been noted, contain only a scattering of Old Norse place names. Therefore, this offers the distinct possibility that a small number of Scandinavians drifted into this sparsely populated area from one of the surrounding regions, probably looking for land, and peacefully founded Leek on a hitherto unoccupied site. The overwhelming preponderance of Anglo-Saxon place names in the Staffordshire Moorlands indicates that these Norsemen most probably arrived tranquilly to avoid antagonising the relatively populous locals, who, in turn, must have at least tolerated the new community of strangers in their midst. Indeed, this hypothesis is vindicated by the rather obvious point that the Old Norse description of the new site was more probably introduced by the Norsemen themselves rather than by the dominant Mercians, who continued to use their own word, *broc*, when referring to a brook.

The case that Harry Ball put forward for the site of the founding settlement at

Leek, although conjectural, is also highly plausible. The well built into the wall of St Edward's churchyard, to which he referred, remains clearly in evidence today on Church Street, just over the brow of the hill, coming from the direction of Stockwell Street to the east. It is easily observed from here that the land falls away sharply to the west, towards Mill Street. The water from the spring now tapped by the well would almost certainly originally have flowed down the valley currently occupied by the A 523, exactly as Harry described, before it joined the Ball Haye Brook and then the River Churnet. This would have proved a handy water supply for the initial settlers, but, intriguingly, Harry's account also referred to a second watercourse, which is known to have run southwards on the western flank of St Edward Street at broadly a ninety degree angle to the first brook. Indeed, as Harry noted, this thoroughfare was formerly called Spout Street (until 1866), which indicates that it originally experienced a regular flow of water. Furthermore, in 1862, John Sleigh referred in his book to the 'oral tradition' which 'affirms that Spout-street took its name from an open channel, or spout, with a flush of water, which formerly ran down the western side of it.'

Harry himself believed that the one spring created both watercourses, but this is highly unlikely because such an occurrence is an extremely rare phenomenon. Therefore, it is far more plausible that the second brook stemmed from a separate source very close to the first, perhaps from somewhere near to the current location of the pay-and-display car park at the top of St Edward Street. Alternatively, the stream which originally ran in the Mill Street valley may later have been diverted to flow down the western side of Spout Street, as Elizabeth Ann Biddulph claimed in 1999 in her book, *Leek's Forgotten Centuries*. Nevertheless, the distinct possibility remains that there were originally two independent springs very close together and, if that was so, it may well have been the precise factor that attracted Leek's founding fathers to this specific location.

Of course, it is not a certainty that the original settlement at Leek was based on this site and the case for other possible locations can be argued. However, a combination of factors strongly suggests that the pioneers put down roots at this very spot. Here, not only did they have fresh water in abundance, but also they were well above the plain across which the River Churnet was liable to flood and probably beyond the dense natural woodland below. In addition, the site of the earliest known church, that of St Edward, was adjacent, on a dry-point position just above the spring or springs, whilst the ancient market place, which probably originally extended westwards from its current location, became established in close proximity to the water supply. Furthermore, this area marks the traditional centre of the town.

According to this, the site of the double sunset was extremely close to, or even in, the heart of the new settlement and it cannot have been long before the midsummer occurrence was noticed. As has already been shown, previous writers automatically assumed that the initial observers of the phenomenon were so profoundly impressed by it that it became the focal point of their religion. This is pure speculation and an exaggerated version of what probably occurred. Nevertheless, the incoming Norsemen were polytheistic heathens and, whilst the Mercians had theoretically been converted to Christianity, their paganism died hard and remained much practised.

Although sun worship was not a central feature of the old Northern heathen religion, the beliefs of its adherents included important references to the sun. Originating from a cold homeland, the Norsemen craved warmth, so that their land of death, Hel, was an underworld of ice and darkness. According to one of their myths, a wolf named Skoll was pursuing the sun across the sky and finally would devour it during Ragnarok, a cataclysm marking the end of the existing order of things. From this, it is easy, but dangerous, to speculate that the Norsemen would have been drawn to the double sunset because the reappearance of the sun after it had set would have symbolised hope beyond the normal pattern and predicted course of events. However, the Norsemen were a very fatalistic and practical people, as indeed were the Anglo-Saxons, and it is difficult to imagine them having been thunderstruck by Leek's double sunset, particularly as it was not the best example of its kind in the vicinity. Nevertheless, as an unusual occurrence in the environment that became so familiar to them, neither can it be realistically conceived that they ignored it altogether.

The predominant Mercians continued to observe at least aspects of their traditional polytheistic nature-based religion alongside their theoretical adherence to Christianity. Their brand of heathenism had involved, and perhaps still did involve, the necessary sacrifice of cakes to the sun in February in order to produce good crop yields, whilst there has survived the Anglo-Saxon incantation and invocation to the sun, Aecerbot. This too was a fertility rite. More importantly, a key festival of celebration, Litha, was held throughout the Anglo-Saxon period on the summer solstice to mark the high point of the solar year and this was precisely when the double sunset was to be seen. Therefore, on clear solstitial evenings, the founders of Leek would have been able, weather willing, to have brought their day's events to a climax by watching the fascinating double sunset occur and it may be that this visual spectacle attracted people from a wider area, as it does today.

It seems inevitable that regular observation of the double sunset began after the initial site at Leek had been occupied and it may well have been conducted in a religious or quasi-religious manner, out in the open, on the *heath*, in true heathen fashion, irrespective of whether the participants were Norsemen or Mercians. As both peoples were polytheistic, adding the new solstitial event onto their existing rites can have been no problem at all.

Furthermore, the double sunset must have served a more practical purpose, that of acting as an important marker in the seasonal calendar. During this period, time was measured with no great accuracy and even the philosopher-king, Alfred the Great, resorted to burning candles of equal length endlessly in an attempt to structure his activities more precisely. Therefore, it is obvious that a small group of Germanic peasants living in the Staffordshire Moorlands had considerable difficulty in determining the passage of time with any great exactitude. They would have found seasonal changes in their environment to have been a reasonable broad indicator, but weather-dependent celestial observations offered more hope of precision. The sun and moon would have been by far the most useful heavenly bodies to them for this purpose and the most specific calculation of all that they could have made was through the observation of the sunrises and sunsets on the summer and winter solstices. On the former day, the sun reaches its furthest point north, as viewed from the earth, and on the latter it arrives at its furthest point south. Indeed, on the day preceding and the day following the summer solstice, the sun can normally be observed as being slightly to the south of its position on the solstice. Because the degree of variation of movement of the sun from one day to the next at this time of year is very slight, it is almost certain to be unnoticeable unless the observations are made from a precisely set viewing position against a clearly delineated fixed point in the distance.

The Cloud, as viewed from St Edward's churchyard in Leek, provides a near ideal point of reference for an accurate calculation of the summer solstice to be made. A day either side of this, the sun sets slightly, but usually noticeably, to the south of its position on the solstice. For the six months following midsummer, the sun sets increasingly further south on the long ridge forming the backbone of The Cloud and beyond until the winter solstice is reached, currently in December. That marks the sun's furthest point south, as seen from the earth. After that date, the sun sets increasingly further north until midsummer arrives once more, presently on 21 June, and the double sunset becomes visible from St Edward's churchyard. Consequently, the founders of the settlement at Leek were able, weather willing, to observe a relatively spectacular sunset which enabled them to confirm with reasonable certainty that their solstitial celebrations were being held on precisely the right day. By following the same principles, all other communities during the Anglo-Saxon period would have been able to calculate similar results, but the people in Leek had a much more spectacular and accurate clock than most!

Despite this appreciable benefit, the double sunset never made sufficient impact for the settlement at Leek to become renamed in its honour. Although Christianity eventually triumphed in England, around fifty contemporary settlement names in the country originated through their connection to the old heathen religion, for example, Wednesbury and Wednesfield in Staffordshire. Thus, for all its apparent associations with heathenism soon after its formation, Leek remained named after a somewhat mundane watercourse. This in itself indicates that the double sunset phenomenon did not have anywhere near the degree of religious impact that previous writers on the subject automatically assumed it had had.

Nevertheless, the early heathen, or perceived heathen, connection to the site of the double sunset is strongly suggested by the very fact that St Edward's Church, the first known Christian building in Leek, was constructed at the same location. It seems near impossible that this can have been a pure coincidence because Leek remained an extremely small settlement, with only 28 recorded households in 1086, and so everyone in the vicinity would have known about the midsummer phenomenon. As Christianity gained a foothold and developed in England primarily through the cunning practice of attaching itself to, and gradually taking over, old heathen festival dates (for example, Yule and Easter) and religious sites, then it is highly likely that the same progression occurred in Leek.

It can be deduced from Kevin Kilburn's historical plan of the shifting double sunset that the midsummer phenomenon was visible from the site of the current church throughout the whole of the Anglo-Saxon period. However, the precise date of construction of the first Christian building at, or in very close proximity to, the location of the double sunset viewing point and the modern church is unknown, although it was probably in the early eleventh century. The sparsity of the local population suggests that it was only a small building, made from wood and/or stone, but its construction was a significant development nevertheless and more formalised the religious ceremonies which had probably long taken place around at least two carved stone crosses erected on the site of the current churchyard.

Although two crosses currently stand in the churchyard and three fragments of two others lie inside the church, they are not identical in style, which helps them to be approximately dated. The most impressive in size, but not in design, is mounted on a base and is located just inside the southeastern entrance to the churchyard. This has long, and perhaps always, stood in its current position. It was dated as 'A.D. 1000 or later' in origin by W.G. Collingwood in his 1927 study, *Northumbrian Crosses of the Pre-Norman Age*; as 'perhaps some time in the 11th century' by Nigel and Mary Kerr in their book, *A Guide to Anglo-Saxon Sites*, published in 1982, and as 'perhaps from the later 10th century' by M.W. Greenslade's *The Victoria History Of The County Of Stafford* in 1996. Intriguingly, it can be calculated from Kevin Kilburn's historical map of the churchyard double sunset that the present location of this cross was firmly inside the midsummer observation window in 1000 A.D. and near to its leading edge. Furthermore, if the viewing zone is adjusted slightly northeastwards, as calculated from the apparent observation point of the most recently witnessed occurrence in 1977, the site of the cross was at virtually the optimum point to enable the maximum amount of solar reappearance to be seen! It is therefore extremely tempting to believe that not only is this cross situated in its original position, but that it was erected there to mark a site of worship that at least initially derived from the practice of observing solstitial double sunsets.

A second cross, containing runic inscriptions, stands outside the church on its south side, having been reassembled from sections of it that were discovered in the churchyard. Unfortunately, the runes are so few in number and so badly damaged that they do not represent even a single word and therefore it remains unknown as to whether they were inscribed by Mercians or Norsemen. Nevertheless, the presence of its carved runes strongly suggests that this stone originates from an earlier period than the first cross and, according to Nigel and Mary Kerr, 'may date from the early 9th century'. Their opinion is broadly concurred with by Harry Ball and M.W. Greenslade. Finally, the Kerrs concluded that the three fragments now housed inside the church 'date to the late 9th or early 10th centuries', which view is likewise generally supported by Harry Ball.

The available evidence therefore indicates that, broadly between the ninth and eleventh centuries, four stone crosses were produced for erection in the vicinity of the double sunset viewing position. This is particularly significant because collections of Anglo-Saxon stone crosses in close proximity to one another are rare and it indicates that Leek became a religious site of longevity and perhaps of some importance.

There is a further stone remnant inside the church, with a possible Scandinavian connection, which Nigel and Mary Kerr described as 'a substantial hog-back tombstone of Anglo-Danish character', although Harry Ball regards it as 'a badly worn cross shaft'. In addition, even the approximate dating of artefacts during the whole of the Anglo-Saxon period is notoriously difficult and consequently it is quite possible that the cross containing the runic inscriptions was actually manufactured later in the ninth century than has been suggested, or even in the (early) tenth century, as was claimed by Keith Warrender in 1982 in his book, *Exploring Leek*. Indeed, this eventuality is indicated by the highly plausible premise that the settlement at Leek was founded by heathen Norsemen. These newcomers to the area would undoubtedly have retained their pagan culture and continued to use the runes for longer than the surrounding Mercians, who had already been at least partly assimilated into Christianity and introduced to the Latin alphabet. Although Harry Ball has expressed serious doubts regarding claims that this particular cross shows signs of Viking influence in terms of its style, the runes it contains could nevertheless have been carved by Norsemen instead of Mercians, in which case a construction date around the late ninth, or even early tenth, century becomes quite feasible.

If the initial settlers at Leek were indeed Norsemen, as seems likely, they would have moved into the area no earlier than the late ninth century. However, if the cross containing the runes was created in the early ninth century, as has been claimed, the Norsemen cannot have been its architects. In this case, an insoluble historical dilemma emerges – either Leek was named after an Old Norse word which was adopted at least forty years before the first Vikings arrived in the vicinity or, alternatively, the stone cross was erected on the site of the initial church forty years prior to the foundation of a settlement to support it! Obviously, neither of these options can be sustained. The alternative is that the Norsemen appeared in the Staffordshire Moorlands in the late ninth century, founded Leek, soon took an interest in the double sunset and later created and erected a stone cross on the site as they absorbed Christian ideas from their surrounding neighbours.

According to this scenario, the founding Norsemen were Danes, who had sailed to England as part of the Great Army in 865 and wreaked havoc until and beyond 877 when they annexed the eastern half of Mercia into the Danelaw. To the west, English Mercia remained nominally independent, but was initially virtually a client state of the powerful Danish confederation. Although the precise boundary line between these two regions remains highly conjectural, the Danelaw certainly included modern Derbyshire and most probably the Staffordshire Moorlands as well. In this case, the Danes who thus apparently founded Leek were able to do so as the site was within their sphere of permitted occupation, albeit towards the western limit of their direct influence and in the midst of indigenous Mercian settlements.

Although these Danes in Leek were a people quite separate from the Anglo-Saxons, they originated from the same roots and their culture and language were by no means dissimilar to those of their Mercian neighbours. From the outset, there must have been considerable communication between the two peoples, not only because it is extremely difficult to imagine the Danes living in complete isolation whilst being entirely surrounded by Mercian communities, but also as a result of their many common bonds. Consequently, it is easy to project the Danes soon including the Christian god in their polytheistic religion under the influence of their neighbours and the nearby Mercians taking an interest in the double sunset. Following this scenario, it can be seen that the erection in Leek of a stone cross containing runes by the Danes, perhaps even in conjunction with their English neighbours, in the late ninth or early tenth centuries constitutes no historical problem at all. In fact, the available evidence indicates that this is by far the most likely sequence of events.

The existence of runes on the cross in question suggests that the early double sunset observations were at minimum influenced by heathenism because runes were not only used as a pre-Latin alphabet by Germanic peoples, but they were also held to have magical properties. However, the sheer fact that a stone cross was erected near to, or even on, the phenomenon's midsummer viewing point shows that Christianity had made inroads onto the site. This may have been by design or by accident and it can only be conjectured as to whether early Christian events at Leek had any direct connection with observations of the double sunset. As the solstitial phenomenon was only a brief, weather-dependent annual event, it cannot have been long before Christian ceremonies were organised at other times of the year until at length they became events entirely independent of the sunset, as they remain today.

Almost certainly by the early tenth century, Christianity had harnessed the power of the double sunset attraction and began to flourish on the site. Although there has been speculation as to the purpose of the stone crosses of the Anglo-Saxon period, the eminent archaeologist of the period, David Wilson, made the following comments in his book, *The Anglo-Saxons*, which was published in 1971:

'The large stone crosses, sometimes 5m. high, which occur especially in the north of England, must be taken as marking preaching places or meeting places. It has been suggested that, when a community could not afford to build a church, a cross of wood or stone was erected and made the centre for Christian worship. There is a certain amount of evidence for this argument, despite the fact that many crosses are so rich that a small wooden church could have been built for the same price and in the same time as it would take to raise a cross . . . The surviving crosses nearly all stood in a churchyard, and such of them as do occur in the market-place of a town, as at Sandbach in Cheshire, were presumably removed there at the period of the Reformation. Even when there was a church they would be used as a centre for preaching. St. Oswald of Worcester, for example, in the tenth century, frequently preached near a memorial cross to congregations that were too big for his church.'

Therefore, if we apply Wilson's informed ideas, the stone crosses in St Edward's churchyard (and those almost certainly once including the fragments currently stored inside the church) formerly indicated the places where Christian worship occurred prior to, and perhaps even after, the building of the first church on the site. As Leek was only a small and relatively poor community, it can be reasonably conjectured that the rune-carved stone cross, and probably the other crosses too, predated the construction of the first religious building at the location. However, when the initial church was built, it drew a clear demarcation between Christian ceremonies, which became held inside the building, and double sunset events, which could continue to be observed outside.

Therefore, in conclusion, there is a plethora of myth and wild speculation surrounding the origins of man's involvement with Leek's double sunset. However, there is no noteworthy evidence to connect human observation of the occurrence from Leek to any period before at least the arrival of the Mercian Angles, no earlier than the fifth century. Even then, it is highly likely that regular viewing of the phenomenon did not begin until some time after 877 when a significant Danish settlement of eastern Mercia took place. The available evidence strongly suggests that, as part of this process, a band of Norsemen founded Leek on a site in very close proximity to the observation point of the double sunset, which these same people soon noticed and used to fine-tune their solar calendar. Finally, it is most probable that their initial viewings of the extraordinary midsummer event had a heathen connection because the Christian Church rapidly occupied the site, in accordance with its usual pervasive practice.

3 The Double Sunset History

Even though human observation of the double sunset at Leek in all probability actually has a much shorter history than has previously been argued, it has still exhibited enormous longevity. Nevertheless, it is not known for certain whether the event continued to be viewed, without interruption, from the Anglo-Saxon period until today. However, there is a vital and relatively reliable piece of written evidence which indicates that there was a break in the continuity of the observations and suggests that the phenomenon was being viewed anew shortly before its publication in 1686. All the other existing written source material, which was produced after this date, clearly indicates the churchyard double sunset observation to have been an ongoing, reasonably well-known custom. Consequently, the historical records reveal what appears to have been a single fracture in the proceedings, which were revived in due course.

Despite this, contemporary practice has shown that human interest in the occurrence is largely self-perpetuating. Although the most recent confirmed sighting of the double sunset from St Edward's churchyard occurred 24 years ago, and even then involved only a small fraction of the sun's disc, many hopeful people continue to frequent the site in good weather on the summer solstice every year without fail. Furthermore, the spectators are not identical from one year to the next – some people give up on the phenomenon, but new people take their place. The point is that the nucleus of interest is quite sufficient for human connection to the event to have survived 24 years of complete disappointment. Tradition dies hard.

It is possible only to speculate upon how long a period would have had to have passed before it could be argued that observation of the phenomenon had categorically ceased to exist, but it seems reasonable to suggest a time span of not less than the memory of the longest surviving witness of the phenomenon. Although it is not likely, at an extreme, this could even be approaching 100 years. Whatever the precise figure, it is therefore clear that once a sizable number of people, especially in a close-knit community such as Leek, begin to observe a regular natural event, interest in it will not easily entirely cease. Old habits also die hard! In addition, for the observation link to the Anglo-Saxon period to have been broken at some point, then interest in the occurrence must have been revived at a later stage, that is, the double sunset had to be rediscovered. However unlikely this may seem, it is exactly what appears to have happened, even though it might be expected that the same old tradition would have prevailed, as have so many other apparently timeless practices in England. A most pertinent case in point is Leek's Pickwood/Milltown Way double sunset observation site, which was referred to in *The Staffordshire Advertiser* on 22 June 1889, but probably fell into disuse the following century before being rediscovered in 2000 as a viewing area for the phenomenon.

Certainly, for the double sunset observations to have continued unbroken for over a millennium until today, they would have had to have exhibited considerable resilience, even taking into account that Leek's relatively isolated position largely sheltered it from the worst effects of the disasters which periodically occurred in England. However, apparently, the custom was not sufficiently established for it to have survived the complete passage of time intact. Although it is possible that interest in the phenomenon declined to such an extent that it simply died out, this is not at all likely, as I have already reasoned. The most plausible explanation by far for a break in the custom of observations is that a momentous event happened at some point, which focused the community's attention so strongly in another direction that people ceased to view the double sunset and all memory of its occurrence faded.

The vital piece of evidence which inferred that observations of the phenomenon had been revived, and therefore had ceased to exist at an earlier time, is contained within the book, *The Natural History Of Stafford-shire*, which was published in 1686. This work included a detailed account of the double sunset and its author was none other than Robert Plot LL.D., the keeper of the Ashmolean Museum, a professor of chemistry at Oxford University and a Fellow of the Royal Society. As it has transpired, Plot's monumental book contained not only the historic first known written reference to the midsummer occurrence, but also, inadvertently, notification that its observation had been in abeyance, perhaps for some considerable while:

'. . . the first thing I met with . . . was a pretty rural observation, of late years made by some of the Inhabitants of the Town of Leek in the Moorelands, of the setting of the Sun in the Summer Solstice, near a Hill called the Cloud . . .'

Plot's whole account is quoted later in this chapter and the rest of it does not concern us here. However, it is crystal clear, even from this snippet of information, that he was referring to Leek's double sunset. The key phrase which provides the clue that observation of the phenomenon had been revived is 'of late years made'. This means that a number of people in Leek had *recently*, in fact *only recently*, observed the occurrence. The sense of the text is quite unequivocal and it is of further significance that neither in this extract, nor in the full account, did Plot make any reference to, or even hint at, an ongoing tradition of double sunset observations. Indeed, if such a practice had been in existence, doubtless he would have mentioned it and most likely stressed it to the exclusion of his incisive comment that the observation had been recently undertaken, but apparently not previously. This is especially so because he specifically investigated the origins of 'strange customs' in his research for his book.

It can, of course, be argued that Plot's phrase was loosely written and not meant to be interpreted so literally, or that he had simply been misinformed. Indeed, as is well documented and shown later, his work was by no means free from error. Ironically, perhaps the most serious criticism that has been levelled at his efforts came from some of the very squires of Staffordshire who had provided him with information and who, apparently, bragged that they had 'humbugged old Plot'!

Nevertheless, these same gentlemen not only subscribed to his book, but also were flatteringly credited in its extensive acknowledgements. In addition, Plot's credentials were impressive. He was an eminent academic, the author of a previously published work on the natural history of Oxfordshire and a Doctor of Laws. Also, he made extensive use of questionnaires to enhance the accuracy of his secondary information sources, whilst he spent several years personally researching the natural history of Staffordshire prior to the publication of his book. Furthermore, Plot was highly critical of a number of the legends that he investigated, whose validity proved unfounded, and the respected historian, M.W. Greenslade, stated that Plot's natural history of the county 'stood alone' in importance for over 150 years. Under these circumstances, it can hardly be denied that Plot was well in a position to express accurately the information at his disposal and it is evident that a long tradition of double sunset observation from Leek was not unearthed by his research.

Having established that human observation of the midsummer phenomenon was most probably not continuous from the Anglo-Saxon age until today, it remains to be discovered as to when the apparent break in the proceedings occurred. This is an extremely difficult fact to uncover and it cannot be detected with any certainty.

The first and most likely cause of a fracture was the influence of the Christian Church upon the solstitial event. Although this was probably surreptitious in intent, it may well have had little adverse effect on the observations in the short run because the new religion's favourite strategy was initially to fit in with and eventually to subsume and harness existing heathen practices. According to this method of proceeding, an attempted immediate ban on double sunset viewing would have been almost certain to have been met with widespread refusal, if not anger, and therefore would have been counterproductive. The long term was considered to be more important and so it is highly likely that Christianity and the midsummer observations continued hand in hand for a while.

However, the status quo would undoubtedly have been altered, perhaps decisively so, when the first church was built on the site, probably in the early eleventh century. This development obviously led to Christian ceremonies being conducted inside the building, whilst the double sunset could only be observed outside, and this can only have served to break the link between the natural phenomenon and the prevailing religion. As Christian worship was a regular practice, but the double sunset an entirely weather-dependent annual event at best, it may well be that the occasional solstitial delight gradually became forgotten amidst the profusion of rites and celebrations occurring inside the church. In addition, in due course, when the firm adherents of Christianity became convinced that their faith had triumphed, it is highly likely that they openly frowned upon the heathen observation of the sun and applied at least moral pressure against perhaps a dwindling band of double sunset viewers to cease their activities.

A second possible threat to the midsummer observations was the cataclysmic Norman Conquest of 1066, with its profound effects on Anglo-Saxon England. This event was arguably the greatest disaster that has ever occurred in this country and consequently conveniently appears to offer the solution to the mystery of the disappearing sunset. The English ceased to be a free people with fundamental legal rights and were quickly reduced to 'subjects of the crown' as they became a distinct underclass of serfs bound to French-speaking lords. The Norman monarch took personal possession of the entire land and by 1086 only one per cent of the original Anglo-Saxon landowners continued to occupy their holdings. Those people who were sufficiently bold to offer resistance to these thefts were invariably forcibly removed, imprisoned or murdered.

Staffordshire itself bore some of the brunt of the worst excesses of the invaders following an uprising in western Mercia against the Norman yoke in 1069. In reprisal, the Norman army laid waste large areas in the county, but Leek seems to have emerged relatively unscathed from the genocide of the period because *Domesday Book* stated that the value of its land had increased from £4 before 1066 to 100s. in 1086. This compares favourably with around 55 villages in Staffordshire which were recorded as being 'waste' in 1086; with a number whose value had dropped over the twenty-year span and with many others whose value was listed as being the same. However, there was a sizable number of settlements in the shire whose worth had increased much more considerably than that of Leek, whilst the values coined before 1066 and in 1086 tend to cloak the situation in between. For example, Cubbington was worth 40s. on both those dates, but had slumped in value to a mere 2s. when King William had handed it out after the Conquest. This suggests that it had suffered devastation either directly or indirectly as a result of the invasion and it is possible that a similar sequence occurred in Leek, but that it was not recorded.

Irrespective of the statistical impact of the Norman Conquest, *Domesday Book* recorded that the land in Leek had passed from the protection of the Mercian earl, Aelfgar Leofricsson (Edwin Aelfgarsson actually), into the direct possession of the new monarch himself, William the Bastard. This meant that the village became ruled by a foreign absentee landlord and an alien culture replaced the community customs which had preceded it. At the same time, the Church fell under the control of foreign lords and its power was extended over the subjugated English serfs, who were forced to labour almost incessantly according to the requirements of the feudal system. If anything, this already dire situation was exacerbated when, by 1093, ownership of Leek was granted to the first Norman Earl of Chester, Hugh the Gross, who became notorious for the appalling neglect of his estate. Consequently, it is tantamount to certain that the new climate had an overwhelming negative effect on the prospect of observing double sunsets in Leek.

Although civil wars and revolts wreaked havoc on England and its people for centuries thereafter, the Staffordshire Moorlands remained backwaters and were therefore mainly closeted from the worst effects of decisive events. However, in 1374, William de Schepesheued recorded in his *Chronicle of the Abbey of Crokysden in Staforshire* that, 'the church of Leek was burnt down together with the whole town by mischance' on the night of 9 June 1297. This date, of course, was based on the old Julian calendar, which by then had retrograded from the tropical year by ten days. Therefore, according to the Gregorian calendar currently in use, the date of the conflagration was actually 19 June, just five days before the summer solstice of that year. Intriguingly, this raises the possibility that the blaze occurred while people from the town were checking the season's progress towards the midsummer double sunset. It can even be conjectured that the fire resulted from insufficient attention being paid to more mundane matters by an individual who became distracted by the excitement surrounding the astro-geographical phenomenon.

However, had this indeed been the reason for the conflagration, then it could be reasonably expected that de Schepesheued, as a monk, would have commented on it because it would have been easy and perhaps obvious for him to have blamed ungodly practices for the disaster. The fact that his annals are silent on this point, but instead use the term 'mischance', may well speak for itself.

Nevertheless, it is almost certain that the precise cause of the blaze will never be known.

Regardless of the specific reason for the fire, the consequent destruction would clearly have given the inhabitants of Leek rather more important things to think about than observing the double sunset on the summer solstice. Therefore, it is feasible that this catastrophic conflagration and its subsequent implications marked an end to the practice of double sunset viewing in Leek for 400 years by preoccupying the townspeople for a considerable time to come with the daunting task of both rebuilding their dwellings and restoring their fortunes. Their midsummer habit broken, it may not have been restored. In addition, if there was indeed a connection between the fire and the double sunset observation, the solstitial event may have become an ill omen thenceforth to be avoided. But that can only be speculated upon.

Another possible contender for the catalyst of the apparent cessation of double sunset observations from Leek was the Black Death of 1349, which killed between a third and a half of the people of the country before it subsided. Unfortunately, the effect of this particularly virulent epidemic of bubonic plague upon Leek was not recorded and therefore can only be inferred. On the surface, an absence of evidence suggests that the people of the town emerged relatively unscathed from this onslaught. However, Leek was only eighteen miles away from the famous plague village of Eyam and a reference in *The Register Of Edward The Black Prince Part III (Palatinate Of Chester) A.D. 1351-1365* hints that all was not well in the vicinity of the town.

Approximately three quarters of a mile to the north of Leek at this time was Dieulacres Abbey, a Cistercian monastery of considerable importance. Unfortunately, the population of the abbey immediately prior to the outbreak of the plague is unknown, but, on 11 April 1351, *The Register Of The Black Prince* noted 'the small number of monks at present serving God there'. In addition, J.C. Russell's *The Clerical Population of Medieval England*, published in 1944, recorded that there were seven monks living at the monastery in 1377 and ten in 1381. This indicates that most of the monks had been killed by the Black Death and that the population of the abbey made a slow recovery thereafter. The close proximity of Dieulacres to Leek in turn suggests that the impact of the plague upon Leek may well have been significant. If this is true, then inevitably the economic infrastructure of the town would have been seriously adversely affected, if not threatened with complete collapse. Such a crisis, of course, would have left little time and scope for observations of the double sunset and it could be that by the time Leek had recovered from its ordeal, the midsummer tradition had terminated. Once more, however, any conclusion can only be speculative.

The final and least likely period in which it can be feasibly argued that regular double sunset observations can have discontinued is that around the seventeenth century Civil Wars. Leek and the Staffordshire Moorlands essentially supported the cause of Parliament and, in November 1642, the locals, perhaps in conjunction with a force of Roundhead regulars, repelled a small band of pillaging Royalists led by Sir Francis Wortley. Although twenty Cavaliers were taken prisoner, this action cannot have amounted to much and it is clear that it caused little interruption to the affairs of the town. However, in December 1643, there was considerable panic amongst the townspeople upon the approach of the cavalry of the Royalist commander, Colonel Gamaliel Dudley, who had just routed the 'English High-landers' at the Battle of Hartington. Some sources have since recorded Leek as having been occupied by these Cavaliers, probably as the result of a tentative report to that effect in number 49 of the Parliamentary weekly news pamphlet, *Certaine Informations*. However, they were actually intercepted shortly before their arrival and defeated by a troop of Roundheads under Major Mollanus, who took about thirty of them prisoner. Mollanus' force then quartered in Leek for a fortnight, thereby bolstering the morale of the locals, before marching out to Derby. Consequently, there was little upheaval in Leek during this period, whilst the two most exciting events, just outlined, clearly occurred near to the opposite end of the calendar from the double sunset and therefore are extremely unlikely to have had any negative effect upon its observation.

According to the 1862 edition of John Sleigh's *A History of the Ancient Parish of Leek, in Staffordshire*, of greater impact on the town was a further outbreak of bubonic plague in 1646, which was apparently so rampant that it raged into the following year. The Plague Stone on Cheddleton Road continues to serve as a reminder of the effects of the epidemic, which were so severe that it is believed that the market was effectively transferred to its vicinity on the periphery of Leek in order to reduce the possibilities of contamination. Apparently, to try to avoid contracting the disease, rural farmers left their supplies by the stone and returned later to collect the vinegar-soaked payments of the stricken townsfolk. Nevertheless, there were few, if any, adverse long-term effects on the prosperity of Leek because in 1670 its market was rated as the third largest in the whole of Staffordshire.

In addition, in the 1883 subscribers' edition of Sleigh's book, the year of the plague was changed to 1699, suggesting that the author had discovered his original dating to have been wrong. Indeed, a footnote in this second edition lists ten dates from 1644 to 1794 when Sleigh believed 'waves of epidemic disease' had 'passed over the town', but 1646 and 1647 were not amongst them, although 1644 was! However, the parish records for 1644 show the number of baptisms to have been not far off double the number of burials, thereby casting serious doubt on Sleigh's accuracy on this count too.

Furthermore, Sleigh's original date of this devastating plague has been recently challenged by the local historian, Robert Milner, the editor of *Cheddleton: North Staffordshire: A Village History*. Detailed research undertaken by Robert on the baptisms, marriages and burials in Leek has actually revealed a normal pattern of events in the years 1646 and 1647, but no baptisms at all in 1699 and 1700, during which years the burials soared to around double their typical number. Therefore, it may well be that there was actually no epidemic in the town in 1646-1647 or that its effects were relatively mild, with the indication that the most serious outbreak of plague occurred somewhat later than Sleigh had originally suggested and, indeed, after the double sunset had first been noted by Robert Plot. Any way round, it appears to be highly improbable that an outbreak of plague in Leek in the mid-seventeenth century can have led to the termination of double sunset observations at the churchyard.

A further factor strongly indicates that the events of the 1640s are extremely unlikely to have caused Leek's solstitial observations to have ceased altogether and that is that it was only four decades later when Robert Plot stated categorically that the double sunset had been seen shortly before 1686. A maximum interlude of forty years seems far too short a period for the occurrence to have been considered a relatively newly observed phenomenon in 1686. Indeed, had the tradition been revived so soon after it had been discontinued, well within the memory span of many of the townspeople, it seems most probable that Plot would either have mentioned its recent restoration or, alternatively, noted that the observation custom was long standing. Instead, he recorded the phenomenon as having been viewed only shortly before the publication of his book.

In summary, Robert Plot's comments regarding the double sunset in his book of 1686 clearly indicate that the phenomenon had been recently, and only recently, encountered by a number of people from Leek. In addition, although Plot had impeccable credentials and discussed the phenomenon in considerable detail, he made no mention of a tradition of midsummer observations, as we would expect him to have done. Furthermore, in a town as small and close-knit as Leek, it seems extremely unlikely that a custom based on such an unusual occurrence would not have come to Plot's attention, especially because the source of his information was the inhabitants themselves. Therefore, it must be concluded that the viewing of the event has most probably not been continuous over the last millennium. However, no other fracture in the proceedings is revealed by the available, and probably sufficiently common, evidence since 1686.

A study of the main crises in Leek's history, which can be reasonably argued to have enabled a cultural collapse resulting in the termination of the solstitial observations, reveals that distant events seem more likely to hold the key to the explanation of the disappearing sunset rather than ones relatively recent to 1686. In particular, there occurred a cluster of developments in the eleventh century that combined, and perhaps individually, appear to have been well potent enough to have halted the observations and eradicated the recollection of the phenomenon from the collective consciousness of the townspeople. However, because of a lack of specific evidence, the precise cause of the probable void until the late seventeenth century will almost certainly remain speculative.

Nevertheless, the double sunset phenomenon first entered known written history in 1686 with the publication of Robert Plot's most opportune book, *The Natural History Of Stafford-shire*. It is of interest that Plot reported the midsummer event as being seen from St Edward's churchyard, even though there are other and better places than Leek to witness the double sunset behind The Cloud, and indeed there are other hills in the southern Peak District which produce a more spectacular event, as I will show later. However, by the 1680s, Leek had a great advantage over its mainly rural, and quite possibly unknown, rival observation points – it was relatively heavily populated and amongst its most frequented spots was the churchyard with its burial ground, its fine views and, of course, its access to the church.

Therefore, it is extremely likely that the double sunset at Leek came to Plot's attention because one or more people from the town accidentally noticed its occurrence when they were out on other business in the churchyard. Consequently, it is highly probable that the prime reason why the occurrence became specifically connected with Leek, rather than elsewhere, had nothing to do with its uniqueness or even any particular viewing excellence, but instead was simply because there were sufficient numbers of people for it to be first spotted and then regularly monitored from that location. Nevertheless, as can be seen from Plot's comments, which are quoted in full because of their historic significance and notable implications, the apparently new discovery was quickly considered to be a rather exciting one:

'To come then forthwith to the subject in hand, the Natural History of the County of Stafford; the first thing I met with relating to the Heavens, and one of the first too that I heard of after I set to work in earnest, was a pretty rural observation, of late years made by some of the Inhabitants of the Town of Leek in the Moorelands, of the setting of the Sun in the Summer Solstice, near a Hill called the Cloud, about six miles distant, in the confines of Stafford-shire and Cheshire; which appearing almost perpendicular on the Northern side, to such persons as are standing in Leek Church-yard, the Sun seems so nicely at that time of year to cut the Edg of it at setting, as in Tab.1. Fig.1. that notwithstanding what is taught by Astronomers, that the Sun whilst it occupies that Cardinal point, appears Stationary for some time without giving any sensible increase or decrease to the length of the days; they can plainly perceive by the help of this Hill, that no two days are equal, but that there is a sensible difference every day: just as at the Temple of Tentiris in Egypt where there are as many Windows as days in the year, so placed, that the Sun rising in a different degree of the Zodiac every day, it also sends in its beams every day into a distinct Window from the day before. For when the Sun comes near the Solstice, the whole disk of it at first sets behind the Hill, after a while the Northern Limb first appears, and so every night gradually more, till at length the whole Diameter comes to set Northward of it, for about three nights; but the middle night of the three, very sensibly more remote, than the former or the following, when beginning its recess from the Tropic, it still continues more and more to be hidden every night, till at length it descends quite behind it again.

Which Phaenomenon though worth notice for its own sake alone, yet might be render'd of much more use to the Publick, would the Curious that for the most part reside thereabout, make annual and more strict observations for the future by suitable Instruments, noteing every year the day precisely, that the limb of the Sun cuts the edge of the Hill, and how many Digits or parts of Digits, of its own Diameter, it daily advances; also carefully noteing the nearest distance 'twixt the edge of the Hill, and the Rim of the Sun, on the very day of the Solstice, and lastly the Mean between both: For by this means in time the Suns greatest Northern Declination (which Astronomers say is less now than heretofore) may be gradually adjusted, and at length perhaps limited; Which I take to be an Experiment of so valuable a Consideration, that I cannot but recommend it to my worthy friends the Worshipful Thomas Rudyerd of Rudyerd Esquire [the Sheriff of Staffordshire], Mr. Parker [probably the lawyer, Thomas Parker], and Mr. Thomas Gent [also a lawyer]; at least that they would take care in some one year or other, when there is least of Refraction upon account of the Atmosphere, from some fixt point, so to adjust the distance betwixt the Hill and the Sun on the day of the Solstice by an Azimuthal quadrant, the new Micrometer, or some other agreeable Instrument, that future Ages however (if it cannot be in this) may see the difference.'

To the modern eye, Plot's account of the double sunset might well appear to be rather rambling and long-winded, but it should be borne in mind that he lived in an age of less speed, or indeed haste, than now and his style is not untypical of learned writing in his era. Therefore, Plot's delivery should not turn us away from the real value of his comments. His description of the phenomenon essentially rings true, but reveals the reappearance of a considerably larger proportion of the sun's disc than might be anticipated through an observation from Leek of the comparative size of The Cloud and the sun. From the churchyard, The Cloud appears on the horizon as a relatively small feature and the sun looms large when set against its summit and scarp slope. Despite taking into account possible minor changes in the shape of the hill since Plot's time, caused by quarrying, it is not geometrically feasible that the 'whole diameter' (even if that means only half) of the disc regularly reappeared at midsummer after the sun had fully set behind The Cloud, as the extract said it did. Although a precise calculation of the exact proportion of the sun to re-emerge during a double sunset was extremely difficult to achieve in the pre-camera age, it is surprising that Plot's dimension was some way adrift of possibility. Consequently, this is one of several factors which indicate that he did not actually witness the solstitial phenomenon himself, but that he transcribed as accurately as he could the details which were related to him.

It is quite possible that Plot had not even visited the churchyard before he wrote his book because his description of the northern slope of The Cloud being 'almost perpendicular' is a fair exaggeration of reality, even taking into account the effects of quarrying since the seventeenth century. However, his description becomes altogether more understandable if it is accepted that he was working from second-hand information. In addition, if Plot had personally observed all the double sunsets he outlined, which clearly stretched over several days around the summer solstice, it would almost certainly have taken him a number of years to have been fully successful because of the unreliable weather experienced in the Moorlands. It is very doubtful whether he could have spared the time to have undertaken all these observations personally, or even have been inclined to have held up the publication of his book for several years until everything was eventually revealed, especially because he was already under considerable pressure from his subscribers well before the date of publication. It seems much more likely that, as the compiler of a tome on the natural history of the whole of Staffordshire, he was to a fair extent reliant on the assistance of other parties and the use of theoretical data, particularly in dealing with tricky and not easily observable phenomena, such as the double sunset.

Furthermore, Plot's Tab.1. Fig.1. is a highly inaccurate depiction of the shape of The Cloud, which is essentially a ridge with a significant scarp slope. However, Plot's version shows an isolated, extremely steep-sided hill, with a profile which is completely unrecognisable as The Cloud and entirely out of keeping with the topography of the surrounding area. Even allowing for the possibility that the illustration was designed to highlight the effect of the double sunset, rather than be strictly accurate, it is still well short of the mark as a representative image. Consequently, this adds further weight to the argument that he had not actually observed The Cloud from the churchyard prior to the publication of his tome.

Finally, Plot also presented information in his book regarding the "Narrowdale noon", the incidence of which was, and still is, much easier to observe than the double sunset, but, unfortunately, his facts were not entirely accurate. He stated that the inhabitants of Narrowdale, near to Alstonefield, 'for that quarter of the year, wherein the *Sun* is nearest the *Tropic* of *Capricorn*, never see it at all; and at length when it does begin to appear again . . . they never see it till about *one* by the *clock*, which they call thereabout, the *Narrowdale noon*: using it proverbially when they would express a thing done late at noone.'

However, when I arrived personally at Narrowdale at 12.15 p.m. on 18 June 1999, to check out this phenomenon, I discovered that the sun was blazing brightly, high in the sky, and it clearly had been doing so for quite some while. Furthermore, the real discrepancy was over an hour greater still, as the actual time in Plot's day would have been approximately 11.08 a.m. This is because British Summer Time was created only in 1916 and a local time system was used in England in the seventeenth century. Therefore, on the first count, in the 1680s, it was an hour earlier and a further seven minutes needed to be deducted because Narrowdale is approximately 1.82° west of Greenwich, so that solar noon occurs slightly later in the Peak District than in east London. Nevertheless, my observations at Narrowdale on 19 November 1999 and 18 March 2000 broadly substantiated Plot's assertion that the sun was not visible at all from the settlement for an extensive period either side of the winter solstice. Consequently, this mixture of fact and error in Plot's account suggests that he dutifully inscribed in his book the provided details on this phenomenon and, consequently, there is every chance that he did the same regarding the double sunset.

Nevertheless, there is much valid substance in Plot's account. It certainly reveals his awareness of the essential astronomical aspects of the phenomenon, for example, the continuing decline of the obliquity of the ecliptic, which was, and still is, gradually shifting the sunset at the summer solstice southwards along The Cloud's dip slope. Plot was also clearly aware that the refraction of light by the earth's atmosphere could affect the apparent position of the setting sun as seen by the viewer and he strongly recommended that the key aspects of the phenomenon should be carefully measured through the use of scientific instruments, although there is no evidence to suggest that this was ever done.

The next known report of the double sunset phenomenon appeared in three consecutive issues of *The Gentleman's Magazine* in 1738. The May edition of Volume VIII featured a letter by R. Brookes regarding 'Whether the Obliquity of the Ecliptick has always continued the same, or whether it has been subject to some little variation.' Intriguingly, Brookes suggested that this problem could be effectively resolved by observing Leek's double sunset:

'Now I have thought of a Method that will go a great Way towards the Determination of this Dispute, especially with regard to the later Observations; and this is to be done by a Quadrant, the Radius of which is no less than six Miles in Length. I make no doubt, but at first Sight this will be taken to be nothing but a wild *Chimera*, and yet nothing upon Examination will appear more plain or practicable. What I mean, is a *Solar Occultation* behind a Hill called the *Cloud*, on the Borders of *Staffordshire*; which Dr. *Plot* has given the World an Account of about 60 years ago. This Hill is so situated with respect to the Church-yard of *Leek*, a Market-Town in the same County, and six Miles distant from the Hill, that a Spectator standing there of an Evening three or four Days before the 10th of *June*, when the Sun enters the Beginning of *Cancer*, beholds the Disk of the Sun gradually emerging from behind the Northward Side of the Hill, which is nearly perpendicular; and this in such a manner, that a very sensible Difference is perceived in the Sun's Motion every Evening, and at length the whole Disk emerges for three Days together, but the second very evidently more distant than the first and last. Now as the Sun's Declination on those three Days does not vary above one third of a Minute, it will be easy to discover, whether the Obliquity of the Ecliptick is the same as it was in Dr *Plot's* Time, or not: For if it is but 23° 28′ 20″ as the *French* astronomers assert, then the Sun's Disk will not entirely emerge from behind the Hill unless Mr *Flamstead's* Observations were faulty: But if the Emersion is entire, and for three Days only, as formerly, we may then reasonably conclude that the greatest Obliquity has been invariable for 60 Years at least, and if for 60, why not for 6,000? However, this *Solar Occultation* will be a very agreeable Sight to the Curious who reside in those Parts; and if they transmit their Observations to you to be communicated to the Publick, it will be a very acceptable Favour to all Lovers of Astronomical Enquiries.'

Although Brookes repeated Robert Plot's proposal for careful observations of the double sunset geometry to be undertaken, he did not seem particularly familiar with the phenomenon, which suggested that he had never seen it nor ever visited Leek. Indeed, his knowledge of the occurrence appears to have been strongly, if not entirely, based on information contained in Plot's tome. Certainly, a lack of empirical experience explains why Brookes believed The Cloud to have been 'nearly perpendicular', when it almost definitely was not, and why he thought that 'the whole disk' of the sun reappeared after setting, which was impossible except perhaps under extremely rare atmospheric conditions. However, his inference that the summer solstice was then on 10 June was quite correct because the Gregorian calendar, which switched the date of midsummer to 21 June, was not adopted in England until 1752. Finally, it seems tantamount to certain that 'Mr *Flamstead*', to whom Brookes referred, was none other than the famous Astronomer Royal, John Flamsteed.

The following edition of *The Gentleman's Magazine*, in June 1738, contained a letter, dated the 26th of that month, from an unnamed author in Leek:

'It is our annual Custom to make Observations from our Church-yard of the Sun's setting some nights before and after the 10th of June, and there's no Person now living that has discover'd the least Variation in its Course, but as it gradually moves to its utmost point, so it returns in the same manner; and that the Curious may have the better Idea how it appears to us I have sent you a Plan. The only ocular Observation that could be made this Year was the 7th, all the other Evenings now Cloudy.'

The plan, which was referred to, actually arrived too late for inclusion in this particular issue and was held over to the following edition. Nevertheless, the letter itself contained a number of interesting pieces of information. Firstly, the writer got straight to the point and stated that there existed in Leek an annual custom of observing the double sunset. This was something that Robert Plot had not done, despite having written at much greater length on the subject, and it therefore provides more evidence that the modern tradition of viewing the midsummer event goes back no further than approximately the 1680s. Also, the letter revealed that the summer solstice was then rightly annually observed at Leek on 10 June, whilst the writer strongly suggested that the double sunset had actually been seen on 7 June that year, in which case it was the very first time that a specifically dated successful viewing of the phenomenon had ever been recorded in writing. Certainly, as the observation window of the occurrence spread across considerably more of St Edward's upper churchyard in 1738 than it has done recently, there is good reason to believe that the double sunset was indeed witnessed three evenings prior to midsummer that year.

Happily, the author's plan was published in the July issue of the magazine and appeared as four diagrams, placed in a vertical row, beneath the following introduction:

'The four following Schemes represent the four successive Phases of the Sun in his approach to, or Recess from the Summer Tropic, as he gradually emerges from, or absconds behind a Hill in Staffordshire called the Cloud 6 Miles distant from a Spectator in Leek Churchyard; as it has been observed from thence many Years, for 2 or 3 Days before and after the 10th of June.'

Unfortunately, the accuracy of these diagrams, as with Robert Plot's drawing, leaves a lot to be desired. The angle of the sunset depicted is far too shallow and, in the third and fourth sketches, becomes almost horizontal, an impossible situation, as a result of which the disc would have taken hours to set, if not been transformed into the midnight sun! In addition, the illustrations portray the whole of the sun reappearing after setting and this is an inconceivable concept given the relative sizes of The Cloud, as seen from the churchyard, and the sun, as well as the angle of the sunset. However, the artist made a much better attempt than Plot to capture the essential shape of The Cloud, delineating both its relatively gentle dip slope and its steeper scarp slope, albeit in considerably exaggerated form and with slight, but perceptible, alterations in its shape in each of the diagrams.

The introductory passage to the diagrams is in itself of interest, telling us that the double sunset had been witnessed from Leek for quite some time and that the event had been observed for up to three days both before and after the summer solstice. This is well believable because a seven-day viewing period would have given quite a strong chance that the phenomenon would have been seen in most years and the observation potential from the churchyard would very likely have stretched to three days either side of midsummer, as has just been noted. Thus the considerable length of the churchyard's north-facing side would probably have enabled the observers to have moved to nearby viewing positions still within its boundaries during the stated period before and after the solstice. In conclusion, these comments and the overall validity of the data as contributed to the magazine indicate that it is almost certain that a number of people did indeed witness the double sunset from Leek for a period up to 1738.

The next writer known to have made reference to the midsummer phenomenon was the Rev. Mr. Nightingale in his book, *A Topographical And Historical Description Of The County Of Stafford*, in 1820:

'This town is remarkable also for the following singular circumstance. By the intervention of one of those craggy mountains which we have already described, at a considerable distance westward of the town, the sun sets twice in the same evening at a certain time of the year; for after it sets behind the top of the mountain, it breaks out again on the northern side of it, which is steep, before it reaches the horizon in its fall. So that within a very few miles, the inhabitants have the rising-sun when he has, in fact, past [sic] his meridian, as at Narrowdale, before noticed, and the setting-sun twice in the space of a very few hours, as here at Leek.'

It is clear that Nightingale had little knowledge and no first-hand experience of the double sunset, as is indicated by his failure to know at what time of year the event occurred and by his erroneous statement that the unnamed Cloud lay to the west of Leek. What little valid fact he did present seems to have been taken from Robert Plot's book because he both mentioned the latter in his account and cited his mistaken details regarding the "Narrowdale noon".

In 1851, William White made a more original attempt to outline the solstitial event in his publication, which was less notable for its accuracy than its remarkable 160-word title: *History, Gazetteer, And Directory, Of Staffordshire, And The City And County Of The City Of Lichfield, Comprising, Under A Lucid Arrangement Of Subjects, A General Survey of the County of Stafford, And The Diocese Of Lichfield & Coventry; With Separate Historical, Statistical, & Topographical Descriptions Of All The Boroughs, Towns, Parishes, Villages, Hamlets, Manors, And Liberties, In The Five Hundreds Of The Shire; Shewing Their Extent And Population, Their Agriculture, Mines, and Manufactures; their Markets, Fairs, Races, and Festivals; their Eminent Men; the Lords of the Manors and Owners of the Soil and Tithes; the Patrons and Incumbents of the Church Livings; the Antiquities, Public Charities, and Institutions; the Civil and Ecclesiastical Jurisdictions; the Names and Addresses of the principal Inhabitants; the Mediums of Public Conveyance by Land and Water; the Seats Of Nobility And Gentry; Lists Of Public Officers; And a Variety of other Commercial, Agricultural, & Biographical Information, In One Volume, with a large Map of the County.*

White had the following to say about the double sunset:

'The higher part of the churchyard commands an extensive view of the "Roches," and the other rocky hills to the north and west; and at the summer solstice, the sun appears to set twice on the same evening, behind the conical peak of one of these lofty mountains, called the Hencloud; for after sinking below the top of this hill, it breaks out again on the northern side of it, before it sinks below the horizon.'

It is a great pity that White did not pay as much attention to his facts regarding the midsummer phenomenon as he did to ensuring nothing noteworthy was absent from the title of his book. Like the Rev. Mr. Nightingale, White was all at sea with his directions because there were no 'rocky hills' visible to the west from Leek and The Cloud was definitely not a 'conical peak'! This description more applied to Hen Cloud, which lies slightly east of north from Leek, but no double sunset occurred behind this hill. Therefore White was in a state of some confusion and, obviously, had never witnessed the solstitial occurrence himself.

In 1862, John Sleigh also commented on the double sunset, in his previously mentioned book, *A History of the Ancient Parish of Leek, in Staffordshire*:

'From the higher churchyard is an extensive and varied view, embracing the Roches, Cloud, etc.; and at the summer solstice the sun seems thence to set twice; for, disappearing behind the latter mountain, he again shows himself on the north side, before finally sinking beneath the horizon.'

Although Sleigh's comments made a reasonable stab at describing the phenomenon, he added nothing beyond what had already appeared in print, which indicated that he too had not actually seen the event for himself. Indeed, he then went on to quote both Plot and Nightingale and repeated the latter's erroneous claim regarding the occurrence of the "Narrowdale noon" around the time of the summer solstice.

However, on 25 June 1870, *The Staffordshire Advertiser* included a precise report on the double sunset, which contained, for the first time, descriptions of specific events on particular days:

'DOUBLE SUNSET – This peculiar phenomenon was witnessed on Monday [20th] and Wednesday [22nd]. Tuesday evening sunset was overcast with thick clouds, which, of course, obstructed any observation, but on the other evening's [sic] mentioned a few of the knowing ones were stationed in the parish churchyard, and with great interest watched the retiring sun sink behind the cloud at Bosley, and shortly after again appear at the extremity of the hill and again fall away in the distance in the usual manner.'

The article then went on to quote Robert Plot and John Sleigh, presumably in order to add more meat to the topic, but, in doing so, covered no new ground. Nevertheless, the newspaper's report of two actual observed occurrences was of historic importance, whilst the scant details which it included were, as it turned out, surprisingly informative. Certainly, the fact that the sun re-emerged only at the base of the scarp slope after setting had a ring of authenticity about it, especially because that was exactly what happened in the video-recorded 1977 midsummer event. In other words, just a small portion of the sun reappeared and only fairly briefly, precisely as was determined from the spectators' viewing points by the geometry of The Cloud. In addition, the article revealed that the phenomenon had been seen from St Edward's churchyard on the evening either side of the summer solstice, which strongly suggested that the double sunset was visible for at least three consecutive nights at that time, weather permitting.

Fourteen years elapsed before a further account of a witnessed double sunset was recorded and this was published by *The Leek Times* in its 18 July 1884 edition:

'The phenomena [sic] for which Leek is famous, namely the double setting of the sun as seen in the old churchyard, was eagerly watched for this year; but except on the evening of the 18th [June], every sunset was obscured. On the 18th, however, the sun went down in right royal splendour, his disc measuring against one-third of the Cloud hill as it is seen from the churchyard. After he had disappeared, the shadows of evening peeped out and were just beginning to steal into the valleys, when the lord of the day suddenly looked forth from behind the foot of the Cloud end, and night and darkness stept [sic] back abashed. In olden days, before the rock (called "Bully-thrumble") on the crest of the Cloud was blasted down, and before the fir trees on the ridge beyond Packsaddle Hollow took off somewhat of the lower height of the hill, the double sunsets must have been glorious sights. We believe that the phenomena may still be seen from Leek Moor for a few nights longer.'

This account was not written by one of the newspaper's reporters, but was credited to *St. Luke's Magazine*, which, it seems, had already printed it prior to its discovery by *The Leek Times*. This explains why the newspaper reported the event rather belatedly.

There can be practically no doubt that the double sunset as described was indeed seen on 18 June 1884. The account contains precise and quite believable details, indicating some disappointment regarding what was actually witnessed. It is of considerable significance that the event was viewed three days before the solstice and it is therefore not surprising that the sun reappeared (almost certainly as just a small fragment) only at the base of the scarp slope of The Cloud because the sunset had still not reached its summer maximum position. From the same viewing point, the reappearance of a progressively greater percentage of the sun's disc could have been expected on each of the following three days had cloud not intervened.

The author of the article showed further familiarity with the phenomenon and the local environment by complaining that alterations to the visible profile of The Cloud had adversely affected the observational impact of the double sunset. Bully Thrumble had been referred to and described by John Sleigh in 1862 and this feature may well have been destroyed during the quarrying of the hill for the construction of the Macclesfield Canal at some point between 1828 and 1830, or possibly the Macclesfield to Colwich and Norton Bridge railway line, which was built between 1845 and 1849. However, the precise location of Bully Thrumble is unknown and it is far from conclusive that its demolition significantly altered the effect of the phenomenon, as observed from Leek. Although the likelihood of this is discussed later in this book, it should be borne in mind that the author of the 1884 feature was commenting on an event which had occurred at least 35 years previously and it is clear that his comments were purely speculative. Therefore, he had no first-hand experience of seeing the double sunset before the destruction of Bully Thrumble and so no direct comparison with the relative visual impact afterwards can be made.

The author's comment regarding the growth of the trees affecting the visibility of the lower section of The Cloud is also interesting as this was most likely a major problem to the viewers because the sun had reappeared so far down the scarp slope owing to the fact that the summer solstice remained another three days away. Had the event on 21 June not been obscured by cloud, an observer standing in the optimum position in the churchyard would almost certainly have seen the sun start to re-emerge higher up the scarp slope and stay in view in varying proportions as it travelled down the edge of the hill before setting near to the spot at which it had been seen on the 18th. In other words, the trees near the base of The Cloud would most probably not have spoiled the main part of the event, which would have occurred above this point.

Finally, the writer's comment that the double sunset was expected to 'be seen from Leek Moor for a few nights longer' is well worth examining. This is the first known written statement to suggest that the phenomenon could be witnessed from somewhere other than St Edward's churchyard and that in itself makes it important. However, Leek Moor is now generally considered to be the area around Mount Road, which was not then in an alignment to produce a double sunset around midsummer and so it must be deduced that the writer was actually referring to Lowe Hill. Although the approximate dates on which the author was indicating that the event could be observed from this location were not given, it is highly likely that he was inferring them to have been from around 25 June onwards and, if so, his impressions were most probably accurate.

The solstitial phenomenon was also mentioned in John Alfred Langford's book, *Staffordshire And Warwickshire, Past And Present*, which is thought by The

British Library to have been published that same year, 1884. However, despite possessing impressive qualifications (LL.D., F.R.H.S.), Langford simply repeated the Rev. Mr. Nightingale's flawed description of the occurrence exactly word for word, apart from correcting the latter's misspelling of 'passed'!

Fortunately, altogether more perceptive information was revealed about the phenomenon by *The Staffordshire Advertiser* on 22 June 1889:

'THE DOUBLE SUNSET – This can now be seen from the churchyard and Pickwood Recreation Ground. It continues to be visible for some days later near Lowe Hill Bridge, beginning at Dale's Farm, and swinging each day further north along the road as the sun goes back and sets at a point further south.'

Perhaps the most interesting aspect of this pertinent item is its matter-of-fact delivery. It simply stated accurately Leek's three main observation sites for the double sunset and commented on their longevity in an unexcited manner, indicating considerable familiarity with the phenomenon. It is noteworthy that Lowe Hill was for the first time specifically listed as a vantage point of the occurrence, in addition to the churchyard, although Dale's Farm is not named on the 1879, 1889, 1900 and 1925 Ordnance Survey maps held by Staffordshire Record Office and its location has consequently not been identified. Nevertheless, the newspaper's reference to Pickwood Recreation Ground is particularly intriguing, providing clear evidence that the event had also been previously seen from this area. However, in the following century, the Pickwood site became so unfashionable as a double sunset viewing point that it was probably abandoned altogether before being rediscovered in June 2000.

Surprisingly, no follow-up report on the outcome of the solar observations that June appeared in *The Staffordshire Advertiser* and the double sunset was next referred to in 1891, in the book, *Olde Leeke: Historical, Biographical, Anecdotal, and Archaeological*, which was edited by Matthew Henry Miller M.I.J. Unfortunately, "W.S.B.", the contributor on this particular feature, added nothing to what had been written previously on the topic and instead extensively quoted the accounts of Robert Plot and *The Gentleman's Magazine*, although a reproduction of the 1738 woodcut enlivened the item somewhat. Nevertheless, a second article in Miller's book, entitled *A "Doctors' Corner" in the Old Churchyard*, contained a brief but pertinent comment about the solstitial phenomenon:

'The fine old elm tree, round which is placed seats for the lame or lazy, is the centre of the "corner," and on the same spot the *savants* used to assemble to watch the "double sunset." '

Thus, for the first time in recorded history, a precise observation position of the occurrence was given, although the text was infuriatingly vague as to since when in time it had been in use. Nevertheless, it can be inferred from the extract that Miller regarded "Doctors' Corner" as a fixed viewing point for the phenomenon, which therefore strongly suggests that the tree marked the spot where spectators assembled to watch the double sunset in the late nineteenth century. Certainly, according to both the extremely slow progress eastwards of the viewing point of the phenomenon and calculations made from Kevin Kilburn's churchyard observation windows map, there is no reason to doubt that this was the case.

Unfortunately, this tree no longer exists, but its stump remains in "Doctors'

Corner" indicating where it once stood. In addition, the well-known local film maker and photographer, Gerald Mee, possesses a photograph which he took of the northeastern part of the upper churchyard and this clearly shows both the tree and a circular seat, along with other currently identifiable features. The stump lies immediately west of the Eli and Isaac Cope tombstones, only a few feet from the north wall of the churchyard and the eastern edge of "Doctors' Corner". Thus Miller had accurately recorded a perfectly valid double sunset observation position, which was most probably the main assembly point in his day, as well as long into the twentieth century.

Leek's midsummer phenomenon also found inclusion in the second edition of *The Official Illustrated Holiday Guide To The North Staffordshire Railway*, which was likewise published in 1891. However, like Miller's book, it quoted Plot's entire report of the phenomenon word for word, apart from errors which were introduced during transcription, and again relied heavily on R. Brookes' letter of 1738. At least this publication managed some original comment, even though it amounted to nothing in terms of substance:

' "What is the most remarkable thing about Leek?" was the question we put to a friend of ours who had spent the best part of his threescore and ten years in that district and was pretty well acquainted with its history, past and present. "The double sunset," was the answer he gave us.

This remarkable occurrence is seen by the spectator standing in Leek churchyard, which is about six miles distant from the "Cloud" which he faces as the sun is setting. It is only noticeable at midsummer . . .'

The only point in this extract that differed from what had gone before was the statement that the event could only be witnessed at midsummer, which was either vague or inaccurate, strictly speaking. This is shown by the 18 July 1884 feature in *The Leek Times*, which had already effectively proved that the occurrence could be viewed to varying degrees of satisfaction for several days either side of the summer solstice.

As the fame of the double sunset spread, the phenomenon found its way into the 1892 edition of *Murray's Handbook For Travellers in Derby, Notts, Leicester, and Stafford*:

'The view from the ch.-yard, looking N., is exceedingly fine. To the W. is the *Cloud Hill* (1190ft.), behind which, for a few days in summer-time, the sun appears to set twice, reappearing on its northern side after sinking out of sight.'

This reference to the double sunset clearly presented the phenomenon in a nutshell, but was somewhat confused in its directions. The Cloud is in fact northwest from St Edward's churchyard, whilst arguably the most spectacular outlook is to the north-northeast in the direction of The Roaches. Also, the extract exaggerated the height of the hill by some 62 feet and was extremely vague as to when the occurrence could be seen.

However, a further successful double sunset observation was announced, by *The Staffordshire Advertiser*, on 29 June 1895:

'THE DOUBLE SUNSET – This was seen, but not well this year. Banks of cloudy smoke lay beyond Cloud Hill on the 22nd inst, and dimmed the radiance of the sun, which nevertheless was seen to set above and again beyond the end of the hill. After its setting on Saturday [the 22nd] it was seen again below Cloud Hill through a rift in the clouds.'

It is interesting to note the report's disappointment that the nevertheless successful occurrence had been a less glorious and spectacular sunset than anticipated. It suggests that the phenomenon's observers at this time were used to seeing altogether brighter double sunsets, in spite of the high incidence of air pollution in this age of steam. Nevertheless, the fact that the event had proved visible regardless of the 'banks of cloudy smoke' on the line of the setting sun indicates the capacity of the phenomenon to survive the adverse effects of man on the atmosphere.

The double sunset progressed from fame to great acclaim in 1905 when the occurrence was promoted by Fredk. Wm. Hackwood in his book, *Staffordshire Curiosities & Antiquities*:

'The county boasts a natural phenomenon which is surely unique.

Is there any other quarter of the world besides Staffordshire in which it is possible to see two sunsets on the same day? This strange phenomenon may be viewed from Leek churchyard on the longest day of June, when the sun descends behind Cloud Hill, only to re-appear shortly afterwards, and afford the spectator the sight of a second sunset.'

It is unfortunate that Hackwood, despite his enthusiasm to proclaim the Leek occurrence to be globally unparalleled, failed to explain what actually caused the sun to reappear after it had initially set behind The Cloud. Therefore, his exuberant account can have contributed little to the understanding of an uninitiated reader with potential interest in the phenomenon, whilst it re-emphasised the myth of the one day per year event.

In 1906, the potential for the legendary double sunset to replace the real one in the public imagination was demonstrated in W.H. Nithsdale's book, *In the Highlands of Staffordshire*:

'The Cloud has given Leek a world-wide fame because of the double sunset. Like many other modern exaggerations, this story of Leek's double sunset has some little foundation in fact. On three consecutive days at Midsummer, provided the weather is fine, the sun does play hide and seek at the extreme promontory of the Cloud. But this is a slender fabric for the American tale, which is frequently journalistically dished for the delectation of newspaper readers at home; that at Leek, far away in the Highlands of Staffordshire, in a little country off the coast of Europe called England, the sun there sets respectably as all suns should, and that in due course the shops and street lamps are lighted. But after a few minutes of darkness, the sun, coming around a tremendous promontory they call the Cloud, again smiles upon the landscape and outshines the incandescence of the ancient gas lamps which still pertain in antiquated places like Leek.'

Undoubtedly, the tale as related considerably exaggerated the reality of the solstitial phenomenon, as Nithsdale indeed stated, but the author himself magnified the importance of the double sunset by claiming that it had achieved 'world-wide fame'. Even today, in a communications-orientated age, there are large numbers of people in North Staffordshire, let alone in more distant parts of the globe, who have never heard of the occurrence and so it is a matter of opinion as to how far the event has actually gained more than local fame.

Surprisingly, Leek's double sunset even featured in W.J. Harper's book, *Mow Cop and its Slopes: A Short History*, which was published in 1907. Harper referred to and quoted from previous information presented about the phenomenon by *The Gentleman's Magazine*, the Rev. Mr. Nightingale and William White, without any qualifying comment regarding their accuracy as sources, except to suggest tentatively that White may have confused Hen Cloud with Cloud End, which he most definitely did.

By 1908, the North Staffordshire Railway guide (now entitled *The Official Illustrated Guide To The District Adjacent To The North Staffordshire Railway*) had got its act together rather better regarding the solstitial phenomenon and stated:

'From the Churchyard of the Parish Church, dedicated to St. Edward the Confessor, a fine view may be obtained of the "Roches," and "Cloud End" near Congleton, and from this point, at the summer solstice, about June 21st, a remarkable phenomenon may be observed, the sun apparently setting twice, it first disappears behind the "Cloud" hill, and shortly afterwards reappears on the north side, before it sinks below the horizon.'

Although the lack of any individual details in this review indicates that its author had not witnessed the double sunset himself, there is nothing to fault within it, except that the summer solstice occurred *on* 21 June that year, rather than 'about' then, and the sun *did* set twice, rather than it 'apparently' did. In any case, the publishers were evidently well pleased with the account because it remained completely intact within the guide until at least the 1925 edition, which was issued under the overall title of *Picturesque Staffordshire and Surrounding Districts*.

Nevertheless, an altogether more interesting account of the phenomenon appeared in *The Leek Times* on 25 June 1927, which reported a successful observation of the sunset:

'The conditions for watching the "double sunset" have not been too favourable this year, the sky having been so overcast as entirely to obscure the sun.

The few local optimists who, in spite of the cloud-packed sky, gathered in the Old Church Yard on Tuesday evening [21 June] however, were not altogether disappointed, as the clouds which were then hiding the sun lay just a little higher than the Cloud and, consequently, the sun was just visible for a minute or so before setting behind Cloud End and on its reappearance before really setting beyond the horizon.

It seems a pity that the trees in the churchyard should have been allowed to grow to such a height as to veil the view of this unique annual occurrence; especially as, without in any way spoiling their beauty, the trees could be sufficiently trimmed so as to give an absolutely clear view.'

Doubtless this report was accurate because it gave specific detail which conforms to now substantiated observational data on the phenomenon. Although the account has an air of disappointment about it, many present-day double sunset seekers would give an arm and a leg to have witnessed even this limited spectacle. It is particularly instructive to note that when the sun reappeared, it was viewed for just 'a minute or so' before finally setting. This means that only a small proportion of the sun's disc can have re-emerged after it had initially set and that it did so near to the base of the scarp slope of The Cloud. Consequently, after the observers of this event had seen the sun set on or around the summit of the hill, like the viewers on 18 June 1884, they had to wait for some time for the sun to return to sight and then at a much lower altitude than one might have expected.

The 1927 report contains two further points of considerable interest. Firstly, the weather shortly before the phenomenon was due to occur did not look at all promising and therefore few people had bothered to turn out for the occasion. Nevertheless, the double sunset was actually observed, albeit in truncated form. The lesson to be learned from this is that the weather can change rapidly and so successful sunset viewing is much dependent on being present even in apparently unfavourable circumstances. The second point to note is that the article complained about the trees in the churchyard interrupting the view of the occurrence and this is a critical factor which is discussed later in this book.

In the mid-1930s, there was both a surge in the interest of *The Leek Post* in the double sunset and a further successful observation of the phenomenon from the churchyard. In the 23 June 1934 edition of the newspaper was printed the following feature:

'It is not everyone in Leek who is aware of the "double" sunset, which can be seen from the Parish Church-yard on certain days in the year.

Mr. Dale, the Verger at the Parish Church, who has witnessed the spectacle for over 20 years, informed a "Leek Post" reporter that the double sunset will be visible providing the weather is favourable, on June 21st, 22nd, and 23rd, that is Thursday, Friday, and Saturday of the present week. It is possible, if the weather is very good, that it may be visible on Sunday night.

At about 9.20 p.m. the sun will be seen setting behind Bosley Cloud, and a few minutes later it will re-appear.

Although the spectacle is attributed to be one of the most mystifying of its kind for many miles around, in recent years it has not aroused the interest which was occasioned in years gone by. This has, no doubt, been due to the fact that the actual dates when the spectacle can be witnessed, are not widely known.

Mr. Dale re-called the days when hundreds of people would gather in the churchyard to see this strange phenomenon of the sky.'

The information presented in this feature is difficult to fault and tallies with, or at least does not contradict, that revealed in the 1870, 1884, 1895 and 1927 newspaper reports. Dale clearly knew what he was talking about, although it should be noted that he did not necessarily see the double sunset every year over the period of his observations. The summer solstice in 1934 occurred on 22 June and therefore the three observation evenings that he gave included a day either side of midsummer. However, the sunset starting time stated in the report was actually a few minutes ahead of schedule, although it would have allowed latecomers more chance to have witnessed the whole phenomenon. Finally, it is notable that reference was once more made to the sun disappearing for some time before, no doubt, only a small proportion re-emerged towards the lower reaches of The Cloud's scarp slope. This further confirms an emerging observational pattern around this time of an initial sunset, a considerable wait and a brief and limited reappearance of the sun.

As it turned out, the event was seen in 1934, as was revealed by the following edition of *The Leek Post* on 30 June:

'The number of people who witnessed the "double" sunset on Friday evening, June 22nd, from the Old Church-yard was far in excess of the previous year. Friday evening's sunset was the only one visible during the week-end, owing to poor visibility.'

This report of observational success must be considered valid, if for no other reason than the volume of its witnesses, and yet, incredibly, it appears to have been the very first specifically documented summer solstitial occurrence! Also, the feature strongly suggests that the event had been viewed the year before. However, the fact that the phenomenon was seen on only one evening out of several by no means indicates that the weather was particularly unkind because absolutely clear skies at sunset in Leek are not common.

The following year, the now renamed *Leek Post & Times* once more had the bit between its teeth and drummed up popular support for the occurrence in its 22 June edition:

'To-night will be the first occasion this year when it will be possible to witness the strange phenomenon known as a "double sunset," which is visible on three evenings in the year – June 21st, 22nd and 23rd – from the Leek Parish Churchyard.

Providing the weather is good, the "double sunset" will be seen at about 9.25 p.m. when the sun will appear to set behind the "Cloud," which lies about seven miles from the town, and will re-appear a few minutes later to the right of the hill. At one time the spectacle aroused great interest in the town and district, and hundreds of people would congregate in the churchyard on each of the evenings when the spectacle was to be seen. Until last year when the matter was brought to the notice of the public by an article in the "*Leek Post*," the event had fallen almost into obscurity, and only a handful of people would gather at the churchyard in post-war years.

Last year, however, a large number of people were fortunate enough to witness the spectacle.'

The newspaper rightly put the summer solstice on 22 June that year and, perhaps because one of its journalists had been an eyewitness of the phenomenon the previous year, it reported the occurrence as starting at an approximately accurate 9.25 p.m. In addition, it reaffirmed both that the traditional gap between the initial sunset and the sun's reappearance continued to be expected and that there had been many successful observers of the event the year before. Nevertheless, it is unknown as to whether the occurrence was actually seen in 1935 because no report of it has been traced and *The Leek Post & Times* lost interest in the event until 1953!

Other than the recorded observation of a 'glimmer' in 1977, the 22 June 1934 occurrence surprisingly proved to be the final double sunset reported by the press. Although the local newspapers thereafter continued to show an intermittent interest in Leek's midsummer phenomenon, their subsequent features consisted of an endless series of laments regretting the failure of the event to reveal itself to the gathered viewers. Consequently, the constant lack of success of the observations gradually transformed the famous double sunset into the puzzling double sunset mystery.

4 The Double Sunset Mystery

Although the previous chapter showed that Leek's double sunset has had a long history, it uncovered only six specifically reported and dated categorically successful observations of the phenomenon, namely those on 20 and 22 June 1870, 18 June 1884, 22 June 1895, 21 June 1927 and 22 June 1934. Even given apparently favourable conditions, the event has not always occurred because subtle weather changes can easily ruin a most promising situation. Therefore, the odds have repeatedly been stacked against the occurrence being viewed, so that at least several observations probably had to be undertaken for each successful newspaper report to be printed. Even prior to the last featured sighting of the double sunset in 1934, the local press had reported a significant number of failures, which helps to put the phenomenon into perspective.

For example, on 27 June 1874, *The Staffordshire Sentinel* stated:

'The curious phenomenon of a double setting of the sun may be seen on the 20th, 21st and 22nd of June, from St. Edward's churchyard. The sun sinks behind the prominence known as Bosley Cloud and, travelling in an oblique direction behind a corner of the hill, re-appears in the course of a few minutes, again shows itself in full glory, and then sinks to rest. Several persons assembled in the churchyard on each evening, but the clouded appearance of the sky utterly prevented the phenomenon being observed.'

The report conformed with the usual local newspaper projection of a three-evening churchyard phenomenon, but it clearly implied that the whole of the sun regularly reappeared after setting, which is geometrically impossible from this location, as I have already stated. Nevertheless, the feature was invaluable in that it reported three consecutive witnessed observational failures.

Two years later, *The Staffordshire Sentinel* reported further disappointment for the assembled spectators in its edition of 24 June 1876:

'On the evenings of Tuesday and Wednesday [20th and 21st], a good many people gathered in the north-east corner of the yard of St. Edward's Church to see the sun set. As is pretty well known in favourable weather on those days the sun can be seen to set twice – once behind the hill called "The Cloud," and again to the east of that eminence. The sight is a pretty one, and several thought it worthwhile on Wednesday to come from a distance to see it. The sky was cloudy on both evenings, and no "double sunset" was seen.'

This time, the reporter saw fit to prune a viewing day from the three which had been given by the newspaper only two years previously and he showed his ignorance of the geography of the phenomenon by claiming that the sun would reappear to the east, instead of the northwest of The Cloud. Nevertheless, the article was invaluable because it gave clear evidence that the occurrence had again been obscured by the elements and, for the first time known in print, it emphasised that the potential observers of the event had assembled in the northeast corner of the churchyard.

The following year, the journal of the North Staffordshire Naturalists' Field Club reported the frustrating end to an excursion undertaken by its members to Waterhouses and the Hamps Valley on 21 June:

'The after-tea proceedings were somewhat hastened, in order to allow the party to reach Leek in time to behold the famed double-sunset annually visible there, the 21st being the day on which it can be seen from the churchyard. The spot was reached in time to see the descending orb touch the summit of Cloud End and disappear; but a cloud intervening, it made no re-appearance, and a disappointment was the result.'

The only point that can be criticised in this otherwise entirely credible extract is its mistaken belief that the double sunset was observable on just one evening a year from the churchyard. Also, it should be borne in mind that the account provides reliable evidence only for the non-observation of the phenomenon on a single evening, albeit the summer solstice, that year.

The double sunset also failed to be observed in 1903, as was reported by the *Leek Post & Times* in its *50 Years Ago* feature, contained in the 25 June 1953 edition:

'The Leek "Sunset" has been a disappointment this year. On Saturday evening [20 June] there was quite a little gathering in the Old Church yard about eight o'clock, but the sun went down in a haze and there was nothing to see. On Sunday evening another little crowd assembled about 8.30 and watched patiently for some time, to be again disappointed.'

Although the obscuration of the sun indicated by this account is virtually indisputable, it is interesting to note that the reporter recorded the spectators as gathering at times half an hour apart on the two consecutive evenings! As the sunset times on these two days actually differed only in seconds, the feature's information must be faulty. Eight o'clock would seem to be a reasonable time for interested people to have been assembling because the initial sunset would have commenced at approximately 8.26 p.m. in this pre-British Summer Time age. Consequently, anyone arriving at the churchyard at 8.30 would perhaps just about have caught the dying embers of the first sunset had the event actually occurred. However, the essence of the article is that it didn't. In addition, it is strange that the extract made no mention of the outcome on 22 June, the date of the summer solstice that year, which may have been considered in the original report but not transferred to the feature of 1953.

In addition, the *Leek Times* feature of 25 June 1927, which was quoted in its entirety in the previous chapter of this book, noted that on only one day that midsummer had the double sunset been visible from the churchyard, whilst the aforementioned 30 June 1934 edition reported two failures out of three viewing evenings the weekend before.

Nevertheless, the sparsity of confirmed sightings of the occurrence did not prevent the inclusion of the double sunset in the laboriously-entitled book, *Staffordshire: An Illustrated Review of the Holiday and Sporting Attractions and the Commercial and Industrial Amenities of the County*, which was edited by H.E. O'Connor and published in 1935:

'From the higher churchyard the curious phenomena of the double sunset may be observed at the summer solstice, when the sun, after disappearing behind the eminence known as the Cloud, appears again on the northern side before finally sinking below the horizon.'

Despite its brevity, this reference was primarily accurate, although the use of the plural term *phenomena* mistakenly suggested that there were several differing spectacles on show rather than the single, integrated, whole occurrence that actually constitutes the double sunset.

Further attention was given to the midsummer phenomenon in 1937 through the publication of the book, *The King's England: Staffordshire: Beauty and the Black Country*, which was edited by Arthur Mee:

'Leek . . . is faced on the north by the rugged group of sinister-looking heights called the Roches, like the turrets and battlements of huge forts raised by a race of Titans.

The Five Clouds, 1500 feet high, outsoar the rest, but the Hen Cloud, solitary and apart, is by its isolation the most impressive in its stark mass and mystery. The form of a section of the range is responsible each midsummer for apparent double sunsets, a rare phenomenon. On three successive June evenings the sun disappears, eclipsed by a flank of Bosley Cloud, and then, having continued its western way, reappears beyond another flank, and, slowly vanishing again, seems to set a second time.'

Despite having detailed contemporary newspaper information available on which to draw, these details presented on the double sunset were woefully inaccurate and therefore served only to confuse public understanding of the phenomenon. The account utterly confused Hen Cloud/Five Clouds with The (Bosley) Cloud, presenting the latter as a feature of the former, instead of as the entirely independent hill some six miles to the west of The Roaches that it really is. Also, although the sun sets broadly in a westerly direction, to an observer of the solstitial event it appears to sink northwards. Consequently, it is crystal clear that neither Mee nor any assistant of his even realised where The Cloud was, let alone understood the phenomenon or had actually witnessed a double sunset. Furthermore, when a revised edition of the book was published in 1971, the only amendments to this extract were made in its phraseology and not its substance. Therefore, the publication continued to promote its own serious original errors to another generation. Unfortunately, in relatively recent times, Mee's book by no means stands alone in its failure to report correctly the basic facts pertaining to the occurrence and thereby in the promotion of mistaken concepts surrounding the double sunset.

The Rev. J.E. Gordon Cartlidge likewise chose to ignore the available newspaper evidence regarding the midsummer event and instead simply quoted in full Robert Plot's 1686 account in his article, *Solar Effects at the Cloud*, which was published by the *Congleton Chronicle* on 23 June 1939. Having laboriously repeated this out of date detail without any comment on it whatsoever, Cartlidge's imagination then ran riot:

'This persistent association of the Cloud with the Sun may seem of little moment to those who live at its foot, or dwell on its slopes today; they may even, with an air of conscious superiority, attribute it to the uncontrolled imagination of races in a lower state of civilisation and mental development in the past; but if they would betake themselves to a point by Crag Hall in Macclesfield Forest, and view the Cloud as it rises out of the vapourous [sic] mists of the Dane Valley and of the Cheshire Plain beyond, outlined against the setting sun, swathed in a glowing haze of gold and amber, they will no longer be surprised that this hill should have become invested with a permanent halo of reverential awe as the abode of the gods, where men could pay their worship to Bride the Goddess of Fire – where the bard could pay his tribute to her as the Goddess of Poetry – a place which could tempt Odin (Old Nick) to turn aside for a moment from his Wild Hunt and leave behind his footprint.'

Although unprovable legends about The Cloud abound, it is extraordinary that a clergyman should have got quite so carried away in print as Cartlidge did and his sensational mythistorical claims were not remotely useful in helping to unravel the continuing mysteries of the double sunset.

In tracing the history of the phenomenon and the emergence of the double sunset mystery, as indicated by the disappearance of reported successful sightings, the intermittent interest shown in the phenomenon by the press since the nineteenth century is not very helpful. The newspapers seem to have had no identifiable policy towards covering the event and their periodic articles appear to have occurred at random, driven by chance circumstances or developments which focused their attention on the phenomenon. Strangely, bursts of coverage can be identified, whereby the occurrence was reported for a short spell, almost as though it became fashionable, before being abandoned to oblivion once more.

Consequently, it is difficult, if not impossible, to ascertain precisely when the double sunset started to become better known to the spectators gathered in the churchyard for its non-occurrence than for its exciting novelty. Nevertheless, a decisive broad period can be identified, that is some time between the recorded sighting of 22 June 1934 and the failed observation of 20 June 1953, reported in the *Leek Post & Times* five days later. It may well be that the date can actually be narrowed down a little more through careful study of the *Leek Parish Church Guide* booklet, written by Prebendary N.W. Waton M.A., R.D. Although the publication was undated, the pertinent passage in this guide is most revealing:

'No account of the church would be complete without some mention of Leek's pride and glory, the Double Sunset, which is best viewed from the seat in the north-east corner of the Churchyard. On the Summer Solstice, June 21st, and on the day before and after, the sun sets behind the distant hill, The Cloud, in the far north-west. Some two or three minutes of darkness elapse: and then the sun reappears just above the horizon on the other side of the hill, and proceeds to set apparently a second time. This spectacle is well worth seeing but, alas! it is very infrequent that the sky is clear of all cloud down to the western horizon. But in seven years, the writer has seen this spectacle on five occasions.'

It is extremely difficult to find anything to criticise in this extract, which stands up to fine scrutiny. Its information is both precise in detail and carefully written, as one would expect from a Master of Arts. It is particularly of note that the feature pinpointed the exact optimum spot from which to view the phenomenon and my own research broadly concurs with this conclusion. Unfortunately, it is unknown as to whether the seat to which Waton referred was the same one mentioned by Matthew Henry Miller in 1891. Alternatively, it may have been a second bench almost immediately to the west of this, which is known from photographic evidence to have existed around Waton's time, or, indeed, it could have been some other seat. Nevertheless, Waton claimed that he had personally witnessed the double sunset five times out of the maximum twenty-one occasions that he stated had been possible in the seven-year period to which he referred. This roughly one in four success rate does indeed appear to be a credible assertion. Consequently, Waton's viewing claims should be accepted as accurate, but it is not easy to dicover precisely when these observed events occurred because the author did not list the dates, nor even the years, of his triumphs.

A copy of the guide is held in the archives section of Hanley Library, with a note to the effect that it was printed in the 1950s. A study of the phone numbers contained in the adverts within the booklet shows that they consist of a mixture of two and three digits, but four-figure numbers came into play in Leek in 1959, so the guide must predate that year. In addition, the St Edward's Church records show that Norman Wace Watson (not Waton) was the vicar between 1943 and 1952. Therefore, the guide was almost certainly published some time between 1943 and 1958, but most likely during the period when Watson was most actively involved with the church, that is between 1943 and 1952. This would also make most sense because newspaper records indicate that the double sunset was not observed between 1953 and 1958. Furthermore, the summer solstice occurred on 21 June in 1944, 1945, 1948, 1949, 1950 and 1952, which suggests that the booklet was probably issued in one of these years. Finally, in the last sentence of his feature on the midsummer phenomenon, by using the phrase 'has seen', Watson suggested that his successful observations had been recent and probably up until the date of the publication of the guide. Consequently, the conclusion that must be reached is that the double sunset was witnessed on five separate occasions in a seven-year spell, probably during the period 1943 to 1952, and that the booklet was most likely published in either 1950 or 1952.

However, the 25 June 1953 edition of the *Leek Post & Times* reported three unsuccessful viewings of the event that midsummer, although an entirely unexpected alternative phenomenon was witnessed on the 22nd:

'While a group of people in St. Edward's churchyard, Leek watched in vain for the "double sunset" over Bosley Cloud on Monday, they were rewarded by another "phenomenon" which looked like a comet.

On the previous two nights the weather had been too bad for the sun to come out and Monday was the last chance this year to see the annual midsummer occurrence, when the sun appears to set twice over the famous hill.

Conditions in the late evening were almost perfect but 10 minutes before the sun was due to make its first disappearance behind Bosley Cloud, it went into the cloud – the nebulous kind.

The disappointed spectators lingered on and as the horizon became a deep red, they noticed high up over the Cloud a glowing streak which at first was comparatively short and moved imperceptibly but after a while became longer and seemed to be moving higher in the heavens.

"Is it a plane?" asked the viewers. The majority, perhaps because they wanted a romantic conclusion, said "No" but as the ever-lengthening trail grew nearer it could be seen that the glowing fiery streak was preceded by an aeroplane which could just be made out high above. The "phenomenon" was just a vapour trail which had been illuminated by the dying sun to a golden consistency.'

Although the reasons for the failure of the spectators to see the double sunset that year cannot be proven for certain, the clear descriptions given by the article do indeed indicate that bad weather was most probably the culprit, and that could be expected in any year, regardless of other relevant factors. That most of the observers were incapable of recognising an aeroplane and its vapour trail seems, at first, scarcely credible, but it should be borne in mind that planes were by no means as common in 1953 as they are today and it is likely that few, if any, of the viewers had ever flown. Nevertheless, this illustrates that the majority of the spectators were not particularly familiar with celestial phenomena and therefore it may be that they were also unreliable witnesses to the nuances of the double sunset that same evening.

1954 proved a vintage year for press interest in the midsummer occurrence because it was covered by both the *Leek Post & Times* and the *Evening Sentinel*! However, both newspapers reported further failed observations and a recent history of adverse weather conditions. The *Sentinel* feature, on 21 June, erroneously claimed that the double sunset occurred 'only at The Cloud on the longest day', but, interestingly, stated that it had been 'first noticed over 260 years ago'. The latter statement was clearly a reference to Robert Plot's written account in 1686, when the phenomenon had actually been first *noted* rather than first *noticed*. More importantly, the report stated that, 'The double sunset has been blotted out in recent years because of bad weather.' Again, whilst this cannot be absolutely verified, it is a quite plausible explanation and it is noteworthy that unfavourable weather conditions were once again held responsible for the failed observations.

The following evening, the *Sentinel* reported further frustration for the viewers of the occurrence:

'Cloud prevented the double sunset being seen at Leek last night.

Despite the overcast conditions all day, a small number of people gathered in the north side of St. Edward's churchyard in the hope that the sky would clear sufficiently for the phenomenon to be seen, but as has now been the case for several years they were disappointed.'

The 24 June edition of the *Leek Post & Times* concurred with the *Sentinel's* summary and thus near conclusively confirmed the reason for the solstitial nonevent:

'Heavy low clouds blanketed out all hopes of seeing Leek's phenomenal double-sunset on Monday, the longest day. A few people went to the north side of St. Edward's Parish Churchyard – the best vantage point – in the hope that there would be a break in the cloud but visibility was so poor that they could not even see Cloud Hill, the Bosley promontory behind which the sun sets first, to reappear a few minutes later and to set again to the north.

The double-sunset has been marred by cloud in all recent years.'

The following year, 1955, the occurrence again failed to be observed, as the *Leek Post & Times* outlined in its 23 June issue, and the weather was blamed once more:

'If Leek's phenomenal double sunset does not soon make another appearance, it will become a legend of the past that no one really believes. In all recent years the event has been marred by cloud or other adverse weather conditions.

On Monday, Tuesday and Wednesday of this week when the "Double" was due to take place again soon after 9 p.m., only one or two young people bothered to go to the North side of St. Edward's Churchyard – the best vantage point to see the sunset.

On Monday cloud was far too heavy and it was impossible to see even Bosley Cloud, behind which the sun sets first, to reappear a few minutes later and set again to the North.

On Tuesday there was less cloud but a haze prevented any of the spectacle being seen. Cloud again was the trouble on Wednesday.'

The most interesting aspect of this article is its worried tone. Clearly, the reporter felt that something had gone wrong with the double sunset because it had not been seen for so long. Although cloud was considered responsible for the lack of a visible occurrence on two of the midsummer evenings, haze was held culpable on the third occasion and the feature also claimed that 'other adverse weather conditions' had marred the observation of the event in former years. This may be of significance. Obviously, if there is dense cloud cover, the sun cannot be seen, but, as will be noted later, haze can easily become a convenient and plausible scapegoat to explain situations when the sun should have reappeared, but didn't. In addition, as in the previous year, the newspaper repeated the belief that, during the occurrence of the phenomenon, the sun would take 'a few minutes' before reappearing after it had initially set.

Although the double sunset had started to become rather elusive, it was nevertheless selected to feature on the arms of Leek Urban District Council, which were granted by the Heralds' College on 7 May 1956. Upon the demise of this local authority in 1974, the arms were inherited by Leek Town Council and still hang outside its office in Stockwell Street. Thus two golden suns continue to be depicted in public, on a blue shield and either side of a gold saltire, 'recalling the well-known Leek phenomenon'.

However, there was still further disappointment for the double sunset spectators in 1956, as was revealed by the *Leek Post & Times* on 28 June of that year:

'As for a number of years past, Leek's midsummer phenomenon of the double sunset was last week obscured by the inevitable bank of cloud.

The double sunset took place on three days last week – Wednesday, Thursday and Friday, the year's longest day and the days immediately preceding and following it.

Although the sun had been hidden by thick cloud for most of Wednesday, the evening was clear and as the sun began to fall towards the horizon the chances of seeing the unusual sunset round Bosley Cloud seemed the best for many years.

With 15 minutes to go there was a group of some ten people waiting at the vantage point in St. Edward's Parish Churchyard. Low lying mist made visibility rather poor but the sun was still clear until the last five minutes. Then slowly it sank into cloud – and wasn't seen again.

On Thursday evening thick cloud persisted all over the sky and with dark mist hanging heavily the sun could not be seen at all.

Friday's sunset again started well and another group waited in the churchyard. But all they saw was a repeat of Wednesday's performance – all clear until the vital time and then into the cloud-bank went the sun.'

From these accounts, it does indeed seem as though adverse weather conditions struck yet again and once more the article went on to reiterate that the sun disappeared for a 'few minutes' whenever the phenomenon was witnessed.

On 26 June 1958, the *Leek Post & Times* reported that there had been more gloom for the frustrated churchyard observers:

'Thick clouds – and rain actually falling – marred all hopes of Leek's famed double sunset being seen this year.

If the climatic conditions had been favourable the double sunset would have been seen on Saturday evening – the longest day of the year – with partial "doubles" on Friday and Sunday, the days before and after.

The phenomenon, best seen from the north-east corner of St. Edward's Churchyard, consists of the sun setting behind the distant ridge of Cloud End. After being hidden for about a minute the sun begins to reappear beyond the Cloud, shines out again and sets for the second time over the Cheshire Plain.

On the day before and the day after June 21, the sun only partly reappears.

But this year – as in so many years – cloud hid the sun from view.'

Invariably, the newspaper pointed the finger at the weather to explain the continuing non-appearance of the double sunset, but, this time, it was noted that the sun was only 'hidden for about a minute' on the now rare occasions when the phenomenon did occur. That was an unexpected change of view, but there is no evidence to indicate what caused it to alter. However, it may be a mistake to read too much into it because the reason could quite feasibly have been slipshod journalism. Nevertheless, from such apparently unimportant switches in emphasis myths are made.

It is also instructive that the article specifically suggested that on the summer solstice the full disc of the sun would reappear after setting, whilst on the evenings either side only a portion would re-emerge. As has already been argued in this book, and will be shown later, the reappearance of the whole sun from behind The Cloud, as viewed from the churchyard in normal atmospheric conditions, is a geometrical impossibility within recorded history. Whilst the re-emergence of the full sun under conditions of extremely anomalous refraction cannot be entirely discounted, such a rare event certainly cannot be predicted. However, the report did reaffirm that the northeast corner of the churchyard was the ideal position from which to view the exciting event and there is reliable evidence to substantiate this claim, as will be presented later.

On 21 June 1960, the *Evening Sentinel* included a feature on the midsummer phenomenon, which supported the prevailing wisdom that it was 'visible only from the moorland town' and stated that it had been 'obliterated by clouds in recent years'. The article also repeated its assertion from 1954 that the occurrence 'was first noticed in the year 1686', but no follow-up report appeared indicating whether the event was seen or not in 1960.

The following year, G.A.L., writing in the *Country Commentary* feature in the 29 June edition of the *Leek Post & Times*, lamented:

'. . . the sight of the double-sunset has almost become a thing of the past too. It has (I believe) been witnessed about once in twelve years – and it was not always so. Has the gradually increasing industrial haze over Cheshire robbed us of another natural phenomenon?'

Clearly, these comments raised once more the question of the mystery surrounding the apparently vanished midsummer occurrence, but, for the first time, as far as is known, suggested a possible explanation beyond simply endless bad weather. Although to blame air pollution is a straightforward and, consequently attractive, argument, which has some merit, it cannot be held valid to account for the entire observational cessation of the event, as will be shown later in this book.

In 1963, the summer solstice occurred on 22 June and the *Evening Sentinel* published an article outlining what the observers hoped to see at the big event that same evening. The newspaper repeated its claims that the double sunset had been first observed in 1686, that it could only be viewed at Leek and that it had been obscured by bad weather in recent years. However, the *Sentinel* failed to print a follow-up review of the outcome of the occurrence that particular midsummer. Nevertheless, it made amends the following year by reporting, on 22 June, that the event had not been witnessed the previous evening:

'Bad visibility last night once more blotted out the longest day of the year phenomenon of the double sunset at Leek.'

Unfortunately, there was no suggestion offered as to what had been responsible for the poor visibility, although the 26 June Leek edition of *The Staffordshire Weekly Sentinel* at least confirmed its sister paper's overall conclusion:

'Once again the longest-day-of-the-year phenomenon of the Double Sunset – which occurs only in Leek – was blotted out by bad weather on Sunday evening and if not seen on June 21st, people hold out very little chance of the evening following when there is the possibility of a glimpse of it.

This Double Sunset has been obscured so often that few people go to look with any optimism, but what it does do most times is to start the discussion about why official summer time starts on the longest day of the year, June 21st and yet midsummer day is on June 24th.

An answer was volunteered this week: "Because summer ends on June 27th!" '

The most important aspect of this article is that it spells out unequivocally that most of the solstitial occurrence adherents were by then congregating in the churchyard more out of habit rather than in high expectation of seeing the exciting event. Also, the report stated that on the 22nd just a fraction of the sun would reappear, whilst the 20th was not mentioned at all. Interestingly, this gives the impression of a shrinking amount of anticipated solar re-emergence compared with earlier accounts and is in line with the actual astronomical progression, although the time factor in which this is occurring is practically imperceptible to an annual observer. In addition, the speculation outlined in the feature regarding the relationship between the summer solstice and Midsummer Day hit a highly pertinent nail on the head. The real explanation of the three-day gap between the two occasions can be found in the great historical struggle to create an accurate calendar in the face of the precession of the equinoxes. Thus when the Julian calendar was introduced on 1 January 45 B.C., the summer solstice (or midsummer) in Britain fell on 24 June and was widely celebrated as a pagan festival. In due course, because of its significance, the Christian Church chose to subsume this date as the fixed feast day of Saint John the Baptist, but, with the adoption in England of the Gregorian calendar in 1752, the summer solstice became hinged on 21 June, in conformity with most of the rest of Europe. Because of the greater accuracy of the new calendar, the summer solstice remains based around 21 June, whilst the 24th continues to be Midsummer Day, the feast date of St John.

In 1966, the aforementioned *900th Anniversary Year Saint Edward the Confessor Leek* booklet was published and it contained a description of the double sunset:

'At the summer-solstice an observer standing in the churchyard can see the disc of the sun disappear behind the distant Hen Cloud only to reappear a few minutes later on the north side finally sinking below the horizon. This 'double sunset' takes place for about three nights but [on] only one night is the phenomenon complete.'

This feature obviously contained no new information about the occurrence, but completely confused Hen Cloud with The Cloud, the actual hill responsible for the double sunset. It was not really clear as to what was meant in the text by a 'complete phenomenon', but, if a fully reappearing sun was implied to be the norm, then it was definitely erroneous.

In spite of the endless reported observational failures, 1970 turned out to be a bonanza year for press interest in Leek's midsummer phenomenon, with the publication of articles in three separate newspapers! The *Evening Sentinel* was the first to strike, with a preview of the event contained in its 20 June edition. The old claims that the phenomenon had first been noticed in 1686, that it could only be seen from Leek and that adverse weather conditions had obscured the event in recent years were dutifully reeled off, but the article also, erroneously, stated that 'It only happens on June 21st,' whilst apparently it had 'been seen only three or four times since the war'. No evidence, nor list of dates, was presented in support of the latter statement and neither the *Sentinel* nor any other newspaper had actually recorded any such successful viewings, so that the claim has to be regarded with considerable suspicion. However, the feature also noted that 'large numbers of people are expected to gather' to observe the solstitial occurrence and that 'With the current run of fine weather, however, there are hopes that the double sunset may be seen this year.'

Despite this optimistic comment, the prevailing tradition of observational failure was maintained, as was reported by the *Leek Post & Times* on 25 June:

'Trust the weather to rob Leek of its annual "spectacle" – the double sunset behind Bosley Cloud. Leek Parish Church graveyard is the best vantage point for this "longest day of the year" event but mist surrounded the Cloud and so once again sightseers were disappointed on Sunday evening [21st].

Outsiders as well as local people were among the large crowd assembled for the phenomenon and after the day-long sunshine hopes were high. But as the sun began to sink mist gathered and it was a case of waiting another twelve months.'

It is interesting that this time the proverbial cloud was not held responsible for the inefficacy of the observations. Indeed, the sunny preconditions were stressed, but still the event was not seen. Unfortunately, the article did not state at what point the mist intervened and so it is unknown as to whether this was before the sun had initially set or if it was after this but before it reappeared. This is of vital importance because whilst the gathering mist, or haze, following a sunny summer's day could easily explain the first possibility, it might well not have been to blame for the sun's non-re-emergence if the initial sunset had been clearly observed.

A further feature on the occurrence appeared in *The Staffordshire Weekly Sentinel* on 26 June, but the unnamed reporter was far more concerned with his own pet proposition than the actual outcome of the recent observations themselves:

'In all the years that the double sunset at Leek has been written and talked about no-one has seemed to realise until it was pointed out this time that the phenomenon has another very unusual aspect – an evening sunrise?

All the concentration has been on the fact that the sun first sets at the side of The Cloud, the wellknown Bosley landmark, and then, after reappearing on the north side of the hill, sets again on the horizon.

So much attention has always been paid to the two sunsets that the "reappearance on the north side of the hill" has been overlooked, but this "reappearance" must obviously be as much of a sunrise as many on the whole think it a double sunset.

By the way, it wasn't seen again this year on Sunday night due to bad visibility at the vital moments.'

Not only did this article produce a weak and vague explanation of the failed observations, but it wasted valuable space on an absurd proposal. The word *rise* means to move from a lower to a higher position and, as the sun is clearly descending in the late evening, it is impossible to give the idea of an evening sunrise any credence whatsoever. When the sun sets, it sinks below the horizon and if it is seen again later on the same day, this can only be as a reappearance, or re-emergence, at a lower point on the horizon owing to the specific topography of the land in view.

On 21 June 1972, the *Evening Sentinel* once again beat the drum for the midsummer event, repeating many of its earlier comments, but on this occasion it claimed that the double sunset had been seen just 'three times in the last 25 years', whereas only two years previously the newspaper had stated that success had occurred 'three or four times since the war'. In other words, the *Sentinel* wasn't really sure as to what the precise tally was and neither did it produce any evidence nor actual dates in support of its statement. However, the article did have a direct input into this book in that it first drew my personal attention to the phenomenon, which I duly went to observe, to no avail, that very evening and on seventeen following summer solstices up to and including 1991.

In 1974, in his book, *Staffordshire*, Vivian Bird described how he had failed to see a double sunset two years previously:

'From the moors in the north of Staffordshire, frosted over with myriad heads of bog cotton, I anxiously watched the mists gathering beneath the setting sun. Not that I had any fear of being benighted up among that loneliness of heather, the lapwing and curlew my only companions – my anxiety rose from the mists, for I had a date with the sunset that night, 22 June 1972, in Leek churchyard five miles distant. I could make it in time, but would the sun be prematurely swallowed in those vapours? Alas, it was as I hurried past that remote hostelry, the "Mermaid", loftily perched on the Morridge and isolated until the Staffordshire Gliding Club came to keep it company.

Once again I was baulked in an attempt to see Leek's phenomenon of a "double sunset" . . .'

Although Bird did not go on to say whether or not he continued on his way to the churchyard regardless, he would have been wise to have done so because there is a substantial difference in the weather prevalent on Morridge and in Leek. Therefore, glorious sunsets can occur in the town while the moors are shrouded in mist and major changes in atmospheric conditions can result from travelling even the shortest distances. Nevertheless, on the balance of the evidence available, this must be counted as yet another failed event.

Also in 1972, the aforementioned *Leek Parish Church Of St. Edward The Confessor: History And Guide* was published. I have already drawn attention to the extreme caution which must be exercised in the consideration of claims made by the Reverend P.D.S. Blake in this booklet, but even less reliable is the essay contained within it about the churchyard, written by the warden, William Francis Brooks. In addition to the usual description of Leek's midsummer phenomenon, Brooks made an apparently absolutely incredible assertion:

'The famous Double Sunset is seen best from the North-East corner of the churchyard. It appears on the Summer solstice, June 20-22. Sometimes the sun sets behind the distant hill, called the Cloud, and after a few minutes reappears and then sets a second time. Another phenomenon is that the sun sometimes doubles into two suns, one above the other, as it goes down and gives the appearance of two suns following each other beneath the horizon. It is a sight worth seeing and still draws crowds of curious onlookers. The North-East corner is also called "Doctors' Corner" because eight doctors are buried there.'

Brooks was clearly wrong to describe the summer solstice as consisting of all the three days, 20-22 June. The summer solstice is the longest day, on which the sun is directly overhead on the Tropic of Cancer, and in 1972 this occurred on 21 June. Also, there is a serious problem with the author's reference to a two-sun phenomenon. As it is astronomically impossible for there to have been literally two suns observable in the sky from Leek on occasions around midsummer, Brooks was presumably attempting to refer to two portions of the one and only sun visible on either side of Cloud End during an occurrence, with part of it reappearing before the whole disc had set. Therefore, he was probably really guilty of a failure to convey his meaning clearly, rather than of making incredible astronomical claims. Although it is not totally impossible that spectators may once have witnessed an event from the churchyard apparently involving two suns through an atmospheric trick, perhaps of extremely anomalous refraction, Brooks suggested that such a phenomenon occurred periodically, which therefore discounts this option. Nevertheless, because the author's comments about two suns were contained within an attractive and authoritative-looking forty-page guide to St Edward's Church, they may well have been believed by some of its more gullible readers and therefore can only have added to the increasing speculation about the double sunset mystery, or, perhaps by now, mysteries. Despite this, Brooks' description of the northeastern part of the churchyard as 'Doctors' Corner' is well worthy of note because that is the name which is still frequently given to that area, especially in relation to its connection with viewing the solstitial phenomenon.

Indeed, this recommended observation point for the double sunset was also referred to as 'Doctors' Corner' by Vivian Bird in his aforementioned book, *Staffordshire*, which was published in 1974. However, as he described the same number of medics buried there in the exact phraseology that William Brooks had used, it may well be that he copied his information from the church guidebook.

The double sunset mystery continued to deepen and my diary entries for both 1974 and 1975 described the midsummer event as 'failed'. Furthermore, on 21 June 1975, the *Evening Sentinel* repeated the essence of the claim which it had published three years earlier, namely that, 'Only three times since the war has the sky been clear enough for the phenomenon, first observed in 1686, to be seen.'

This statement made it clear that the newspaper believed both that the occurrence had not been witnessed in the previous three years and that the explanation of the absence of sightings was due to adverse weather conditions. In addition, the article once again held Leek to be the only place where the event could be observed, but now claimed that it could be viewed 'principally [although not solely] on the longest day'. The reason for this minor change of opinion was not expressed, but was most likely because the reporter didn't actually know when the double sunset could be seen and therefore precise and accurate phraseology was not used.

The following year, on 22 June, the *Evening Sentinel* specifically reviewed a failed midsummer observation:

'Crowds who gathered on the north side of St. Edward's churchyard, Leek, last night, hoping to see the double sunset were disappointed once again.

Only twice in the last 30 years has it been visible and again last night, although the first setting was clear, the second was blotted out by cloud.'

By now, it had become rather obvious that the *Sentinel* was not on the ball with regard to the history of the phenomenon, creating variance even to the extent of disagreeing with its own previous reports without any apparent reason for doing so. In the entire absence of the dates of the supposedly successful observations, the newspaper had by now presented four different assessments of the double sunset's track record in four consecutive articles! In 1970, the *Sentinel* had claimed that the occurrence had been seen 'only three or four times since the war'; by 1972, this had changed to 'only three times in the last 25 years'; by 1975, it had been further modified to 'only three times since the war' and in 1976, it had shrunk to 'only twice in the last 30 years'. Consequently, it is hardly surprising that the increasingly frustrated solstitial spectators were in considerable disagreement with one another as to the essential background to the double sunset mystery.

The clarity of the picture was not helped at all by the *Sentinel* reporter's ultimately imprecise statement that 'although the first setting was clear, the second was blotted out by cloud.' The problem with this is that it is entirely uncertain as to when the sun finally disappeared from view and that is the critical factor which needs to be known. For example, did the sun fail to reappear after it had initially set or did it indeed re-emerge but then become swallowed by cloud before it set for the second time? In the latter case, the weather conditions would almost certainly explain why the final sunset was not observed, but, if the former situation applied, there is less chance that adverse atmospheric conditions can have been to blame because of the shortage of time and space in which these could have dramatically altered.

However, in 1977, contrary to many expectations, the double sunset was finally observed again from the churchyard, as was reported by the *Evening Sentinel* on 22 June, although the newspaper failed to realise its full implications, almost certainly because the reporter had not seen the phenomenon before and therefore did not know what to expect. Nevertheless, the review itself was most instructive:

'The "longest day" phenomenon of the double sunset was partly seen last night – for the first time in years.

The double sunset can be seen only at Leek – best vantage point the north side of St. Edward's Parish churchyard – and bright weather during yesterday built up hopes that it would be visible. Several hundred people, more than for many years, packed the churchyard to see the first sunset – and then just a "glimmer" on the horizon for the second.

There is a possibility of the double sunset being seen again tonight, when more crowds are expected.'

The implication of this is that Leek's midsummer occurrence had at long last been both seen and reported, albeit in less splendour than many people had anticipated. It is clear that only a very small proportion of the sun reappeared after setting and that it did so near to the visible base of The Cloud's scarp slope. However, this is approximately, or even entirely, in keeping with several earlier accounts of the event, which have previously been described in this book, including those that inferred such an outcome by reporting that the sun took several minutes to reappear after setting. During this time, the sun could be expected to have sunk considerably in the sky and therefore its re-emergence at a much lower point on the horizon should come as no great surprise. Furthermore, this very event was captured on video, as is discussed in more detail later, and this fortunately provides conclusive confirmation of the *Sentinel's* account.

In addition, two aspects of the newspaper feature require brief comment. Firstly, it is not accurate to say that the phenomenon was 'partly seen'. It *was* actually seen, even though the re-emergence and final disappearance involved only a fraction of the sun's disc. As has been already argued in this book, the double sunset, as successfully observed from Leek, entails just a partial reappearance of the sun and consequently the occurrence described by the *Sentinel* cannot be regarded as untypical. Secondly, as such a tiny proportion of the sun re-emerged on the horizon of a landscape feature 6½ miles distant, it is doubtful that there would have been any reappearance from the same viewing point the following evening because of the sun setting further back (south) along the ridge. This is so, even taking into account variable refraction and the slightness of the solar declination within the 24-hour period.

I was present personally in the churchyard on the evening of the successful observation, on 21 June 1977, but I did not see the sun reappear after it had first set. Although, at first sight, this might seem to cast doubt on the authenticity of the *Sentinel's* report, I am now confident that the failure was on my part. For example, I may have departed in disgust before the full time had elapsed for the sun to re-emerge or, more likely, I (and many other people) may have stood in the wrong place to have observed the occurrence, as the following article written by G.A. [George] Lovenbury in the *Leek Post & Times* on 4 August that year suggests:

'I have been aware of the "double sunset" for more than sixty years and yet, believe it or not!, until this year of grace I had never made my way – which would have been easy enough – to the churchyard of St Edward the Confessor to witness the phenomenon.

The fact is that I had never looked upon it as a phenomenon in the usual meaning of the word. The sun just happens to pass temporarily behind an eminence – and there is nothing phenomenal in that, surely. It must happen in many places at some time or other during the course of a year. How very unromantic of me! How prosaic!

If the escarpment we know as The Cloud had extended only a little further northwards there would never have been any fuss – and there may not have been a church on that spot either! The first builders might have chosen the site, they might have considered it significant, because they could see, on that significant day in their year, the double setting of the object of their worship.

As it is, at midsummer for just three days The Cloud acts like a cloud and obscures the setting sun for a period of time.

However that might be, this year I was asked to accompany some friends on the middle evening, 21st June, to see the sunset – and I was keen to accept. Readers will remember that at the time we were experiencing a spell of fine, sunny and exceptionally clear weather. We had several cloudless days, free from haze despite the heat. Like everyone else I knew that our chances of seeing the sunset were high – odds-on in fact. So very often, in the past, watchers in the churchyard have been disappointed. What with low cloud over Cheshire or (as more of that county's rural acres have been surrendered) the increase in industrial haze, the sun had not even been visible; it was not to be seen to set. So, this year it was the clearness of the atmosphere each evening that was phenomenal, not the double sunset!

We arrived in good time and took up our stand – in the Doctor's [sic] Corner, near the seat – with a comely crowd. There was a pleasant buzz of conversation, pleasant greetings as newcomers arrived, and people moved about to find good viewing positions beneath the lime trees. There was an air of expectancy. Some of the optimistic gathering had their cameras "at the ready".

The sun had still some way to go in the cloudless sky and we stood in the golden glow which lit up the stones of the church and the buildings behind us. As it sank slowly (it took an unconscionable time, it seemed!) and the golden rosy light of the gloaming intensified (it was something you could 'feel' as well as see!) anticipation increased – and the animated buzz decreased.

At length the sun seemed to fall more quickly, tension increased, the awaited moment had come and in an almost dramatic silence the lower rim of the sun touched the hill. In a blaze of light the great sphere-that-was disappeared and we saw it all – right to the final flicker – leaving just the rosy glow.

"It's gone" was the spontaneous remark on a hundred, or more lips! And two hundred, or more, eyes moved slightly to the right (and the north) in eager expectation. And thus we waited. Was that a faint glow, a harbinger, on the north face of the escarpment? Was the sun about to reappear where [Robert] Plot's illustration said it should? To us in the Doctor's Corner there was, sadly, no reappearance.

Then to our right and below us there was a spontaneous but little burst of clapping! This rather took me by surprise for, I thought, whom are they applauding? Evidently some of the persons had seen the rim reappear and had saluted the fact in the usual way the British have when a feat has been accomplished. This is enthusiasm for you! I thought. And as I walked away I still hadn't seen the "double sunset" . . . and I still wondered who the enthusiasts had applauded so unselfconsciously. In a way a little thing like that makes me feel glad to be an Englishman!'

Lovenbury's report of this event has been quoted at length (although not in its entirety) primarily because it stands as by far the finest known account written by an observer of the sunset from the churchyard, complete with its evocative atmosphere of expectation and, ultimately, disappointment, which has been experienced by most of the phenomenon's recent viewers. However, aspects of the article have deeper implications.

In a scientific sense, Lovenbury hit the nail on the head when he stated that the midsummer occurrence simply involved the occultation of the setting sun through its passage behind a feature of the landscape and he was the first known person in recorded history rightly to suggest that this type of phenomenon was visible from many other places beyond Leek. There is also much value in his inference that, had The Cloud extended further to the north, double sunset observations might never have taken place from the site of the churchyard and indeed that the church might not have been built on that spot. However, his idea that the builders of the first church were specifically sun worshippers is bizarre and inconceivable.

Lovenbury explicitly stated that his viewing point for the events he outlined was 'in the Doctor's Corner, near the seat', which gives a fairly precise location of where he stood. Unfortunately, it is not clear as to which particular seat he referred, as such conveniences have long been a feature of the northeastern nook of the upper churchyard. For example, Gerald Mee's aforementioned photograph, taken not later than the 1950s, shows both the circular seat around the now felled tree and a bench almost immediately to the west, facing the railings to the north. In addition, there is currently a green wooden seat which faces the church and dates from 1973. Nevertheless, these benches were all situated in close proximity to one another. Therefore, according to the previous evidence which has been presented in this book, Lovenbury should have witnessed the double sunset from his position that evening because the weather conditions were so conducive to success and both his article and that of the *Evening Sentinel* reported that the occurrence was witnessed from the vicinity of the churchyard. However, he did not!

Nevertheless, he revealed that the 'rim' of the reappearing sun was seen by a group of people to his 'right and below', which places them between the upper and lower churchyards, near or at the junction of footpaths immediately to the north of "Doctors' Corner". Had Lovenbury drifted a little to the west of his stated spot, he almost certainly would not have watched the sun reappear after setting because the various seats were already located towards the trailing edge of the projected viewing window. However, his account strongly suggests that he took up a relatively fixed position at a place which should have yielded success. Therefore, the conclusion that is inferred by this is that the double sunset was no longer visible from at least the western end, and perhaps the whole, of its traditional observation point, but that the ideal viewing position had moved a short distance to the northeast. This is possible astronomically, but, as far as is known, no investigations followed to confirm or deny this apparent discovery. Consequently, if anything, the successful sighting of 1977 served only to deepen the double sunset mystery.

However, on 21 June 1979, the actual story was all too familiar, as was revealed by *The North Staffordshire Field Club Transactions* of that year at the end of its review of a field trip to The Cloud and Rushton Spencer, under the leadership of David and Florence Dodd:

'As the day was the longest of the year the leaders hoped the party would see the double sunset from St. Edward's churchyard at Leek. The sky was clear until just before nine o'clock when a huge bank of cloud came up from the west. Members had to be content with seeing colour photographs taken on the last occasion when the sunset was visible, but they consoled themselves with a brief visit to the inn.'

There seems no reason to doubt the accuracy of this account and David told me on 1 April 2001 that the intriguing photographs which were mentioned had been shot by him on 21 June 1977. They were apparently taken 'every so often' and recorded both the setting sun and its reappearance, but, unfortunately, he could no longer find them. Neither was he able to recall with any precision where he stood that night, but he did say:

'I particularly remember people clapping when it reappeared in the nick between the two hills. I was right in the middle of the viewers and it did happen.'

The gap 'between the hills' is actually a feature of just the one ridge, The Cloud, but David's description put the re-emerging sun well down its scarp slope and therefore indicated that his viewing position was towards the trailing edge of the observation window.

I have not been able to uncover any newspaper reports relating to the midsummer occurrence in 1980, 1981 or 1982, but there is an intriguing entry in my diary on 21 June 1980. It simply states, 'Double sunset (fractional).' At that time, I was purely an annual pilgrim to the churchyard and took no further interest in the phenomenon. I had never previously seen the sun reappear and was not familiar with its nuances. As a result, I was probably unable to distinguish between a very strong glow and a fractional re-emergence of a dim sun. It is also possible that my wish to see the sun reappear was greater than my objective visual senses. Indeed, this is suggested by the fact that my girlfriend of the time, Jill Evans, who was with me on that evening, is certain that she has never observed the occurrence. Consequently, without further evidence to support my diary, I am rather sceptical about having seen the double sunset that solstice and, even if I did, it is unknown as to precisely where I stood. Nevertheless, the uncertainty merely served to compound the double sunset mystery.

On 21 June 1981, I noted in my diary that the solstitial event did not occur because it was 'hazy', whilst on the longest day in 1982 I recorded that it had been 'still slightly drizzling' after a cold, rainy day and that The Cloud was barely visible from the churchyard. Therefore, I am confident that the double sunset was not observed at midsummer in either of those years.

Despite the intriguing new perspective introduced on the phenomenon by George Lovenbury in 1977, a traditional version of events was faithfully churned out by Keith Warrender in his aforementioned book, *Exploring Leek*, which was published in 1982:

'From the churchyard on June 20th and 21st a curious "double sunset" can be seen. The sun sinks behind Cloud End and then appears to set again further North . . .'

As can be seen, this extract added nothing to what was already known about the solstitial phenomenon and it mentioned neither the mystery of the rarely seen event nor the interesting question recently uncovered by Lovenbury. However, it did succeed in perpetuating the myth of the rather obliging double sunset.

The following year, in its 22 June edition, the *Evening Sentinel* reported that the occurrence had again failed to be observed on the solstice:

'Seen only three times in the last 50 years, the last time in 1964, the longest day of the year phenomenon of the double sunset at Leek was once more blotted out by clouds last night . . .

Best vantage point is on the North side of the St. Edward's Parish Churchyard and last night as customary between 50 and 60 people – some armed with complicated photographic equipment – waited patiently.

Shortly before the scheduled time of setting – 9.20 p.m. – the sun was a large red ball in the sky and there were hopes that the double setting would be clearly visible.

But as so often happens a bank of cloud obliterated the sun, which completely disappeared even before dropping down behind the side of the hill.

The weather has been sufficiently clear enough to see the double sunset only twice since the last war.'

Although it is not explicitly clear from this account, it seems that the sun vanished from view before it had set for the first time on the back of the ridge. The fact that the sun was described as a 'red ball' prior to 9.20 p.m. indicates that its visibility was already waning considerably and it is probably unlikely that the complete phenomenon (actually due to commence at approximately 9.26) would have been seen regardless of cloud interference because of the apparent haziness of the atmosphere. Indeed, this scenario was confirmed by a brief entry in my own diary, which stated, 'Disappeared into haze 5 minutes before sunset.' Cloud and haze are often confused and it is not always possible to distinguish clearly between them at sunset.

Although the *Sentinel* article repeated its assertion from 1976 that the midsummer occurrence had only been viewed twice since the Second World War, it also presented an entirely new claim, that it had been witnessed just 'three times in the last 50 years, the last time in 1964'. There was no indication where this information had come from and it is very tempting to believe that it must have been hearsay. Indeed, the *Sentinel's* own report of the 1964 solstitial event stated, 'Bad visibility last night once more blotted out the longest day of the year phenomenon of the double sunset at Leek.' Not only was the newspaper's 1983 feature in error on this point, but also the successful observation of 1977, which it had reported on 22 June of that year, was completely ignored. Therefore, as the *Sentinel's* reporter had made little or no effort in this instance to research even his own newspaper's files, and consequently offered erroneous facts to the public, his overall conclusion about the number of successful viewings since 1933 can only be regarded with considerable suspicion. Furthermore, the feature continued to press the inaccurate claim that the double sunset could only be seen from Leek. Therefore, the outcome of the *Sentinel's* efforts in 1983 was that members of the public became even more confused about the midsummer phenomenon than they had been beforehand!

Regardless, the *Sentinel* produced another article on 22 June 1984, which described the observational failure of the previous evening:

'The double sunset phenomenon at Leek, which was last seen just over 30 years ago, was again obliterated last night . . .

It is invariably blotted out by cloud, but each year people gather on the north side of St. Edward's churchyard, the best vantage point, in the hope of seeing it.'

Strangely, the newspaper had altered its claim regarding the last successful viewing from '1964' in its 22 June 1983 edition to 'over 30 years ago' in this issue and, as usual, no reason was given for this change of opinion. This thrust further dubious information into the public domain, although it would no doubt have appeared factually reliable to most of the *Sentinel's* readers because, during the time lapse between the two reports, any memory of the earlier feature would almost certainly have long disappeared. Nevertheless, my diary entry for 21 June 1984 broadly concurs with the *Sentinel's* version of events on that solstice: 'Cloudy evening – no double sunset – the sun appeared briefly 5 minutes before setting.'

The 1985 summer solstice offered yet another observational nonevent at the churchyard, as is shown by the entry in my diary for that date. It had rained and been overcast all day and at sunset time The Cloud could just about be seen, although the sun could not. The outcome was no better the following year, as the *Evening Sentinel* reported on 23 June:

'With a clear blue sky all evening hopes were high on Saturday that the longest day of the year double-sunset . . . would have been observed.

But not even one sunset was seen for just at the vital moment a bank of cloud descended once again and obliterated it, much to the disappointment to over 200 people who had waited patiently and optimistically at the best vantage point, St. Edward's parish churchyard . . .

It has been seen only twice since the war – in 1948 and 1956.'

Although the *Sentinel* repeated its claim of 1976 and 1983 that the event had been witnessed just twice since the Second World War, it asserted for the very first time that 1948 and 1956 had been successful viewing years, even though there was no known written evidence to support this argument. Worse still, a report in the 28 June 1956 edition of the *Leek Post & Times* had stated unequivocally that the double sunset that year had been obscured by cloud on the summer solstice as well as the day immediately before and afterwards. Furthermore, only three years prior to making its claim, the *Sentinel* had stated that the occurrence had last been seen in 1964! By now, it was clear that the newspaper's version of the history of the phenomenon had more connection with myth and legend than it did with tangible reality and the public perception of the double sunset had well and truly entered the realms of mythistory.

Nevertheless, the *Sentinel's* description of the 1986 midsummer observational failure is essentially supported by the comments entered in my diary for 21 June that year:

'It was very bright and then the sun disappeared into cloud on the horizon, which had suddenly got up. Then, within half an hour, the whole sky clouded over and strong winds and swirling mist made it look like January.'

The double sunset was also referred to in 1986 by John Dearden in his book, *Tale of the Backbone: A Journey Along the Watershed of England*:

'The churchyard is the grandstand for seeing that unique Leek phenomenon, the double sunset, which occurs at about 9.30 p.m. on three successive evenings at the summer solstice. Having set behind Bosley Cloud, 7 miles to the north-west, a portion of the sun reappears about two minutes later round the north flank of that hill and is seen for a brief period before it finally sinks into the Cheshire

Plain. All too often, clouds of another sort intervene, so that sometimes the phenomenon is not seen clearly for periods of 10 years or more, and it is rare to find among those assembled in the churchyard at the critical time, anyone who has witnessed it before. Unlike the Loch Ness monster, there is a time and place to see it, but its reappearance cannot be guaranteed under English weather conditions.'

There is much of value in Dearden's account and the only serious criticism that can be raised about it is that Leek's double sunset is definitely not 'unique'. Nevertheless, his description of *the* actual occurrence is in reality an outline of just *one* possible event within the viewing window. In addition, it was no longer known as to whether the phenomenon could still theoretically be seen from the churchyard on 'three successive evenings at the summer solstice', whilst interludes of ten years or more between successful observations, given a clear sight line, is a rather pessimistic appraisal of the circumstances. Finally, although many, and perhaps most, of the spectators who had typically gathered in the churchyard in the years shortly before 1986 had not previously seen the event, to have encountered individuals who had successfully observed the phenomenon was certainly not 'rare'.

I continued to be present at the churchyard on the summer solstice, but, according to my diary, the occurrence was not observed from that location on 21 June 1987 because the sun disappeared into cloud approximately fifteen minutes before it was due to set. However, the next evening, I decided to go to the churchyard again and saw the sun set on the back of The Cloud, but it did not reappear from the unrecorded spot where I was standing. This clearly made me ponder the situation, as my diary noted: 'It was very bright, so the angle [from the previous evening] must have changed.' By now, I was becoming rather frustrated with the consistent lack of double sunsets and I was actively seeking an explanation, although I had little spare time to pursue the answer.

1988 proved no respite from the double sunset mystery, but it did give me food for thought. The evening of the summer solstice was ruined by drizzle and there was no one other than my wife, Rosalind, and me in the churchyard. The next evening, I recorded in my diary that 'the cloud cleared and there was a superb sunset,' which I saw from the churchyard through my father's tinted binoculars, but 'the sun didn't reappear; the angle is wrong.' Having experienced the same outcome two years running, at least I'd resolved to my satisfaction that I was not going to see the double sunset from the churchyard on the evening after midsummer!

However, Michael Raven struck a relatively optimistic note with his reference to the occurrence in his book, *Staffordshire and the Black Country*, which was published in September of that year:

'On the 20th, 21st and 22nd June it is possible, weather permitting, to see a double sunset from Doctor's [sic] Corner (where 8 doctors are buried) in the churchyard. The sun sets over Bosley Cloud 7m. NW beyond Lake Rudyard, disappears and re-emerges to set a second time over the Cheshire Plain.'

Michael was quite sensible to stress the need for good weather, but, within that parameter, clearly believed that the phenomenon remained observable from the northeastern corner of the upper churchyard. This was primarily because he had not witnessed the event himself and was therefore reliant on outdated secondary sources for his information.

Nevertheless, by 1988, the double sunset phenomenon had essentially been superseded by the double sunset mystery or, perhaps more accurately, the double sunset mysteries. The classical concept of the phenomenon hinged upon its aesthetic strangeness and yet, at the same time, it was simple in form. It could be interpreted both romantically, in a quasi-religious way, and scientifically, as an astro-geographical event comprised of geometric angles. Either way round, it was ultimately predictable within the sole confines of cloudless weather and good atmospheric visibility. However, the classical image of the double sunset was in tatters by 1988. There had developed a puzzle regarding its almost annual nonoccurrence which stretched well beyond the confines of bad weather and haze, but this was not appreciated by the press and so utter confusion and disagreement abounded amongst the public as to the cause of the missing double sunset.

This, of course, was not the only problem with the phenomenon. The lack of observable double sunsets meant that there had long ceased to be any certainty about precisely where the event, or nonevent, should be viewed from. The churchyard had been consistently presented down the ages as the prime, or only, viewing position and, periodically, a particular case had been argued for "Doctors' Corner", but the contribution of George Lovenbury in 1977 had thrown both of these options into the air. Neither was it really known as to when the, by now almost mythical, occurrence could be seen. Opinion had long varied, and still did, as to whether the phenomenon could be observed on evenings other than that of the summer solstice. My own recent investigations had cast serious doubt upon whether it was possible to see the sun reappear from the churchyard after setting on the back of The Cloud on the evening after midsummer in any year – but nobody had a definitive answer, or even much evidence, to offer in order to resolve any of these questions. Finally, the chameleonesque mythistory endlessly presented to the public by the *Evening Sentinel* over an extensive period of time had so distorted the history of the double sunset that it could be argued that its real history had almost entirely been replaced by myths and legends, believed in various combinations by different people.

Therefore, it can only be concluded that at this point the mystery of the double sunset had become paramount and that the phenomenon itself had essentially ceased to exist independent of the various mysteries surrounding it. The key question was whether these mysteries would be resolved and the double sunset become prised from a nether world within the imagination and restored to a predictable real event which could actually be observed by interested people.

5 The Double Sunset Investigations

The 1989 summer solstice experience for the gathered hopefuls in St Edward's churchyard was typically unrewarding. My diary entry for that evening states that the event was ruined by 'thick cloud' and that this was 'the first day for ages there hasn't been a sunset'. Superficially, therefore, it seemed as though the almost endless pattern of non-observation of the double sunset was being predictably maintained. However, breakthrough developments were afoot that would rescue the phenomenon from the realms of myth and legend and restore it to its rightful place in the real world.

In July of that year, Roy Parker, a resident of Leek, offered to the *Leek Post & Times* for publication three colour photographs of a double sunset, which he had recently taken from Lowe Hill, but, apparently, the newspaper was not interested in printing these gift-horses because they had not been shot in black-and-white! Nevertheless, Roy was keen to share his new-found experience of the midsummer occurrence with the general public and so had the following notice, along with his phone number and copies of his photographs, placed in the window of Fred Hill's Bookshop in Derby Street:

'Having had a passing interest in the Summer Solstice double sun-set phenomenon of St. Edwards Church Yard, but never able, for one reason or another, to participate in the annual attempt to view, I was delighted when, in April 1988, I moved to live in Leek Town Centre, and my interest was re-awakened. This was brought about by a visit to the church yard to exercise the dog. It was at this time I found an ideal viewing spot.

Come the 21st June, and true to form, overcast conditions prevented observation. 1989's wonderful Summer, therefore, held great promise of a good sighting, clear skies on both 20th and 22nd but no double. 21st yet again cloudy!

Some of the people present had been attending for over 18 years but due to cloud cover, rain, etc., have never witnessed the event.

In the lively conversations while awaiting sun-sets, I suggested that if one was to continue the line of sight (Bosley Cloud – St. Edwards Church) to the higher ground East of Leek and by angling round to the South or North to compensate for the daily changing sun-set (maximum North on 21st) then a possible double would be seen. Having plotted a sight line on an ordnance survey map, I proceeded on the next two or three evenings to search along this line for an unobstructed view of the Bosley Cloud.

During this search I met Mr [Peter] Chimes who was also looking for the same thing. Together we discovered a good place. All we had to do now was to wait for the first clear night. This occurred on the 29th June and the photos demonstrate what we observed. The camera position was not moved during filming. I can understand the significance of the combination of Church/Summer Solstice but we are now convinced that it is not the only place to observe the phenomenon.'

Roy's notice and photographs remained in the bookshop window for three weeks, but, in spite of his efforts, he did not receive a single phone call as a result, although he had not specifically touted for communications. Nevertheless, his efforts were ground breaking and represented the most significant development in the history of the double sunset since the apparent rediscovery of the phenomenon in the seventeenth century and its subsequent promotion by Robert Plot. There is nothing that can be faulted in the contents of Roy's notice and his photographs do stand up to careful scrutiny as a splendid historic sequence showing an actual double sunset. However, not only had Roy captured the long-sought occurrence on film, but, perhaps more importantly, he had broken free from the traditional orthodox thinking that had placed the sole observation point as being in St Edward's churchyard. Indeed, so significant were the consequences of Roy's achievements that it is fitting to regard him as the father of the modern double sunset.

At this time, and possibly for nearly another year, I was entirely unaware of Roy's endeavours, although I pursued my own independent investigations with a little more vigour than previously. On 20 June 1989, I visited the churchyard and that night noted in my diary that, 'There was a good full sunset and possibly a fractional reappearance (a strong glow on the scarp side).' I am now unconvinced that I actually saw the sun re-emerge because my experience of observing numerous double sunsets since then has led me to realise that, other than in the most hazy conditions, the brilliance of the sun's light dispels any doubts about it when it does appear. Furthermore, unknown to me, Roy was in the churchyard that same evening and categorically stated in his bookshop notice 'no double'.

As already stated, I had no joy from the same location on the solstice and the following evening confirmed my previous two 22 June experiences: 'Like Tuesday [20th], there was a strong sunset and no sign of a reappearance – the alignment mustn't be right on this night.' However, after this disappointment, prompted by my fellow double sunset seeker, Carl Hambleton, I provisionally checked out the viewing possibilities from Lowe Hill ('probably better [than the churchyard] and at a slightly better angle, to the right') and Bradnop ('possibly better still').The next evening, I returned to both places in the hope of finally seeing a double sunset and, having gauged that Bradnop was 'well off' line, I awaited events at Lowe Hill. Although the outcome was that 'the sun sank into cloud that appeared on the horizon,' I saw enough to note in my diary that, 'It does look as though you have to be in alignment with St. Edward's Church.' I also wrote that, before I departed, I talked about the phenomenon 'to an older and a younger guy who were fascinated'. Of course, there is a strong likelihood that the two people concerned were none other than Roy Parker and Peter Chimes.

Roy was on the lookout for an early observational opportunity during the evenings leading up to the summer solstice in 1990, but his notebook on the phenomenon reveals that 'poor conditions restricted viewing'. He visited the churchyard on 20 June, but this proved futile visually because 'There was a bank of cloud on the horizon,' according to my diary. However, I was also present that same evening and, by chance, engaged in conversation with Roy. I was both amazed and very impressed when he told me, in a rather casual way, about his photographic success at Lowe Hill the previous summer and this breathed new fire into my quest for the mysterious double sunset.

Although I went to Lowe Hill on the evening of the summer solstice, nothing further was learned because of adverse weather conditions. My diary stated: 'An absolutely dismal day – rain from lunchtime and incessant at night, so the double sunset was completely washed out.' This was concurred with by the *Evening Sentinel* in its following edition, which said that the occurrence had been 'blacked out by bad weather'. Nevertheless, the newspaper took the opportunity to reassert its erroneous claim that the event had last been seen from the churchyard in 1956!

On the 22nd, I struck unlucky again, with cloud entirely obscuring the phenomenon, although the sky had become so clear by midnight that I saw a meteor from my back garden in Alsager. However, this frustrating failure finally marked the prelude to success the following evening. Inspired by Roy's success, I decided to join him at Lowe Hill to try again to see what the location had to offer. My diary recorded my uncontained joy as I finally observed my very first double sunset after seventeen years of patiently trying:

'Although there was much grey cloud around, the red disc set and at least 25% reappeared, with a considerable amount obscured by the cloud. There may even have been a full double sunset, but it [the viewing position] was to the left (not the right, as expected) of the line between the farmhouse [Home Farm] gate and the split tree. It was very exciting.'

My observation point, referred to in this extract, was actually on the grass verge, to the southwest of the entrance to Home Farm, in the direction of the first split-trunk sycamore tree. However, at this stage, like many people, I was still under the impression, or at least believed the possibility, that the whole sun would re-emerge after setting, as seen from the churchyard, and I applied this concept to Lowe Hill, even though it was just over another mile further away from The Cloud. The significance of the distance from the hill, as I came to realise, is that the further you travel from it, all other things being equal, the smaller the proportion of the sun that reappears after setting. This is because the hill shrinks in size, especially in relation to the sun, which remains the same. Consequently, despite my euphoria, Lowe Hill was actually a move in the wrong geographical direction and the one third or so solar re-emergence, which Roy had witnessed the previous year, turned out to be the greatest proportion that could be expected to reappear from this location.

Neither Roy nor I experienced any more joy at Lowe Hill that summer, but, as the sun gradually set further south along the ridge of The Cloud each evening, we compensated and steadily moved north until we reached Mount Road in early July. The only additional success at this location occurred on the 12th when Roy and my wife, Rosalind, observed the sunset on the dip slope of The Cloud and then, according to my diary, 'saw a slight reappearance of probably the top edge [of the sun] at the bottom of the [scarp] slope, from [a location to] the left of the first house'. Importantly, Roy captured some key moments of the occurrence with his camera. However, I took up a viewing position 'past the house' and observed the initial sunset, but saw no re-emergence whatsoever. Nevertheless, this event proved that the phenomenon occurred well beyond the summer solstice and from a location at some distance from the sight line of that date. It also demonstrated that by moving even a short distance north or south from a successful viewing point, failure could result. Therefore, the critical nature of the precise observational position of the double sunset became apparent to us.

On 14 July, Roy and I decided that there were too many obstructions to the north along Mount Road for this sight line to be worth continuing to pursue any longer that summer and so we began to look for a better alternative. This initially took us to Knivedon service reservoir above the road, but we were bellowed at by an irate farmer and consequently decided to scrap that possibility. Out of our subsequent discussions regarding other feasible options was born the idea of investigating potential viewing positions on the opposite side of Leek, that is closer to The Cloud. The logic of this was that the hill, as observed, would become larger and this would enable the viewing point to be determined more easily and more precisely, whilst consequently improving the accuracy and effect of further photographs. However, we still did not realise that a location nearer to The Cloud would hold another advantage, that is that it would theoretically increase the proportion of the sun that could re-emerge after the initial sunset.

Consequently, Roy drew a sight line on his Ordnance Survey map between The Cloud and our last observation point on Mount Road and discovered that it crossed the A 523 above Rudyard Reservoir. He tested this position on 15 July and observed a further double sunset, with approximately a 50% reappearance. The following evening, he took a series of photographs of another fine occurrence at this location, which produced further evidence to back up the information that we were rapidly gathering. Then, on the 17th, I joined him for an additional success slightly to the north, which my diary recorded as involving a 'partial' re-emergence of the sun and rather loosely described the event as having been seen from 'to the left of the farm by Rudyard'.

On the following two evenings, the occurrences were ruined by haze and I then abandoned my efforts in order to undertake an extended holiday on the Outer Hebrides. Nevertheless, Roy photographed another interesting and successful double sunset sequence on 20 July, but, according to his notebook, ceased his endeavours the next evening because of impending 'sight line obstructions'.

In preparation for the resumption of our investigations in 1991, Roy drew up two maps, scaled eight inches to one mile, showing the estimated double sunset viewing positions and their projected dates on the Lowe Hill-Mount Road line (between 29 May and 14 July) and along the A 523 from the southern end of the lay-by above Rudyard Reservoir to Wolf-Dale (between 22 May and 21 July). On 24 May, he had his first success of the year, approximately a 50% reappearance, on the A 523 near to the spot that he had estimated. I joined him for further good fortune on 1 June, but, more importantly, we paid a visit to St Edward's churchyard afterwards.

Roy showed me the precise location of what he believed to be "Doctors' Corner", in the northeastern nook of the lower churchyard, which had been projected as the best viewing point of the midsummer phenomenon. His premise was based on the position of the tombstone of the surgeon, Peter Milner, virtually in the apex of that part of the graveyard, and further investigation revealed that another medic, James Robins, had been buried in the next row. Thus it seemed categoric that we had identified "Doctors' Corner" and no additional enquiry appeared necessary. From that spot, The Cloud was obscured by trees and I quickly realised that by the summer solstice the foliage would be even more dense, thereby making a double sunset observation well nigh impossible. Indeed, I could not remember ever having noticed any spectators standing there to see the event, for that very reason no doubt.

It then struck me that the actual places where people gathered in the churchyard on the summer solstice were simply those from which The Cloud could be perceived, rather than necessarily those from which the double sunset occurred. It also became apparent that these two groups of viewing positions might well not coincide. Although we had little evidence to go on at this stage, we formulated the opinion that the steady growth of the trees in the churchyard over time had forced the midsummer spectators to shift their position gradually because their view of The Cloud had become increasingly obscured. In other words, we now believed that the observers had moved away from the potentially successful viewing points, westwards along the top of the tall north wall of the upper churchyard in order to be able to see The Cloud through diminishing gaps in the trees. According to our postulation, the price they had paid for doing so was endless frustration because of a non-reappearing sun on the summer solstice.

Roy and I continued to follow the line of the A 523 southwards beyond the middle of June and enjoyed several further observational successes. As the month progressed towards the 21st, it steadily became obvious that Roy's map of projected dates and viewing positions was increasing in its degree of inaccuracy. The distance between each observation point and the next, the following evening, quite noticeably decreased as the solstice approached until there was only a small amount of movement per day. At this time of year, the summer standstill is approaching, whereby there is little change in the position of the sun in relation to fixed points on the earth at a fixed time each day for a short period around the solstice. This can effectively be confirmed by checking the sunrise and sunset times throughout the year and it can quickly be noticed that the day-to-day variation at the equinoxes is much greater than at the solstices.

There was another unexpected development on 19 June, which I observed from the A 523 and recorded in my diary:

'The double sunset [occurred from] 2 posts in front of the first tree back from the iron gate in the lay-by. There was a bright yellow sunset and one-third bright reappearance. The sun started to set at 9.22; set 9.26; final set 9.33. It was a surprise that it was only one-third when we've seen a half earlier in the month! The sun must be setting at too high an angle – it's doubtful if a full double takes place from the [A 523] because the altitude perhaps isn't high enough.'

What I actually saw was recorded as accurately as possible without the aid of any relevant equipment, but my speculative thoughts clearly indicated that the double sunset mysteries were still far from entirely resolved. However, the main reason for the apparent discrepancy in the amount of solar re-emergence proved to be rather more mundane than I'd projected. Because the reappearing sun was so bright that night, my estimate of its size cannot have been very precise and later observations from approximately the same location around the same date, assisted by solar filters, showed a maximum proportion consistently of about 45%. It transpired that there was also a possible secondary explanation, in that the shape of The Cloud as visible from the progressively southern viewing positions along the A 523 changes noticeably. Furthermore, my observation techniques were not then as refined as later and it may well be that my viewing position was not on the leading edge of the window. Finally, my knowledge of the relative angles of sunsets throughout the year was at this stage uninformed and I eventually discovered that the sun strikes a flat horizon at approximately 37° on the equinoxes and 29.9° on the solstices. Consequently, the reverse of my assumption of a rising sunset angle as midsummer approached was true!

On the 19th, for the first occasion on the same evening, we undertook more than one sunset observation, primarily because of the importance of the time of year. Roy was at Lowe Hill, from where the sun disappeared into a bank of cloud at 9.32 p.m. before setting, whilst his friend, Rose Tipton, saw the sun set a bright yellow from the churchyard, but only a red glow appear afterwards. The conclusion we reached from this experiment was that viewing from the closest position to The Cloud also had a distinct weather advantage in that this would reduce the effects of haze and mist. It was, of course, possible that my observation, from the A 523, had struck very lucky and been completed just before cloud drifted in, but a scrutiny of the relevant times of events recorded by Roy and me suggests not and that instead poor visibility had been responsible for the Lowe Hill failure.

The media came alive on the 20th, with, apparently, features on the double sunset on both Radio Stoke and the TV, whilst the *Evening Sentinel* published a preview of the occurrence, which it now claimed was visible for three nights around the summer solstice. The importance of "Doctors' Corner" was emphasised, but the erroneous assertion that the phenomenon had last been seen in 1956 was once more repeated. Finally, the newspaper engaged the services of the Leek-based historian, Harold Bode, to predict the outcome of the events:

'All the rain we have had has cleared a lot of dust from the atmosphere and if it stays dry, then we may get a good view.'

Roy and I covered Lowe Hill and the churchyard that same evening, but haze, or perhaps cloud, entirely ruined the occurrences. Nevertheless, at the former position, I met Colin Burgess, a really keen viewer of the phenomenon, and together we moved on to the churchyard, where we found Roy already in deep conversation with Peter Chimes. The outcome of this gathering was that we decided to form ourselves into an observation group, to be co-ordinated by Roy, which would meet and discuss each evening's developments in The Swan, opposite the church, after sunset.

On the solstice, the *Evening Sentinel* published an article by Phil Edmeades, who confirmed our verdict about the 20 June churchyard event:

'A rare double sunset failed to materialise last night after low cloud blocked spectators' views of the event . . . A group of more than 50 people gathered in the churchyard last night . . . But a bank of mist and low cloud on the horizon meant that the sun disappeared from view several minutes before it was supposed to, ruling out any possibility of seeing the double sunset.'

Unfortunately, two other aspects of the feature did not inspire confidence in the newspaper's familiarity with the phenomenon. Accordingly, it confused the pre-solstice evening with Midsummer's Eve and repeated the mistaken claim that the occurrence had not been seen since 1956.

That evening, the sunset observation group put a plan into action to cover the key eventualities. Colin was at the lay-by above the reservoir on the A 523, from where he saw the sun set and approximately one third of the disc reappear. However, Peter observed only a slight re-emergence of the sun on a generally cloudy (or, actually more likely, hazy) horizon at Lowe Hill. Roy stood on his stepladders (which we thought was hilarious) on the car park immediately to the north of Moorlands House, in order to see The Cloud above the trees, and he witnessed the bottom half of the sun clip the hill, while the remainder passed by above it without being obscured. This therefore proved that Roy's elevated position was too far to the northeast for a double sunset to be seen on the longest day. At the same time, I was in the churchyard, taking up the most suitable spot I could find. My diary recorded the outcome:

'I struck lucky because the sun reappeared out of the cloud shortly before setting and brightly set, between 9.26 and 9.31, but there was no reappearance, only a red glow, even though it was basically clear. It set too far back on the ridge to reappear, so there's no double sunset from the normal place.'

In summary, the phenomenon *was* successfully observed on the summer solstice of 1991 from the lay-by on the A 523, but there was no such success from the best-placed clear viewing point in the churchyard because this did not match the angle needed for the sun to reappear after setting. However, the double sunset almost certainly did occur from the grounds of the church, but unfortunately from a position where The Cloud was not visible because of tree cover. This conclusion was supported by the evidence of the overshooting sun discovered by Roy on the council car park. In addition, we now believed that during the traditional event, as formerly seen from the grounds of the church, no more than approximately one third of the sun re-emerged at peak viewing on the summer solstice because that was the amount which we had recorded as having reappeared on the A 523 three miles closer to The Cloud. However, as it transpired, our projections for the latter location were a little pessimistic. Regardless of this, the fine weather had enabled us to make further substantial breakthroughs in the quest to resolve the problem of the missing double sunset. Nevertheless, after this immediate success, the observation group shrank to just Roy and me.

On 27 June, I visited the churchyard and saw the sun set further south along the dip slope of The Cloud, thus confirming that its annual migration to the tropic of Capricorn was well under way. I also checked the situation from the vicinity of what I believed to be "Doctors' Corner", but sun did not reappear from there either. The following evening, Roy ascended his stepladders on the council car park once more and this time observed the set of the whole sun, except for a thin crescent, with approximately a quarter of the disc re-emerging. After that, we returned to action on the A 523 and continued to record our data, noticing in particular the relative increase, both in the distance between the viewing points and, apparently, the proportion of the reappearing sun, as the days passed.

When the view of The Cloud from the A 523 eventually became obstructed, we moved on to the minor road running parallel, to the east of Barnswood. From this location on 3 August, we had a novel and very interesting experience, which was recorded in my diary:

'The sun set into cloud about 8.54 or so, but reappeared (a quarter to a third); set at 9 p.m.; a pinprick reappeared, set and slightly more reappeared (i.e. 3 reappearances), but finally set at 9.02. This was because we're closer and because of the variations in the hill face as the sun moves down it. So it was a quadruple sunset and Roy got very excited!'

There was an even more important development on the 14th. After sunset, Roy suggested that we take a look at Woodhouse Green as a possible viewing point and my diary noted the outcome:

'There certainly was a vantage point! It's only a mile away from The Cloud, which [looks] huge from there, and it decreases the chances of mist . . . As we were driving away, round the corner, I realised the face [of The Cloud] had become vertical, so I pulled in and pointed it out to Roy. It's roughly on the solstice alignment, so next summer we may have a full double.'

However, Roy considered the steepest angle of the scarp slope to be located slightly too far south in order to be a midsummer observation position and, in due course, he turned out to be right. Nevertheless, on 17 August, I saw what I thought to be approximately a quarter of the sun reappear [later observations put it more reliably at about 10%] from my viewing point on the semicircular minor road running north from Woodhouse Green, by the first gate east-northeast of the track crossing Raven's Clough. However, the initial sunset was at 7.52 p.m., compared with 8.36 on the flat Cheshire horizon and consequently the sun was still so bright that it was dazzling and dangerous to observe. As it turned out, when I had completed this viewing, there was still time to drive to join Roy on the Ryecroft Gate to Heaton road and see a second double sunset on the same evening! I then spoiled myself and took a further short trip to watch a normal (single) sunset occur against the Cheshire Plain.

The following night, we decided to investigate the higher ground to the west-northwest and move closer still to The Cloud. However, we encountered human interference in the shape of a farmer, who told Roy that he was 100 yards off the footpath, but that we could cross his land 'providing that hippies and sun worshippers from Gun Hill don't come down'! Our reward was approximately a 50% reappearance. We then explored a likely viewing position just beneath The Cloud on its eastern flank, on Cloud Side, in our continuing search for the elusive full double sunset. We got the opportunity to put this to the test on the 21st, armed with Perspex observation filters (which thenceforth became our most vital equipment) produced by Roy to counteract the intensity of the early evening sun. I finally recorded in my diary the completion of this part of our quest:

'A full double! At last, a full set, a full reappearance and set again on the slope, about 6.11 p.m. from the back side of the road, opposite a gate and telegraph pole. [The sun was] very bright and observed through a double block of Roy's filters. It was very exciting and a cyclist pulled up and started asking questions at the critical moment!'

Further successful observations on the 29th and 30th confirmed these conclusions, although it quickly became apparent that the precise viewing point was absolutely critical in affecting the proportion of the reappearing sun after its initial set. The primary objective became to stand in such a position as to get the sun setting as close to its point of re-emergence as possible. By doing this, the greatest proportion of the sun would reappear and, over time, we developed the technique of gradually positioning ourselves at the initial sunset so that the final fraction of the sun would vanish just the briefest moment before the first speck re-emerged. Nevertheless, on 30 August 1991, Roy's notebook stated: 'Handshakes all round as we had finally done it.' All that seemed to require doing from then on was periodically to observe and note the progress of the event, perhaps once a week, I thought. However, after 15 September, bad weather and then work pressures brought my efforts to an end for that year.

Nevertheless, human response to the phenomenon in 1991 had not yet finished because it featured briefly in Doug Pickford's book, *Myths and Legends of East Cheshire and the Moorlands: a cabinet of curiosities*, which was published in December of that year. At the tail end of a section covering The Cloud, Doug made the highly speculative statement: 'Also, carved in the rock on top of the Cloud there is a sun falling out of the sky. It could have something to do with the double sunset seen over the Cloud.' He pressed the same point a little further in his 1996 publication, *Earth Mysteries of the Three Shires*, whilst discussing the rock carvings on the hill: 'Another appears to represent the Double Sunset of which Bosley Cloud is very much a part.' I investigated these claims on 27 April 2001 and, although I spotted in the region of 300 separate incisions on the rocks around the summit of the hill, the vast majority consisted of people's initials, whilst none of the few pictorial carvings appeared to have any noticeable connection with the double sunset. Therefore, I rang Doug, but he was too busy to point them out to me and instead described their approximate location. However, my subsequent careful investigation of the relevant rock faces on 27 May 2001 still revealed no likely contenders for these images.

I swung back into action on 25 February 1992, saw a full double sunset on Cloud Side (with the sun disappearing for the first time at 1.10 p.m.!) and entered my findings in detail in a new file, which I opened, with the object of recording the data approximately fortnightly for inclusion in this publication. However, this proved more easily intended than done because of adverse weather conditions and it was not until 9 April that I had any further success! I followed the road southwards as the sunset progressively moved northwards, but, by 26 April, the fully reappearing sun had been replaced by three quarters of the disc and this proportion continued to shrink.

The following month, a new sign appeared on Ashbourne Road in Leek, just southeast of its junction with Mount Road, notifying motorists that they were entering the town. Its design had been created by Reg Barks of Ipstones and featured two yellow suns, representing the double sunset, arranged either side of a yellow saltire. Most interestingly, the sign was, and still is, located extremely close to a position from which the phenomenon can be seen, albeit not on the summer solstice.

On 13 May, Roy and I combined our efforts for the first time that year on the Woodhouse Green line, but we were not particularly impressed with the shape of The Cloud as viewed from this position. However, we knew that the hill would appear more vertical from the viewing point around the summer solstice. By 9 June, Cloud Side had become unproductive and I began to search for a new position in one of the fields to the east of the road. Two evenings later, Roy and I saw a double sunset with approximately a 50% reappearance from a field on the western side of Woodhouse Green and Roy filmed the event with his camcorder. This turned out to be a rather slow-moving seventeen-minute spectacle suitable to be viewed only by an absolute fanatic on double sunsets!

On 12 June, we discovered a good viewing place in the field immediately to the northeast of Woodhouse Green Farm, from where we saw an impressive two-thirds or so reappearance, which was videoed by Roy. However, it became increasingly clear that, by the solstice, we were not going to have reached the spot which would give the ideal view of the steepest angle of The Cloud's scarp slope and the greatest chance of a fully re-emerging sun. Therefore, I briefly explored the possibilities of the Rushtonhall area as an observation zone, but quickly realised that it was less favourable than Woodhouse Green.

The 17th provided a further breakthrough because Roy saw a double sunset, with perhaps a 25% reappearance, from the garage forecourt immediately to the northeast of St Edward's lower churchyard in Leek. This was the first known recorded successful viewing of the phenomenon in the town proper since 1977. The following evening, I found an ideal location to continue the Cloud Side observation line from the field opposite the entrances to Duke's Well and East View and across the road from the car pull-in used by walkers en route to the summit of The Cloud. The subsequent event was impressive and extensive as the sun rolled down the ridge and returned fully into view a quarter of an hour after it had first set.

Although there were no visible occurrences from any of our sites on the solstice because of complete cloud cover, I observed a double sunset, with almost a three-quarters reappearance, from Woodhouse Green, on the 19th and the 23rd and a full double from the field below Cloud Side on the 22nd. Fortunately, from these sightings, the events of the solstice could be pretty accurately determined.

Roy videoed the occurrence from the garage forecourt in Leek on the 19th, from where the sun failed to disappear entirely from view because of partly overshooting, but Carl Hambleton stood near to what we believed to be "Doctors' Corner" and apparently saw the sun set too far back on The Cloud's dip slope to re-emerge. Peter Chimes bumped into Roy in the churchyard on the 22nd and reported that he'd observed a double sunset, with approximately a one-third reappearance, three evenings before from Lowe Hill, 'by the wall of the farmhouse [Home Farm]', according to Roy's notebook.

On the 24th, Roy once more saw a double sunset, with about a 25% re-emergence, from the garage forecourt, as the sun began to move southwards again, but, this time, he had to stand on his stepladders because of tree interference at that particular spot. The following evening, he reaffirmed to me the precise location of what he believed to be "Doctors' Corner", in the northeast of the lower churchyard, which, intriguingly, was located only a few paces away from the garage forecourt, thus being in contention as an observation point of the midsummer phenomenon, according to our calculations. However, as the view of The Cloud from this position remained entirely obscured by trees, we continued to project that spectators had once stood on that spot to watch the double sunset, but that the tree growth had forced them to shift to the current position in the churchyard. The problem with our hypothesis was that it hinged on the observers having moved some 100 yards up the path from the lower churchyard and along the north wall of the upper churchyard, which seemed a relatively long distance to travel on an unlikely route behind a screen of trees.

Roy and I continued to monitor and record the data from the various double sunsets on the Cloud Side and Woodhouse Green lines and along the A 523 until the end of September, without making any startling new discoveries. Further progress was made, but nowhere near as much as we would have liked because of the limitations imposed by the weather and work commitments. Nevertheless, I was keen to investigate as to whether the phenomenon occurred on or around the winter solstice and was able to do so on 24 December. Although I had no real idea of what to expect, nor what time it would occur, I thought that the sun might well pass the edge of The Cloud in the morning and thereby become a double sunrise rather than a double sunset. Consequently, I arrived at Cloud Side at 10.35 a.m., but the sun was nowhere near high enough in the sky to appear at the required point. I was also unable to distinguish any viewing places based on the Woodhouse Green line and it became clear that the occurrences needed to be followed through the autumn in order to make any progress on the winter solstice.

As Roy and I largely kept our discoveries under wraps, outdated and second-hand information about the midsummer phenomenon continued to be promoted, for example, in Ros Prince's book, *Curiosities of Staffordshire: A County Guide to the Unusual*, which was published in 1992 and stated:

'From the vantage point of St Edward's Churchyard in Leek at midsummer, 20 to 22 June, it is possible to watch the sun set twice. It disappears behind Bosley Cloud and then reappears over the Cheshire Plain.

Weather conditions have to be right, of course, to be able to see this, but every year many hopefuls turn up to watch.'

Although Ros was not writing from personal experience of the event, because she had never seen it, and the flaws of her account should by now be obvious to the readers of this book, the ideas that she was representing remained essentially unchallenged until evidence was published to the contrary.

The double sunset investigation wasted no time at the beginning of 1993 when Roy made a highly successful observation from the A 523 just south of St Mary's Church in Bosley on the very first day of the new year. In doing so, not only did he pinpoint a viewing position and a time from which it would be relatively easy to line up a winter solstice reading, but also he recorded an impressive 50% reappearance of the sun after it had initially set. I then undertook two positive observations on Cloud Side in March, but work commitments and adverse weather conditions prevented me from achieving anything else until June.

On 18 June, Roy and I took sightings at exactly the same positions that I had covered on the same evening the previous year, from the field off Cloud Side and that in Woodhouse Green. The readings were absolutely identical and therefore, we believed, could be expected to remain so every year. Although on the 20th, for the first time, I had complete success at Cloud Side and saw the maximum reappearance at Woodhouse Green, dense cloud once again ruined the solstitial observations. However, over the next few evenings, we confirmed the essential accuracy of our data from 1992 and, on the 27th, Roy, Carl and I all observed a double sunset, with a sizable re-emergence, from the rear of the car park at the back of Moorlands House in Leek, despite immense problems with trees obscuring the view. Little else was achieved that year and our observations ceased entirely after 12 August. Indeed, nothing further was recorded in Roy's notebook until 21 June 1996.

Nevertheless, my own efforts were more extensive in 1994 and, on 8 February, I saw a second sunrise and the initial sunset of a later double, all within 21 minutes and from exactly the same location! I discovered the position to observe this unusual spectacle with considerable difficulty and found myself in a field to the north of Tunstall Road, beyond the scarp slope of The Cloud. This was the best place I could locate in order to view the phenomenon from a reasonable extension of the Cloud Side line. I didn't get there in time to see the sun rise at daybreak, but I did observe it disappear behind the edge of The Cloud at 11.49

a.m.; fully, or almost fully, re-emerge and then set at 12.10 p.m. Around 12.25, the sun reappeared once more from the same viewing point and, although I missed this because of cloud interference, I did observe the whole of the sun shining brightly yet again.

The following month, I discovered a feasible location to continue the Woodhouse Green line to the north, beyond the summer, and this was along the no through road from Raven's Clough to Toftgreen. The main value of this was that I had identified it as the closest off-the-hill viewing line, that is the one from which the maximum amount of reappearance of the sun could be seen. As the observation positions on and off Cloud Side were nearer to the summit of The Cloud, they produced a greater proportion of the re-emerging sun, but technically were located on the lower eastern slopes of the hill. However, the Woodhouse Green to Toftgreen line could not be criticised on that basis and it also had the advantage of showing The Cloud as a more identifiable hill, looming ahead. Thus the two separate locations had their own specific advantages and so I felt that both were worth pursuing for different reasons.

Nevertheless, my main activity on the project was once more concentrated in June. Unfortunately, on the 20th, I had my first difficulty with an irate farmer, who spotted me standing in a field at one of my observation sites, awaiting developments. As a rule, I asked for permission before exploring private land for possible viewing sites, but, on this occasion, I had forgotten to do so. My attempts to reason with the farmer failed and I was escorted off the land under threats of the police being contacted. I wasn't impressed by that, but, as I needed to return to the field the following evening, I realised that it was in my interests to conclude a peace settlement. I'd ascertained from the farmer that he was not the owner, so I went to the farmhouse afterwards, apologised for my behaviour and requested permission to return to the field, which was granted immediately!

As usual, the double sunset was not seen on the summer solstice, which turned out to be a really dark, dismal day, with dense cloud and intermittent rain. Nevertheless, I was present at both Cloud Side and Woodhouse Green in case a miracle occurred, but it didn't. However, I was lucky the following evening when the intermittent cloud cleared and left me with perfect conditions to observe a full double sunset from the field below Cloud Side and approximately a 72% reappearance from Woodhouse Green shortly afterwards.

I undertook observations in July, August and September, but my main thrust was reserved for the winter solstice. Although I had not followed the events through the autumn, my 8 February viewing had produced a continuation of the Cloud Side sight line and so I needed to move broadly north from that position in order to discover the relevant observation point. Amazingly, I had to put my alarm clock on in order to be sure of getting there and fixing a viewing spot on time! On 20 December, I set out from my home in Cotes Heath in brilliant sunshine, but when I got there, it rained most of the time and The Cloud was shrouded in mist!

However, two days later, I made a second attempt at a midwinter reading, despite the fact that I started from home in a thick freezing fog. Although this seems irrational, a work colleague had told me that he had woken the previous morning in Mow Cop to bright sunshine, while the Cheshire Plain below was covered with fog. Being aware that valley fogs and hill fogs rarely occur at the same time, I decided to take a chance and it proved well worth my while. After walking through three fields to the north of Tunstall Road, beyond Cloud End, and crossing an infant stream, I finally discovered a suitable location to view a most interesting occurrence. At around 11.17 a.m., the sun disappeared behind the edge of The Cloud, which, at this angle, was visible as only a small protrusion on an elongated ridge. I had placed myself so that the sun began to re-emerge immediately, although it was another twenty minutes before it came fully into view. The most interesting aspect of the observation was that the reappearance was actually the second sunrise from my viewing position on that day and, as such, was part of my first recorded off-the-hill double sunrise. In addition, this was the first known occasion on which the full sun had reappeared from an off-the-hill location. Therefore, as can be imagined, I was most pleased with this reward for my gamble in having set out that morning and I drove back to the continuing Cotes Heath fog in buoyant mood. The following morning, there was another dense freezing fog in my village, but I returned to my viewing point to fine tune my observations and once more struck lucky.

There was further activity concerning the double sunset in December 1994 with the publication of Issue 8 of *The Green Dragon Mysteries Society Newsletter*. In this, it was announced that Andrew Collins, the author of *The Seventh Sword*, had 'offered (without any arm twisting) to be the speaker at the June meeting next year to coincide with the Double Sunset – if it should be witnessed.' Remarkably, the newsletter then stated that Collins 'suggests we could go across to the Church after his talk and he will employ some "psychic energy" to ensure the Sunset is seen.' Therefore, according to this, Collins possessed a phenomenal supernatural power which could be invoked to command the elements!

Also in 1994, the occurrence was featured in David Bell's book, *Ghosts & Legends of Staffordshire & The Black Country*:

'IN Leek, it is possible to gain yourself twelve months worth of good fortune, lasting from one midsummer to the next. You need to visit the churchyard of St Edward the Confessor on the 20th, 22nd or 23rd of June, and to stand in the part known as Doctors' Corner, where the graves of eight doctors are situated. If the weather is fine, all you have to do is to look west towards the rocky hills called the Roaches. It is unlikely that you will be alone, because people come from all over the world to be in that spot at midsummer, and to watch a unique natural phenomenon.

After watching the sun set behind the hill called Bosley Cloud, you should wait patiently. Your fellow watchers will hold their collective breath until the sun unsets itself! It slowly reappears from behind Bosley Cloud, only to set again over the Cheshire plain.

This rare double sunset only happens on these three days of the year, and can only be observed from the vantage point of Doctors' Corner in St Edward's churchyard. Those who are privileged to see it can count themselves doubly lucky, because the year that follows will bring them good fortune in both love and business affairs.'

Bell's comments clearly represented a peculiar mixture of fact, fiction and error, which served only to veil the real double sunset even further. It is difficult to imagine why the author believed that all the observers of a successful occurrence from the churchyard should experience good luck for a year, but, more importantly, this is not a tale which I have encountered anywhere else at all during my research for this book and Cathryn Walton, the secretary of the Leek and District Historical Society, has never heard of it either. Indeed, the writer's lack of familiarity with the phenomenon was revealed by a series of factual mistakes in his account, the most notable of which was his inexplicable omission of the current summer solstice (21 June), the key viewing evening, from his list of possible observation dates! In addition, he failed to realise that it is The Cloud and not The Roaches which is responsible for the double sunset and that the former lies northwest of the churchyard, whilst the latter are approximately to the north-northeast. Furthermore, Bell gave the impression that "Doctors' Corner" was full of foreigners on midsummer evenings, which is certainly not true, whilst also it is obvious that he was unaware of Leek's other observational locations. Finally, he fell into the old trap of describing the churchyard occurrence as 'unique' before contradicting himself and deciding later in his text that it was only 'rare'!

I was able to commit more time to my investigations throughout the year in 1995, especially in the spring when I undertook a series of successful observations along the Toftgreen to Woodhouse Green line. In addition, my efforts on the summer solstice were finally rewarded with a double sunset from the field below Cloud Side in very fine weather. I estimated the sun to have started to set around 8.16 p.m.; set and re-emerged at 8.30; been fully in view between 8.47 and 8.49 and then gradually disappeared into the trees on the lower slopes of The Cloud. Because of the ideal conditions, I had an experienced photographer, Chris Lovatt, with me to record the event, but he had considerable difficulties with the intensity of the light of the direct sun, so much so that both the prints and the negatives were effectively ruined by flare. Also, the solstice was unkind to me afterwards at Woodhouse Green, from where cloud interference diffused and partially obscured the sun, so that I was unable to fix a precise viewing point or to record any specific details of the event. Thus, the double sunset retained one of its few remaining secrets for another year!

The observers in St Edward's churchyard were also disappointed, as was revealed by *The Sentinel* on 22 June:

'Spectators hoping to see a rare double sunset – not seen for nearly 40 years – were disappointed again last night.

The double sunset, last observed in 1958, should happen at Leek on the longest day of the year – June 21.

From certain points in and around the town watchers are supposed to be able to see the sun set first behind Bosley Cloud near Congleton.

Then, because of the rotation of the Earth, the sun should reappear before dropping below the horizon a second time.

Last night, crowds gathered in Leek's St Edward's churchyard and on The Mount, a hillside overlooking the town.

But as on many previous occasions hazy cloud obscured the view preventing the watchers from witnessing the double sunset event.'

It is unknown why the newspaper switched its allegiance in this article from 1956, the year it had previously promoted, to 1958 as the date of the last successful viewing from the churchyard. No evidence has been discovered to support this claim, whilst the 26 June 1958 edition of the *Leek Post & Times* categorically stated that, 'Thick clouds – and rain actually falling – marred all hopes of Leek's famed double sunset being seen this year.' Nevertheless, *The Sentinel's* feature accurately recorded the 1995 solstitial observational failure and correctly noted that the occurrence could be viewed from locations other than the churchyard, although it clearly confused the Mount (from where there is no double sunset on the longest day) with Lowe Hill.

The Sentinel's report of the double sunset nonevent was substantiated by a brief reference to it in an article on The Green Dragon Mysteries Society in the *Leek Post & Times* on 28 June of that year:

'One of the largest audiences yet came to the society on Wednesday 21 June to hear Andrew Collins talk on psychic questing . . .

There was a short question and answers section as everybody was keen to adjourn to the Mount in great anticipation of the double sunset for which Leek is famous.

About 60 to 70 people gathered to see this sight. Unfortunately, it was not to be seen this year, this was a shame as the meeting had been especially arranged to coincide with the summer solstice sunset last seen about 17 years ago.

This in no way detracted from Andrew's talk which was excellent, informative and very well presented. He explained that through the axis of the earth changing slightly this may effect [sic] the double sunset.'

Doug Pickford confirmed this observational failure in his previously mentioned book, *Earth Mysteries of the Three Shires*:

'Andy . . . and some fifty or so others trotted off to, hopefully, witness the Double Sunset – the unique event experienced only at Leek – but it was not to be. The sun set behind Bosley Cloud and, instead of re-appearing to the right as it should at this time of year, it vanished from sight, save for a faint white glow. No-one was surprised for it is very rare these days to be able to see this mystical double sunset.'

A further account of the events of this evening was related to me on 22 June 2000 by Geoff Channon of Leek, who had been present at both Andrew Collins' talk and the failed observation:

'He [Collins] was straining credulity and we were looking forward to going out to see the double sunset. Then Doug Pickford announced that they were all going up to the Mount and we said okay because they seemed to know what they were doing. We were being led as followers, so we drove up and parked on the verge at Mount Road. There were 70 at least stretched out along the road. We were thinking, all these people must have seen it here before. Even before it had set, I said, "It's going to miss by miles!" Doug Pickford and Andrew Collins were looking intently at the sun and I thought, they must know it's going to miss. It missed by so far that I felt a right pillock. They all stayed and watched it miss and set way off to the right. I was a bit bemused. I was watching Andrew Collins and Doug, who were to my right, and they looked blank! We thought it was very strange, so we then decided to follow it up ourselves.'

Therefore, Collins' "psychic energy" did not ensure the observation of the solstitial phenomenon from the Mount in 1995, primarily because he and the party with him were standing in entirely the wrong place in order to see it! Consequently, the alteration in the tilt of the earth's axis, to which Collins referred, was completely irrelevant in explaining the absence of a viewable double sunset to a group of people located over a quarter of a mile away from an actual contemporary sighting position.

Throughout the autumn, my observations from the Cloud Side and Toftgreen lines continued and more useful data was collected, but the most memorable incident of that period involved a herd of large, frisky bullocks inhabiting the field immediately southwest of Toft Green Cottage. On 21 October, I entered the flat lower part of their field in order to find the closest off-the-hill position to view the double sunset that afternoon, but the bullocks were most inquisitive about my presence and determined to distract me from my purpose. Nevertheless, I achieved my objective and left my carrier bag to mark the viewing spot while I took the necessary measurements to determine the precise location for future reference. As I walked away, they gathered around my bag, desperate to smell it, and when I returned it was so drenched in slobber that it had to be discarded!

On 13 December, my double sunset project took another big step forward when I first met Chris Doherty, a photographer who had been highly recommended to me. He was very keen to take on the challenge of filming the phenomenon for my projected book and showed me some impressive photographs he had shot of a solar eclipse from the South China Sea. These successful images proved decisive because they strongly suggested that he would be well capable of producing the required goods and so I decided to engage his services. I was hoping to start work with him shortly afterwards, but fate intervened just five days later when his bicycle was struck by a pick-up truck and he was rushed to intensive care with serious injuries!

Also in December, I switched my attention to the A 523 at Bosley, which culminated in a highly successful observation on Boxing Day. From a position at the side of the road, near to that recorded by Roy Parker on 1 January 1993, I too saw what I believed to have been a 50% re-emergence after the sun had initially set behind The Cloud at 3.15 p.m. and it dropped below the horizon for the second and final time at 3.34. However, sunset viewing at this time of year can have its disadvantages and it was so cold that my pen stopped writing just as I was completing the recording of my data! Nevertheless, the winter conditions had one big advantage and that was that I was able to mark my observation position by drawing a line in the snow with my boot and I then stood with one foot on each side of it.

I resumed my observations in April 1996 after a winter break and, the following month, Doug Pickford's aforementioned book, *Earth Mysteries of the Three Shires*, was published. This endeavoured to explain the reason for the recent non-observation of the midsummer phenomenon:

'. . . it is very rare these days to be able to see this mystical double sunset. At one time it was a matter-of-fact annual event but either a slight tilt in the Earth's axis, or a 'wobble' or different air pollution or whatever, has meant it has not been seen for many a year. Technically, it is the obliquity of the ecliptic causing a change – a fact mentioned in the 1800s Official Guide to the North Staffs Railway.'

Unfortunately, despite putting forward a variety of options, Doug did not identify the real cause of the long-lost churchyard phenomenon, whilst his use of rather loose language did not help in making his explanation sound convincing. For example, in spite of Doug's claim to the contrary, the solstitial double sunset never has been and never will be an 'annual event' because adverse weather conditions can and do prevent successful observations of the occurrence from even the most promising locations. As is commonly known, for instance, the sun is rarely visible through dense cloud and Leek unfortunately suffers from that atmospheric condition more than most other areas of the country. Indeed, Richard Stephenson made the point that, 'A horizon phenomenon is not the easiest to observe; clouds seen edge on are thicker and the layers of the atmosphere are thicker.'

Also, it is not at all clear what Doug meant by either 'a wobble' or 'different air pollution'. If, in the former instance, he was referring to slight irregularities in the rotation of the earth caused by seasonal changes, tidal friction and processes within the interior of the planet, then the impact of these forces on the double sunset is absolutely infinitesimal, especially in comparison with the rate of obscuration of the view of The Cloud from the churchyard through tree growth. Alternatively, he may have been alluding to the variation in the tilt of the earth's axis over a cycle of about 40,500 years on average, but Kevin Kilburn has calculated that this has the effect of moving the observational position of the double sunset a mere ten feet per century northeastwards across the churchyard. Therefore, the gradually changing tilt cannot explain the relatively sudden cessation of successful double sunset observations. Finally, Doug was perhaps vaguely hinting at the precession of the equinoxes, which, as already stated, has major implications for the calendar, but does not directly affect the astro-geography of the double sunset phenomenon.

With regard to air pollution, it is difficult to comprehend why Doug believed a change in the *type* of atmospheric contamination could explain the apparently endless absence of a churchyard midsummer event, particularly because the occurrence had been visible during the age of dreadful coal smoke fogs prior to the passing of the Clean Air Act in 1956. Before Parliament thus acted, air pollution was such a serious hazard that more than 4,000 people died as a result of the great smog of December 1952. Indeed, it was that catastrophe which provided the very catalyst for belated action. It is also notable that the prevailing winds in Leek blow from Stoke-on-Trent, to the southwest, and the Potteries suffered from terrible air pollution in the days of unregulated chimney emissions, much of which drifted towards the Staffordshire Moorlands. Neither can smoke from the home fires of Congleton, immediately to the west of The Cloud, have helped the hill, let alone the sun, to have been clearly visible from St Edward's churchyard before the 1950s. Furthermore, the sight line of the solstitial setting sun crosses southwest Lancashire, which also experienced appalling air pollution in the heyday of industrial Britain.

Interestingly, the consequences of reduced visibility from an alternative, anticyclonic, weather system were perceptively put to me by Kevin Kilburn in a letter dated 21 June 2000:

'As a gross generalisation, to see the setting sun clearly and unobstructed from Leek, [the] line of sight must be cloudless. Haze must also be at a minimum, especially over south west Lancashire and Merseyside.

Last weekend, the strongish wind was from the southwest and, combined with cloudless skies, the sunset was brilliant. No doubt through the centuries this combination has occurred many times. But what about the alternative situation; low wind, especially from the east, combined with high pressure over the heart of the industrial northwest? Even now, haze develops within a couple of days over Greater Manchester. Combine this with the smoke from industrialised south Lancashire drifting westwards, especially between the early 19th century and, say, forty years ago and the prospects for seeing the sunset would be severely reduced.'

Although today, there remains plenty of scope for improving the cleanliness of the air, there is no justification in the argument which claims that observation of the double sunset is more adversely affected now by atmospheric pollution than it was prior to 1956. Indeed, this very point was put succinctly to me in a phone conversation on 15 March 2001 by Joe Buchdahl, who co-runs Manchester Metropolitan University's Atmosphere, Climate and Environment Programme: 'Visibility through man-made pollutants is greater than it was before 1956.'

Joe's statement was supported by Steve McQuade, the Pollution Co-ordination Officer for Staffordshire Moorlands District Council in a phone interview with me on 13 March 2001:

'Pollution levels were far worse before 1956 when coal was the primary source of fuel. Leek is now primarily a smoke-controlled zone and the use of gas and smokeless fuels helps.'

A similar picture was painted by Frank Grayson, an environmental technician for St. Helens Metropolitan Borough Council, whose operational area is located approximately across the sight line of the midsummer setting sun observed from Leek. Frank sent me a copy of a graph which showed a dramatic reduction in the average levels of smoke and sulphur dioxide in St. Helens between 1964 and 1998 and told me on the phone on 26 March 2001:

'The air is a lot cleaner up here than it used to be. Virtually the whole of the borough is now a smoke-free area. Certainly the particulate matter from the burning of coal has lessened over the years.'

In addition, as there have been several relatively recent documented viewings of the solstitial occurrence in June from Lowe Hill, which is over a mile further from The Cloud, then the air must be clear enough for the double sunset to be observable from the right location in or around the churchyard. Indeed, this was conclusively proved to be so by Roy Parker's previously discussed successful observations from the council car park and the garage forecourt, near to the churchyard, in Leek.

Doug also regarded 'a slight tilt in the Earth's axis' as another valid explanation of the midsummer nonevent. It is actually not the tilt in itself which is the issue, but the fact that the angle between the plane of the earth's orbit and that of the celestial equator varies over time, as previously noted. This is called the obliquity of the ecliptic, a phrase correctly used but not explained by Doug. The switch between the minimum and maximum obliquity takes on average around 20,250 years and gives a 0.234° change in latitude in 2,000 years. This does indeed affect the viewing position of Leek's churchyard solstitial phenomenon, but, as has already been stated, only to a very slight extent over a person's lifetime and therefore it cannot be held responsible for the dramatic recent fall-off of double sunset observations.

Finally, having listed three incorrect possible alternatives in an attempt to explain the non-observed midsummer occurrence, Doug inadvertently indicated that he was really at a loss to understand the problem by finishing his list with an entirely inconclusive fourth option: 'or whatever'!

Nevertheless, Doug's views on the lack of a visible phenomenon were quoted in an article printed in the *Leek Post & Times* on 12 June that same year:

'Intrigued visitors descending on Leek for its famed double sunset a week on Friday may be wasting their time, according to author Doug Pickford . . .

But it is many years since the spectacle was seen in its full glory with Mr Pickford describing the last full sighting as being back in 1958.

And in his latest book, Earth Mysteries of the Three Shires, Leekensian Mr Pickford advances two theories to explain the apparent demise of the double sunset – which can also be viewed from Lowe Hill and The Roaches.

One suggestion is that either the earth has tilted slightly on its axis or that air pollution has obscured the phenomenon . . .

The other theory propounded by Mr Pickford is that the shape of The Cloud has been radically altered by quarrying over the years.

Certainly, stone from the hill was used to construct both the nearby canal and the foundations of the railway viaduct in the valley below.

It was probably at this time that an unusual rock formation, a huge corkscrew-like structure called Bully Thrumble, was demolished.

In any event, there can be no doubt that the shape of The Cloud now bears no resemblance to that depicted in Miller's History of Leek . . .

Having thus consigned the double sunset to history, what's the betting on a glorious spectacle this year?'

Doug's claim of a successful double sunset observation in 1958 is particularly interesting because, in conversation with me, he stated that he had witnessed this event personally, from "Doctors' Corner". Although it cannot be categorically proved otherwise and it seems that he genuinely believed his assertion to be true, it is nevertheless extremely difficult to accept the validity of his claim because of the existence of contemporaneous documentary evidence to the contrary. This is contained in the aforementioned 26 June 1958 edition of the *Leek Post & Times*, which reported that no double sunset had been seen that year because of 'thick clouds – and rain actually falling'.

The 12 June 1996 newspaper feature was also notable in that it correctly promoted Lowe Hill as a bona fide viewing point of the double sunset, although the phenomenon cannot be observed from The Roaches on, or even near, the summer solstice, as will be shown later. In addition, Doug's claim that 'the shape of The Cloud has been radically altered by quarrying over the years' (which he had previously made in 1991 in his book, *Myths and Legends of East Cheshire and the Moorlands*) was based on speculation and is therefore open to considerable doubt. Furthermore, even if this assertion should be proven to be true, it still remains to be established that the change in the landscape had an effect on the midsummer observations, particularly adversely.

Evidence seemingly in support of the altered profile of The Cloud can be found in John Sleigh's book, *A History of the Ancient Parish of Leek, in Staffordshire*, which was published in 1862:

'Some 30 years ago, before the mountain was defaced for the sake of providing materials for the Macclesfield canal works, and still later for the Liverpool and Manchester railway, there were four curious points jutting out of that portion of the Cloud standing in Rushton Spencer, viz., the *Sugar* rock, the

Raven rock, the *Mareback*, and the *Bully Thrumble*, which last-mentioned point was most remarkable, resembling a gigantic cork-screw, and rising sixty or seventy feet above its parent rock.'

An important aspect of this account is its reasonable proximity to the dates of the construction of the canal (1826-1831) and the railway (1845-1849) and therefore of the quarrying of The Cloud. This helps considerably in accepting its authenticity and Sleigh's specific descriptions of the various landscape features originally existing on the hill appear to be so definite as to be virtually irrefutable. Furthermore, it is well possible that these rock outcrops had actually been known to the family of Sleigh, a native of Leek, who was born in the same year that the construction of the canal began.

Sleigh's comments on the quarrying of The Cloud for the new transport arteries in the nineteenth century were substantiated and expanded upon by John L. Brown in his excellent and detailed article, *The Macclesfield Canal – Why and How*, which was published in the *Journal of the Congleton Historical Society* in 1979:

'One stonework contractor was John Ward – the writer's Great Grandfather – of Rainow . . .

Ward . . . obtained his stone from . . . Tegg's Nose, Bosley Minns, Cloud, Under Rainow (Buglawton), and possibly Mow Cop. The stone would be 'dressed' at the quarries. Scores of men would be engaged in quarrying the stone alone, and as many dressed the stone. At the quarry on Cloud, 10 blacksmiths did nothing but sharpen the stone punches, bezels, and other chisels used by the dressers. The quarrying of the stone for the canal, and afterwards, the railway – for John Ward built many railway bridges – accounted for the familiar 'bite' out of the end of the Cloud.'

The quarry was opened on The Cloud in 1828 and its production of stone was sufficiently significant for the construction of a railway to take it to the line of the canal. In addition, a week after the aqueduct over the River Dane had been completed, the *Macclesfield Courier* stated: 'The very superior stone of which the aqueduct is composed, and also the twelve adjoining locks . . . have been procured from the adjacent mountain.' Furthermore, it was contemporaneously recorded that the impressive brick and stone Dane Valley Viaduct was rebuilt on stone foundations after four of its original piers had subsided.

Therefore, extensive quarrying of The Cloud is well documented and, indeed, considerable scars are still visible near to the summit, especially on the northern face of the hill. However, the detailed *Plan of the Township of Buglawton in the Parish of Astbury and County of Chester*, produced in 1841 at a scale of six chains to an inch, showed a quarry on Black Heath Common and three others clustered around Timbersbrook, but no sign of any workings in the vicinity of the peak of The Cloud. Nevertheless, the map was sufficiently specific to reveal a 'Mark on Rock' in proximity to and perhaps indicating the actual summit of the hill.

By 1911, all doubt had been ended because the six-inch Ordnance Survey map of that year showed a series of quarries on and around The Cloud, including those marked on the map of 1841 and two immediately off the northern face of the hill. These are the very ones that would have had some effect on the shape of The Cloud in relation to double sunset observations, although almost certainly not those undertaken from St Edward's churchyard, as it transpired. The upper and, to us, more significant of the two quarries was also shown, as an extensive feature just below the northernmost edge of the summit, on map SJ9063 of the Ordnance Survey 1:2500 series, published in 1993.

However, John Sleigh's extract specifically stated that the 'four curious points' jutted 'out of that portion of the Cloud standing in Rushton Spencer'. The first point of interest in this is that the account suggests that they (or at least three of them) primarily stuck 'out' and not *upwards* from the hill and therefore in all probability had less effect on a double sunset observation than they would have done had they been more vertical. Indeed, it is quite possible that their removal had no impact on solar viewing at all. Secondly, Sleigh categorically located these rock features on the Rushton Spencer side of The Cloud, that is to the east of both the summit and the county boundary dividing Staffordshire and Cheshire. The accuracy of his positioning is very much suggested by the continuing existence of a number of unusual outcrops jutting out from the same eastern flank of the hill, but, intriguingly, none of the aforementioned maps shows any quarries at all on this part of The Cloud. Consequently, it cannot be determined with any certainty as to whether or not the 'four curious points' were situated at places on the hill critical to double sunset viewers.

Finally, Sleigh provided a vivid description of the 'most remarkable' Bully Thrumble, which resembled 'a gigantic cork-screw, and rising sixty or seventy feet above its parent rock'. Such a natural feature would certainly be considered remarkable by any standards and most extraordinary even for a hill composed of Millstone Grit, a rock that can and does weather into unusual shapes. The Cloud in essence is a not untypical Pennine hill, with its flatish summit ridge and steep scarp slope, but Bully Thrumble-like features are not easily found on other northern Gritstone mountains. Therefore, it is difficult to believe that the outcrop in question actually looked precisely as related by Sleigh. Consequently, it may be that his description was embellished somewhat for effect or that he faithfully recorded an exaggerated second-hand representation of the feature, which he never saw personally.

Nevertheless, Bully Thrumble clearly existed and must have been a notable feature, although Sleigh's comments do not make it apparent as to whether the outcrop rose above the summit ridge of The Cloud or simply above the bedrock to which it was attached. Even if the former is true, it would have had to have been extremely broad to have radically altered a double sunset observed from Leek because it is very doubtful whether the sun could entirely have set behind a thin feature before reappearing. However, most pertinently, it is obvious from Sleigh's account that he did not regard Bully Thrumble to have been particularly broad and it therefore may well be that its demolition had no impact on the churchyard viewers of the midsummer phenomenon.

As the key visual and map evidence of former quarrying in the vicinity of the summit of The Cloud is to be seen on the northern face of the hill, none of the aforementioned features can have been affected by it because they were clearly stated by John Sleigh to have been located on the eastern side of the county boundary, whereas the main quarries were, and their scars still remain, to the west of the border. Neither these northern quarries, nor their areas of impact, are in fact visible from the centre of Leek, but are hidden by the northeastern flanks of the hill. Indeed, it may well be that the northern edge of The Cloud has never been seen from St Edward's churchyard because the contours of the hill are already inclining downwards towards the scarp slope before the quarried section is encountered. This suggests that the current summit of The Cloud is also the traditional peak, which remained as such even after the quarrying had taken place. Furthermore, the northern extremity of the hill itself is not visible from the churchyard and so what appears as the northern edge to an observer is, in fact, part of its northeastern flank. Thus the combined visual and map evidence indicates that the projected link between the quarrying of the hill and 'the apparent demise of the double sunset' is tenuous in the extreme.

Additionally, had the double sunset ceased to be observed from St Edward's churchyard immediately after the quarrying of The Cloud had taken place, then the cause of the new nonevent would have been obvious and irrefutable. However, that is not the case. As has been shown, historical evidence suggests that the most extensive damage done to the hill occurred in the second quarter of the nineteenth century and the key quarries which concern us were marked on the six-inch Ordnance Survey map of 1911. Despite this, the double sunset was witnessed from the churchyard or its immediate vicinity, according to reliable contemporaneously-recorded evidence, on 20 and 22 June 1870, 18 June 1884, 22 June 1895, 21 June 1927, 22 June 1934 and 21 June 1977. Consequently, no amount of quarrying of the hill prevented these successful observations.

Furthermore, it is obvious that the quarrying of The Cloud removed rock from the landscape, rather than added to it. Therefore, the way in which there should have been an impact on the viewing of the midsummer phenomenon is that the very existence of the initial sunset should have been threatened. The reason for this is that the removal of a chunk of the hill, should, if anything, have meant that the sun would not entirely have disappeared in the first place because there would have been less of The Cloud for it to have set behind. Alternatively, if, when viewed from the churchyard in the mid-nineteenth century, the sun set a short distance back from Cloud End, then a greater proportion of the disc should have reappeared after quarrying had occurred.

Therefore, the one effect that could not be expected to have resulted from the removal of the northern part of The Cloud was the obscuration of the sun. In other words, the quarrying hypothesis, projected to explain the recent non-observation of the double sunset, falls down because its consequences must be the opposite of what its proponents have claimed. Also, only quarrying on an absolutely monumental scale can have made any notable difference to an observer of the solstitial phenomenon from the churchyard in Leek because The Cloud appears to the naked eye as a very small feature indeed, especially in relation to the size of the setting sun.

One final point regarding the mining of the hill needs to be made. In support of the quarrying postulation, the *Leek Post & Times* article of 12 June 1996 stated that 'there can be no doubt that the shape of The Cloud now bears no resemblance to that depicted in Miller's History of Leek.' By doing so, the newspaper was suggesting that the four diagrams included in Matthew Henry Miller's book of 1891 depict the hill in its exact form, but that is not the case. As I have noted earlier, these illustrations were taken from the July 1738 edition of *The Gentleman's Magazine* and each shows a slightly, but noticeably, different version of The Cloud, which is broadly, but not specifically, recognisable to the modern eye. Although the exact pre-quarrying shape of Cloud End can only be conjectured, the vertical and, even in places, concave northern face of the hill presented in the diagrams seem exaggerated forms, designed to illustrate the double sunset occurrence rather than to represent The Cloud with absolute accuracy. Indeed, this is strongly suggested by the woodcut's portrayal of a steeper dip slope than existed in reality. Therefore, in conclusion, the hill today does bear some resemblance to its depicted shapes in Miller's book, but it never did appear to an observer precisely as it is shown in that publication.

In June 1996, Chris Doherty finally joined me in the field, having recovered sufficiently from his horrendous accident to photograph the phenomenon. Over a week from the 18th, he took a series of shots of double sunsets from the Cloud Side and Woodhouse Green locations, in varying conditions and with variable results, and, although there remained much to do in order to capture the key seasonal occurrences on film for posterity, we were happily under way.

On 19 June, the *Leek Post & Times* made a useful contribution to helping to resolve the double sunset mystery when it published an intriguing and pertinent letter by Anthony Bode:

'In the 1930s my father took me to the 'Doctor's [sic] Corner' in St Edward's churchyard to view the double sunset.

The first three or four occasions the weather had been warm and sunny and each time heat haze aborted the eagerly awaited phenomenon.

Eventually we had a spell of wet weather with rain up to about 8 p.m., the air was crystal clear and one small boy saw his first double sunset.

How many times in the last few years have we had rain followed by a clear sky at the right time?

Unfortunately the trees in the churchyard have been allowed to grow wild, ruining the view from the Doctor's Corner, unlike the park in Avranches in Brittany.

There is one spot in that park where the trees are cut to frame a superb view of Mont St Michel, some eight miles to the west.

Judicious pruning of the trees in St Edward's churchyard would restore the attractive view towards Bosley Cloud, tidy up Doctor's Corner and add one small amenity to those which have, in the past few years, made Leek a much pleasanter town.'

Although it was not entirely clear as to whether Tony understood the full implications of his comments about the overgrown trees in the churchyard, his letter actually hit the nail firmly on the head. As Roy Parker and I had already discovered, the obscuration of the view of The Cloud from the critical position in or around the churchyard on the summer solstice provided the entire explanation of the mystery of the non-reappearing sun and the consequently unobserved double sunset. However, Tony's appeal for 'judicious pruning of the trees' was not acted upon and The Cloud remained visible in late June only from points within and proximate to the churchyard which were not at the right angle to the hill to enable the midsummer phenomenon to be viewed.

Chris Doherty and I had a frustrating time on the summer solstice in 1996 (and on the two days either side) because adverse weather completely ruined our activities at both the Cloud Side and Woodhouse Green locations, although Roy had better luck on the A 523 on the longest day when the sun dropped out of a bank of cloud just in time to enable him to fix the observation point for the first time at this site. In addition, an article in the *Leek Post & Times* on 26 June contained two interesting reports of events on the solstice, as well as the traditional description of the occurrence and the repeated claim of 1958 as the last sighting:

'It is still not clear whether the sun has finally set on a unique phenomenon associated with Leek . . .

And, according to one witness who spent Friday evening [the 21st] in the churchyard, the event again failed to materialise.

Said Mike Brittan, who works for the Congleton Chronicle newspaper: "A great cheer went up as the sun disappeared – then we waited and waited for it to rise again but it never did.

By 10 p.m., the 15 or 20 of us who had gathered there had had enough, and we went home", he recalled.

But one local resident said he saw the phenomenon from the top of Thorncliffe while Central Television reported that, for the first time in many years, the event had been witnessed from a number of locations.

Said the resident, who wished to remain anonymous: "It was the first time I had ever seen the sun go down and then reappear.

I thought I was seeing things", he confessed.

These reports give backing to theories advanced by Leek author Doug Pickford on why the double sunset may no longer be visible from the churchyard.'

The newspaper's account of Mike Brittan's experience in the churchyard once more confirmed that the available observation points at that location were at the wrong angle for the sun to have re-emerged after setting behind The Cloud. As the Leek sunset begins slightly later than that seen from the A 523, the spectators at the churchyard, like Roy, struck lucky because the sun descended from a layer of cloud shortly before it set. However, they then suffered misfortune because, from where they were located, the sun does not reappear. In addition, it is clear that Brittan had very little idea of what to expect because the sun categorically cannot 'rise again' as it sets and, in any case, by 10 p.m., the sun had finally disappeared below any possible horizon visible from the churchyard for over twenty minutes, so that twilight was well under way.

The anonymous local resident quoted in the *Leek Post & Times* definitely did not see a double sunset occurring behind The Cloud, as viewed from 'the top of Thorncliffe', because that area is well off the sight line at the summer solstice. Nevertheless, it is not impossible that he saw the phenomenon occur as set against another object, natural or otherwise, although my own investigation of the high ground above Thorncliffe has uncovered no natural landscape feature with the potential to provide a double sunset, except perhaps for the northern edge of Ramshaw Rocks. However, even this possibility can be discounted because the rocks lie virtually due north of the viewing area, a direction in which the sun never sets. In addition, the Central Television report of successful observations of the occurrence from 'a number of locations' is entirely mystifying and contradictory to the information presented by the local newspaper, other than that dubiously proposed by the anonymous Thorncliffe spectator. Consequently, it can only be concluded that either the TV company was mistaken in its claims or the newspaper erroneously reported Central's broadcast.

Also on 26 June, the *Leek Post & Times* printed a letter from Jill Crawford of Bedford, who gave another report of the solstitial events in the churchyard:

'Although born and bred in Leek I have never got around to seeing the Double Sunset.

So I arranged to visit my parents in Leek this particular weekend.

On Friday June 21 after 9 o'clock I made my way up to the St Edward's Church and waited with the small group which had gathered. I managed to find a spot to peer through the trees and see Bosley Cloud.

The sun appeared to come down out of the clouds as a frothing fireball and set behind Bosley Cloud but did not reappear. A mere orange glow seemed to show up through the cloud and heat haze at the other side of the Cloud . . .

Better luck next year!'

This account is particularly relevant because it provides a description of the near archetypal recent midsummer churchyard experience. Crawford quite naturally positioned herself at a spot where she could see The Cloud, but, by doing so, thereby inadvertently ensured that she would not observe the sun reappear after it had set behind the hill. She inferred that 'cloud and heat haze' were responsible for the non-re-emergence of the sun, but the 'orange glow' off the northern flank of The Cloud indicates that the disc had set too far south on the ridge to reappear beyond its scarp slope.

I was active through much of the rest of the summer and the autumn, observing and recording the data from sunsets along the Cloud Side, Woodhouse Green-Toftgreen and A 523 lines. On 20 July, I made a particularly exciting visit to Woodhouse Green, where I saw my first quintuple sunset as the edge of the sun rolled down The Cloud's scarp slope, alternately setting and reappearing according to the precise contours of the hill! Around the autumnal equinox, Chris Doherty and I concentrated on photographing the occurrences from Cloud Side and the Toftgreen road, which were essential to my objective of producing quarterly illustrations for this book. In late October, I focused my attention on the A 523, from where the shape of The Cloud promised a solar reappearance of considerable proportions, but, in the event, only a disappointing 35% or so of the sun re-emerged during a successful observation on the 25th. Finally in 1996, Chris photographed the second sunrise from my favoured position north of Tunstall Road in a biting easterly wind on the winter solstice and the day afterwards, whilst I undertook a successful viewing of the double sunset, with approximately a 70% solar reappearance, from the A 523 at midwinter in equally bitter conditions.

However, the weather became colder and, whilst watching a second sunrise on 3 January 1997, I stood in about two inches of lying snow and did not regain feeling in my left big toe for around an hour after completing my observations, in spite of the best efforts of my car heater! Nevertheless, this was just the start of a very busy year for me on this project as I sought to drive it closer to completion. On 8 March, I witnessed approximately a 40% solar reappearance from the A 523, but, more importantly, I made appeals for information about the phenomenon, which were kindly published in *The Sentinel* on 9 June and the *Leek Post & Times* on the 18th. The relevant article in the former included an interesting quotation from the Reverend Keith Jones, the vicar of St Edward's

Church:

'To see a double sunset you do need a beautifully clear evening and over the years trees have grown which partially obscure the view. Although I have been at St Edward's for nine years and have not seen it yet.'

It is noteworthy that the vicar of St Edward's had still not observed the phenomenon despite the length of his service at the church and, although he clearly appreciated that tree growth had limited the possible viewing points of The Cloud from the churchyard in June, it was apparent that he didn't realise just how critical this factor had become.

My public appeals proved well worth while because I received particularly interesting written responses from Jean Bode, the wife of the historian, Harold, and from Doug Moller, more commonly known as the King and Lord of the Roaches. The former had the following intriguing information to offer in her letter of 14 June:

'The June 20-22nd sunset in the Leek area has been seen so rarely in recent years because of cloudy weather and pollution over the Mersey estuary. However, the churchyard is not the only place where a double sunset can be seen. Bosley Cloud is visible from Mount Road, and, depending on the viewer's position on the road the double sunset can be seen on clear days throughout June and early July. I saw it myself on July 8th in the early 1980s. Travelling home along the Ashbourne road I could see the setting sun clearly, and anticipating a double sunset I turned off along Mount Road, and found a suitable position to view the sun setting behind the Cloud and partially re-appearing several minutes later.

In the 1970's we also saw a double sunset in early July from the window of the Arts Club room in the Nicholson Institute, but that view is now obscured by the new Moorlands District Council offices which were built later.

Regarding double sun-rises: During the early 1960's our family spent several holidays at Llandudno. We stayed at a family hotel overlooking the promenade and had a view from our window of the Little Orme. We rose early one morning (late August I think), we saw the sun rise over the sea, disappear behind the Little Orme, and re-rise some time later over the hill.'

Clearly, Jean had not realised the key significance of the tree growth in and around the churchyard as a factor additional to adverse weather conditions and atmospheric pollution in explaining the recent non-observation of the midsummer phenomenon. Nevertheless, the contents of her letter revealed her strong understanding of the concept of the double sunset and the only other point with which I could quibble was that the viewing position of the occurrence from Mount Road technically gives way to the extension of its line on to Lowe Hill in the period around the summer solstice. However, there is no reason to doubt the validity of Jean's sightings from both Mount Road and the Nicholson Institute, whilst a personal examination of the geography and geometry of the Little Orme, during my visit to Llandudno on 28 July 2000, indeed confirmed the feasibility of a double sunrise involving the hill in the very late summer.

Doug Moller's letter of 18 June 1997 also appeared to be on the ball and noted other apparent places from which double sunsets could be observed, in addition to St Edward's churchyard:

'The double sunset . . . depends on (1) The time of the year (2) The location (3) Also the contours of the land.

I have seen the double sunset both in Rockhall, and even travelling from the main road to here [Knotbury End], also I have seen it in Africa. I have never bothered to take notice of the times, next time I will.'

The phenomenon indeed depends on the three factors that Doug listed and can most likely be viewed from Rockhall Cottage at the foot of The Roaches in April and September each year, weather permitting. However, evidence later came to light which indicated that the occurrence is not observable from any fixed point along the minor road linking Knotbury End with the A 53. Doug's further correspondence on the subject on 19 September and 2 October 2000 revealed that he had been on the move ('passing through') when he saw the solar events from the Knotbury End road and in Africa. It thus became clear that Doug had not realised the vital importance of standing still in order to witness a double sunset of the type concentrated on in this book.

The weather was absolutely dreadful around the summer solstice in 1997 and I recorded not a single successful event between 18 and 28 June inclusive! Neither did Roy have any joy during this period, which produced by far the worst viewing conditions of any spell since I had first embarked on the project. Nevertheless, I plugged on regardless and on 7 July saw a beautiful sunset and remarkable afterglow from the summit of The Cloud, which I described in my notes for this book:

'After it set, the horizon was pinky, but a bright red line (like fire) spread along the horizon both north and south for perhaps 10 minutes. It was incredible! One section, at the left end, seemed like a small ring of fire – presumably there was an intrusion of higher ground there?'

Even the well-known astronomer, Paul Doherty, was somewhat at a loss to explain these effects and could only suggest that they may have resulted from refraction, although Richard Stephenson said: 'This has to be an atmospheric phenomenon with clouds of the right density.'

My experience marked the beginning of a short purple patch in my observations and the following evening I struck lucky in my very first attempt to see a double sunset behind a natural feature of the landscape other than The Cloud. I arrived at the top of Lin Dale at 8.14 p.m. and straight away saw a triple sunset, with approximately a third of the disc reappearing, behind the angular peak, Thorpe Cloud, which flanks the southern entrance to Dove Dale! I quickly realised that there were many easy observation positions of this event because the ground round about was completely open with an unobstructed view of the hill. Therefore, the occurrence was visible both earlier and later in the evening than my own sighting. However, as I afterwards investigated the possibilities of seeing the phenomenon at different times of the year, I concluded that it was doubtful whether much more than a third of the sun would re-emerge on any other occasion.

After this triumph and before I returned home, I provisionally explored the likelihood of further double sunsets at other locations by investigating the shapes of several hills in the vicinity. Subsequently, I concluded that Chrome Hill and Parkhouse Hill, to the north-northwest of Longnor, were well worthy of specific examination, but that Ramshaw Rocks, Hen Cloud and The Roaches were not formed in such a way as to provide any realistic prospect of success.

Roy also made progress on 8 July when he checked the observational possibilities of the double sunset from the north-northwesterly-facing offices of Moorlands House in Leek. He saw a clear sunset on the dip slope of The Cloud, but the sun disappeared too far south along the ridge for there to be any solar re-emergence, even from the most east-northeasterly of the overlooking windows of the building. His conclusion was that the phenomenon would most likely be seen from this location, but at a date closer to the summer solstice.

The following evening, he joined me at Glutton Bridge, just over the River Dove in Derbyshire, to investigate whether Chrome Hill would provide a double sunset. Roy found a suitable viewing point in a field on the western side of the B 5053, but the sun vanished into cloud shortly before it reached the summit of the hill. However, I positioned myself closer to the peak, on the southern flank of Parkhouse Hill, and saw the sun set and around 80% of the disc reappear before the event was obscured by cloud. I was extremely pleased with even this incomplete reading because it had given a greater solar re-emergence from an off-the-hill position than The Cloud could provide at this time of the year.

I returned to the same place on Parkhouse Hill at the next opportunity, three days later, and, although my observations were thwarted by cloud, it turned out to be an eventful evening. Firstly, I had to shelter briefly under a tree from a sharp passing shower and then, during my descent, I came off worse in an encounter with a patch of nettles, especially because I was clad in just a T-shirt and shorts. As I continued to descend the hill, I became aware of three young farmers walking abreast directly towards me, with shotguns resting over their arms, and it was obvious that they weren't approaching to enquire after my good health! In fact, the scene briefly seemed reminiscent of the build-up to the gunfight at the O.K. Corral, but I had no fear that I was about to be shot. One of the farmers informed me that I was on private land and it quickly became obvious that they intended to guard the hill against all-comers. They were worried about the spectacular peak being damaged by an influx of tourists, apparently as a result of inaccurate publicity that the hill was open to the public. Anyway, the discussion ended amicably and I was given personal permission to continue my research on the peak.

The following evening, I investigated and subsequently discounted the possibility of Shutlingsloe, a flat-topped hill to the southeast of Macclesfield, being a feature capable of producing a significant double sunset because of its unsuitable shape. I then returned to my previous night's location and was rewarded with a superb double sunset occurring behind Chrome Hill from 8.21 to 8.53, with the full sun reappearing for all of 21 minutes (8.27 to 8.48), broken only by a small intrusion of the hill into the disc shortly before the sun began to disappear for the second and final time. I was euphoric about this, the first occasion that I had seen the sun fully re-emerge during a double sunset from an off-the-hill location. However, the viewing position left something to be desired because it was surrounded by thorn bushes and had only been reached after a scramble up a steep slope. Nevertheless, as I returned to my car, I had an unexpected additional pleasure when I saw the full moon rise, a beautiful silver, from the southern flank of Parkhouse Hill, which I had just descended.

On 2 September, an interesting video, *Leek: The First Millennium: 1000 Years Of Leek History*, was premiered at The Swan in Leek. This had been written by Paul Anderton and produced by Gerald Mee. *The Sentinel* stated that the film contained 'a sequence recording the famous double sunset, as seen from St Edward's churchyard' and consequently I contacted Gerald with considerable excitement. Although he was friendly and helpful, his reaction to my query was not as I expected. In fact, he denied that the video presented a double sunset and explained that the moving footage, taken by John Cunningham, merely showed the sun setting on 21 June 1977, but not reappearing, probably because of pollution in the atmosphere. This was disappointing news, but I decided to have a look at the sequence regardless. I was unable to do so until 13 June 1999, but, in the event, I was very glad that I did.

To my great surprise, the film did include a double sunset after all, even though Gerald was not very impressed with it. The sequence showed the sun setting on the back of The Cloud; a small portion of the disc re-emerging after quite some time, well down the scarp slope of the hill, and an outcrop of the landscape intruding into the visible section of the sun before it finally set at the foot of the slope. The only drawback to this historic film was that the camera had clearly moved position after the sun had first set, but before it had re-emerged. However, the tripod holding the camera had apparently remained stationary throughout the whole sequence, whilst it seemed almost certain to me that a small piece of the sun would have reappeared on the film even if the camera had never moved.

It was initially a mystery as to why Gerald did not recognise the footage as revealing a double sunset, but I eventually concluded that this was because, perhaps like most people, he considered that a significantly larger portion of the sun should have re-emerged after it had initially set. This seemed to be borne out in our further discussions, whereby he remembered having seen several double sunsets, with approximately 50% solar reappearances, from the 1930s until the 1970s. Certainly, from the right location in or around the churchyard, a greater proportion (although almost definitely not a half) of the sun should have re-emerged in Gerald's film than actually did, as Roy and I had already proved through our observations from the more distant Lowe Hill. Therefore, it can only be concluded that John Cunningham did not shoot the sequence from the optimum position, but rather from a spot where he could clearly see The Cloud. The two places were almost certainly not one and the same. Nevertheless, the occurrence as shown in the video essentially tallied with the independent verbal account of the same event related to me by David Dodd in April 2001.

I took Gerald to the churchyard and he showed me the location where he thought filming had occurred 22 years earlier. This was above the north wall of the upper churchyard, immediately to the west of the vicar's garage and virtually opposite the electricity substation. This is particularly interesting because it does not tally with the account of George Lovenbury, who, as described earlier, failed to observe any reappearance of the sun on the same evening from a more hopeful position in "Doctors' Corner", further to the east. However, a group of spectators to Lovenbury's 'right and below' him apparently viewed a similar event to that captured on Gerald's historic film. Therefore, it appears that the footage was not shot from where it was believed to have been.

Having calculated a plausible time of year when a double sunset might occur behind Parkhouse Hill, I duly returned to the location on 21 September 1997. As it transpired, I was already too late in the season to see such a phenomenon from the B 5053 as I'd hoped, but, with permission, I observed the event from the side of an outbuilding at the back of the farmhouse at Glutton Grange. Just as expected, the shape of Parkhouse Hill produced a double sunset, with the full sun reappearing in view for 22 minutes. This was therefore an occurrence which in many ways visually surpassed the events created by The Cloud and rivalled the one that I had recently witnessed against nearby Chrome Hill.

I persisted in my various observations through the autumn, but, on 21 November, was given a curt reminder of the need to be prepared at all times when researching, literally, in the field. I was hurrying to get to a viewing position to the north of Tunstall Road, beyond Cloud End, in time to see a solar event, but, as I ran down a slippery slope in a pair of worn trainers, I lost my footing and fell flat onto my back in the mud! I was then harangued by a flock of hungry sheep and finally arrived in a rather bedraggled condition at Leek Library to check the old newspapers for references to the midsummer phenomenon for use in this project!

By the end of 1997, it appeared that my double sunset investigations were not far from concluded, with all the key aspects of the occurrence seemingly having been resolved. Therefore, I believed that it only remained for me to undertake some final observations in order to complete my data and enable my book to be published. Therefore, the double sunset resolution seemed quite close at hand, but, as it transpired, the phenomenon had not nearly finished with me yet.

1. THE PARISH CHURCH OF SAINT EDWARD THE CONFESSOR IN LEEK. The upper churchyard is the traditional observation site of the midsummer double sunset.

2. THE CLOUD, as seen from the southeast, from the lay-by on the A 523 above Rudyard Reservoir.

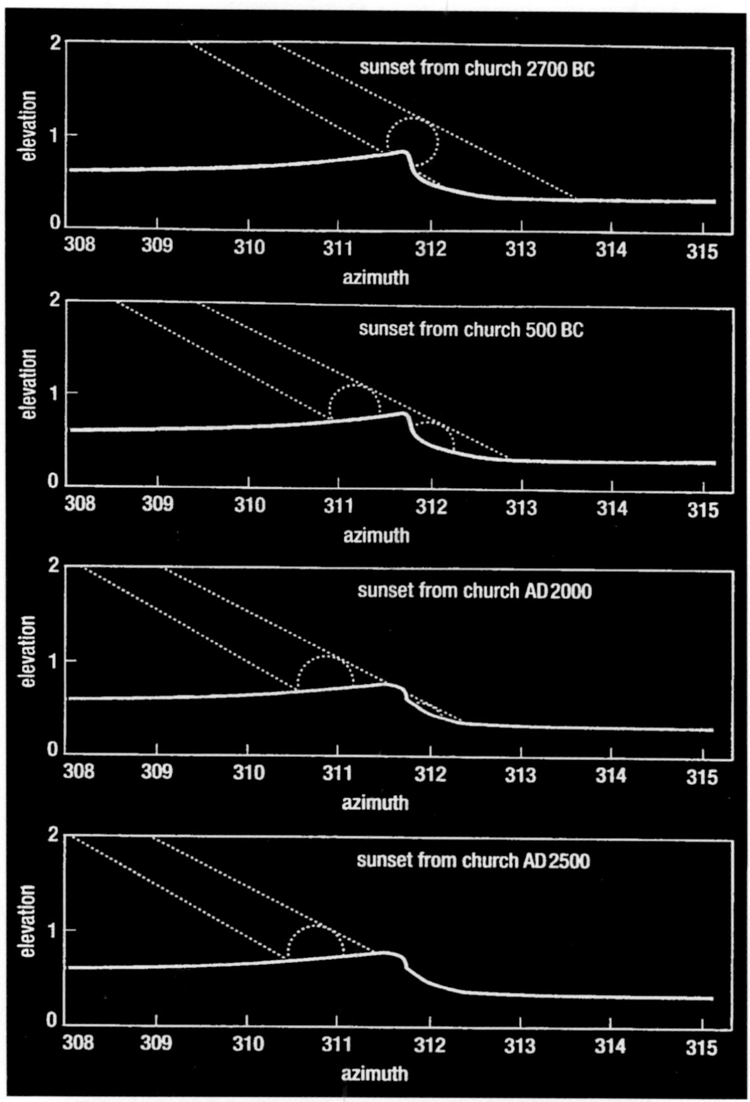

3. A SERIES OF DIAGRAMS ILLUSTRATING THE INTERACTION OF THE SETTING SUN AND THE CLOUD OVER TIME AS OBSERVED FROM THE SITE OF ST EDWARD'S CHURCH ON THE SUMMER SOLSTICE. These diagrams formed part of an article by the astronomer, Kevin Kilburn, in the *Astronomy & Geophysics* journal in February 1999 and their implications are discussed on pages 4 - 7.

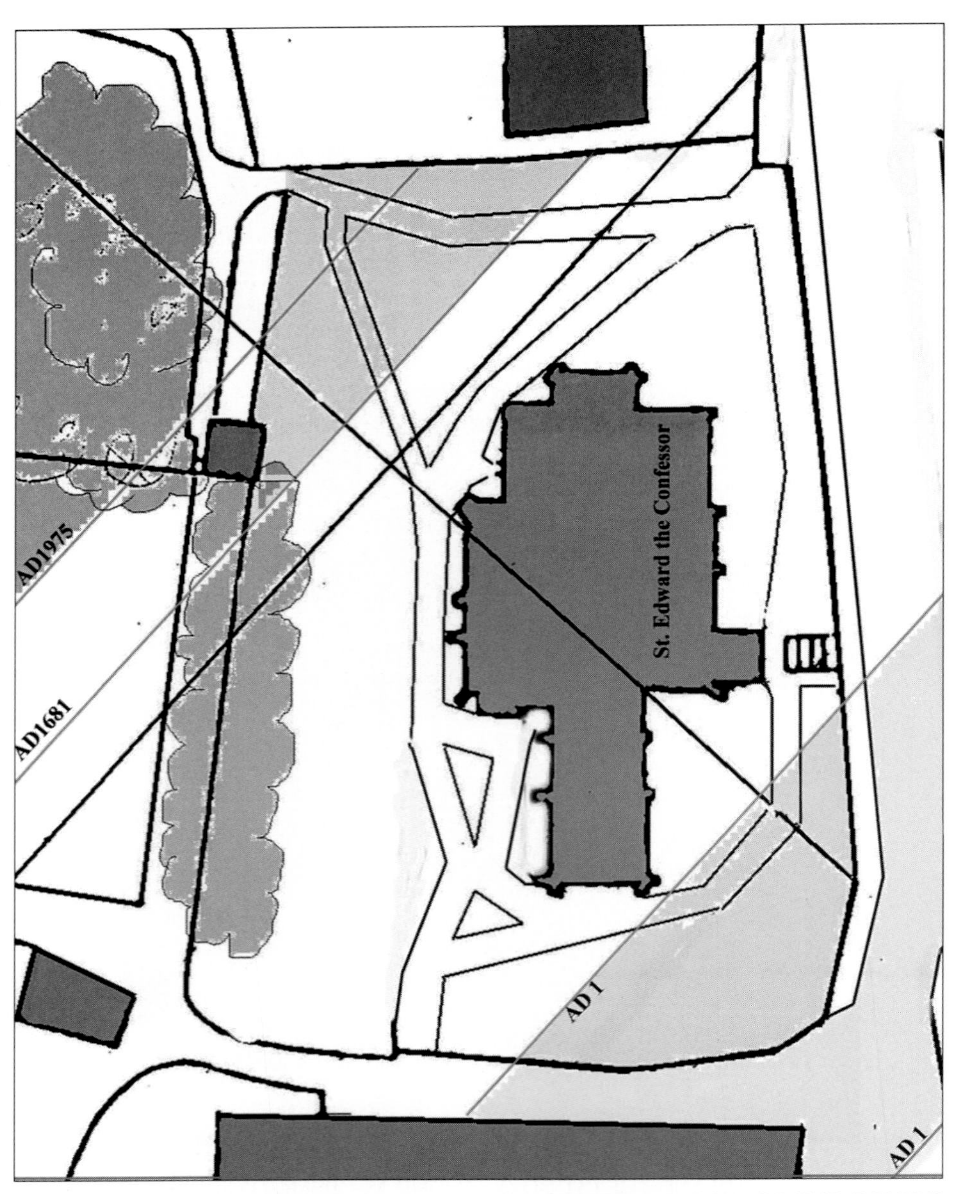

4. A PLAN OF THE EFFECTS OF TIME ON THE VIEWING WINDOW OF THE DOUBLE SUNSET FROM ST EDWARD'S CHURCHYARD ON THE SUMMER SOLSTICE, produced in March 2000 by Kevin Kilburn. Its implications are discussed on pages 7 - 9.

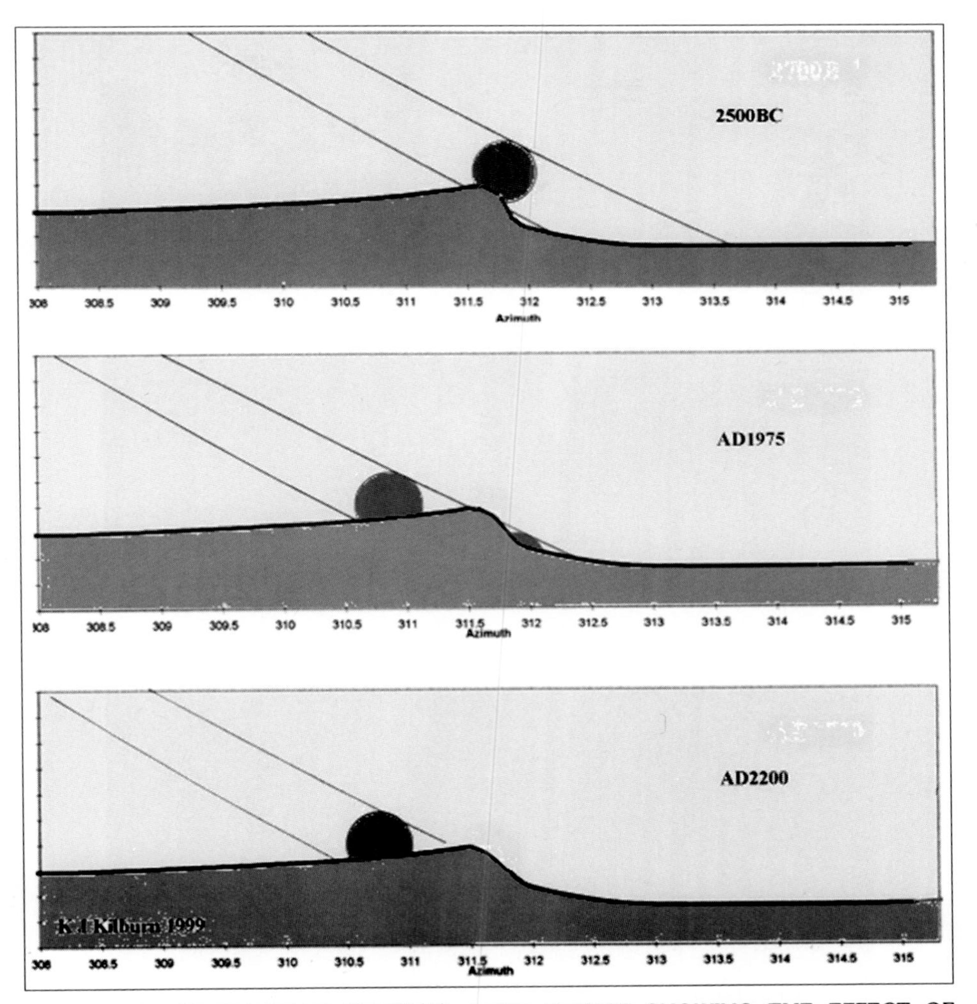

5. A SERIES OF DIAGRAMS ENTITLED, *LEEK SUNSET SHOWING THE EFFECT OF CHANGES IN THE OBLIQUITY OF THE ECLIPTIC FROM ST. EDWARD'S CHURCHYARD,* produced by Kevin Kilburn in 1999. Their implications are discussed on pages 9 - 11.

6. ONE OF TWO CARVED STONE CROSSES FROM THE ANGLO-SAXON PERIOD CURRENTLY STANDING IN ST EDWARD'S CHURCHYARD. It is believed to have been constructed around 1000 A.D. and is situated at a point from which the double sunset could be seen at that time. "Doctors' Corner", a more recent observation position of the phenomenon, is in the distance.

7. AN ILLUSTRATION OF THE CHURCHYARD REAPPEARING SUN, PUBLISHED IN ROBERT PLOT'S BOOK, *THE NATURAL HISTORY OF STAFFORD-SHIRE*, IN 1686.
Its depiction of The Cloud is highly inaccurate and the diagram is discussed in detail on pages 40 - 41.

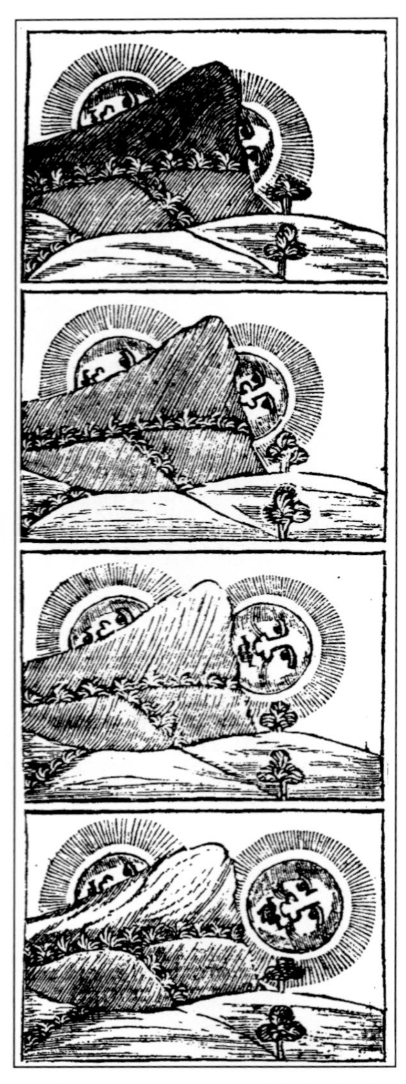

8. A PLAN OF THE CHURCHYARD DOUBLE SUNSET, PUBLISHED IN *THE GENTLEMAN'S MAGAZINE* IN JULY 1738. The diagrams are not notable for their accuracy and are discussed in detail on page 44.

9. THE ARMORIAL BEARINGS OF LEEK TOWN COUNCIL AND FORMERLY LEEK URBAN DISTRICT COUNCIL. On the shield are depicted two golden suns symbolising the double sunset.

10. THE 1977 SUMMER SOLSTITIAL CHURCHYARD DOUBLE SUNSET:
(i) A photograph, taken by Gerald Mee, showing the sun about to start to set on the dip slope of The Cloud.

(ii) A print from a film, shot by John Cunningham, showing a small portion of the sun, having reappeared from the lower scarp slope of The Cloud after setting.

11. A NEAR-DOUBLE SUNSET ON THE CLOUD, PHOTOGRAPHED FROM LOWE HILL ON THE 1977 SUMMER SOLSTICE BY HAROLD BODE:
(i) The sun setting on The Cloud, but it did not entirely disappear behind the hill.

(ii) A portion of the sun visible off the scarp slope of the hill, but it had not completely set before reaching this position.

12. A DOUBLE SUNSET ON THE CLOUD, PHOTOGRAPHED FROM LOWE HILL ON 29 JUNE 1989 BY ROY PARKER:
(i) The sun setting on the dip slope of The Cloud.

(ii) A portion of the sun visible off the lower scarp slope of the hill, having reappeared after setting.

13. A DOUBLE SUNSET ON THE CLOUD, PHOTOGRAPHED FROM THE A 523 ABOVE RUDYARD RESERVOIR ON 16 JULY 1990 BY ROY PARKER:
(i) The sun setting on the dip slope of the hill.

(ii) A portion of the sun visible off the lower scarp slope of the hill, having reappeared after setting.

14. A DOUBLE SUNSET ON THE CLOUD, PHOTOGRAPHED FROM WOODHOUSE GREEN ON 18 JUNE 1996 BY CHRIS DOHERTY:
(i) The sun, just starting to set on the summit of the hill.

(ii) The Cloud, with the sun having set behind its northern edge.

(iii) Approximately the maximum reappearance of the sun off the scarp slope of the hill.

(iv) The sun gradually setting on the lower scarp slope of the hill.

15. THE CLOUD, as seen from the A 54 to the north-northwest. A nick in the scarp slope, just below the summit, is the site of a former quarry for stone, which was used in the construction of the railway viaduct that is shown.

16. A DOUBLE SUNSET ON THE CLOUD, PHOTOGRAPHED FROM A FIELD OFF CLOUD SIDE ON 24 JUNE 1996 BY CHRIS DOHERTY. Unfortunately, the sun is not clearly delineated in the sequence, but its progression is visible nevertheless:
(i) The sun, just starting to set on the top of a ridge on the hill.

(ii) The Cloud, with the sun having set behind the ridge.

(iii) A portion of the sun, having reappeared beyond the northern edge of the ridge.

(iv) The full sun, having completely reappeared.

17. A SECOND SUNRISE, PHOTOGRAPHED FROM THE NORTH OF TUNSTALL ROAD, NEAR TO TOFTGREEN, ON 22 DECEMBER 1996 BY CHRIS DOHERTY:
(i) The full sun, still rising, approaching the summit of The Cloud.

(ii) The Cloud, with the sun having set behind its summit.

(iii) A portion of the sun, having reappeared beyond the summit.

(iv) The full sun, having completely reappeared.

18. A DOUBLE SUNSET ON PARKHOUSE HILL, PHOTOGRAPHED FROM THE B 5053 AT GLUTTON GRANGE ON 3 APRIL 1999 BY CHRIS DOHERTY:
(i) The sun, just about to start to set on the summit of the hill.

(ii) Parkhouse Hill, with the sun having set behind its summit.

(iii) The full sun, visible off the northern flank of the hill, having reappeared after setting.

(iv) The full sun, near the foot of the northern flank of the hill, just about to start to set.

19. THE SETTING SUN, PHOTOGRAPHED FROM ST EDWARD'S CHURCH TOWER ON THE 1999 SUMMER SOLSTICE BY CHRIS DOHERTY:
(i) The sun, having dropped out of a bank of cloud and just about to start to set on the dip slope of The Cloud.

(ii) The sun setting too far south on the ridge in order for it to reappear, thus showing that a double sunset does not occur from the church tower.

20. "DOCTORS' CORNER", IN ST EDWARD'S CHURCHYARD, LOOKING TOWARDS THE CLOUD ON 22 JUNE 1999. The photograph shows the viewing line from this traditional observation site as being completely obscured by trees.

21. ONE OF THE FEW POINTS IN ST EDWARD'S CHURCHYARD FROM WHICH THE CLOUD COULD STILL BE SEEN IN THE DISTANCE IN JUNE 1999, BUT, UNFORTUNATELY, ALL OF THEM WERE, AND REMAIN, TOO FAR WEST TO PRODUCE A DOUBLE SUNSET.

22. A DOUBLE SUNSET ON THORPE CLOUD, PHOTOGRAPHED FROM THE TOP OF LIN DALE ON 8 JULY 1999 BY CHRIS DOHERTY:
(i) The sun, just starting to set on the summit of the hill.

(ii) Approximately the maximum reappearance of the sun after having set behind the hill for the first time.

23. A DOUBLE SUNSET ON CHROME HILL, PHOTOGRAPHED FROM PARKHOUSE HILL ON 11 JULY 1999 BY CHRIS DOHERTY:
(i) The sun, just about to start to set near the summit of the hill.

(ii) Chrome Hill, with the sun having set behind its summit.

(iii) The full sun, visible off the northeastern flank of the hill, having reappeared after setting.

(iv) The sun setting near the foot of the northeastern flank of the hill.

24. A DOUBLE SUNSET ON THE CLOUD, PHOTOGRAPHED FROM THE B 5053 SOUTH-WEST OF BOTTOM HOUSE ON 11 JULY 1999 BY CHRIS DOHERTY:
(i) The sun setting on the dip slope of the hill. As can be seen, from this position the sun does not fully set.

(ii) Approximately the maximum reappearance of the sun after having set, shot from a point to the northeast of the position of the first photograph.

25. A DOUBLE SUNSET ON THE CLOUD, PHOTOGRAPHED FROM CLOUD SIDE ON 21 SEPTEMBER 1999 BY CHRIS DOHERTY. This sequence is also representative of the occurrence on the equivalent date in the spring:
(i) The sun, just about to start to set on the summit of the hill.

(ii) The full sun, having completely reappeared after setting.

26. A DOUBLE SUNSET ON THE CLOUD, PHOTOGRAPHED FROM THE VICINITY OF CLOUD HOUSE FARM ON 18 MARCH 2000 BY CHRIS DOHERTY. This sequence is also representative of the occurrence on the equivalent date in the autumn:
(i) The sun, about to start to set on the summit of the hill.

(ii) Approximately the maximum reappearance of the sun after having set.

27. THE SETTING SUN, PHOTOGRAPHED FROM ONE OF THE FEW REMAINING VANTAGE POINTS OF THE CLOUD IN ST EDWARD'S CHURCHYARD ON THE 2000 SUMMER SOLSTICE BY DAVE RANDLE. The sun can be seen setting too far south on the ridge in order for it to reappear, thus showing that a double sunset is no longer visible from the churchyard.

28. A NEAR-DOUBLE SUNSET ON THE CLOUD, PHOTOGRAPHED FROM PICKWOOD VALE RECREATION GROUND ON 26 JUNE 2000 BY GEOFF CHANNON:
(i) The sun, about to start to set on the dip slope of the hill.

(ii) The sun setting near to the summit, but it did not entirely disappear behind the hill.

(iii) A portion of the sun visible off the scarp slope of the hill.

6 The Double Sunset Resolution

My main observational efforts in 1998 were based on filling in the gaps left after my extensive viewings of the phenomenon involving The Cloud over the previous few years, but it was not easy to draw my investigations to a close because the weather often frustrated my attempts to do so. However, the conditions were ideal on the summer solstice and consequently I saw double sunsets both from the field below Cloud Side and, for the first time on that particular evening, from Woodhouse Green. As it turned out, this was a stroke of good luck because there were almost certainly no complete double sunsets on the following nineteen nights at least!

Thereafter, I was tied up with more pressing matters, but, in November, I resumed my gap-filling activities and, on 4 December, suffered from another hazard of the occupation. To get to my intended observation point for the anticipated double sunrise in a field to the north of Tunstall Road, I had to cross the infant brook, whose banks I already knew to be boggy at the best of times. However, the whole area around the stream had turned into a quagmire and I increasingly sank into the bog until my legs were stuck in mud to a depth of nearly an inch above the top of my rubber boots, so that I extricated myself only with considerable difficulty!

I was out observing in the field in every month in 1999 as I attempted to bring the project towards a close. On 8 January, I was unfortunately spotted by an enthusiastic border collie when I was returning from an unsuccessful visit to the same field just mentioned. Its playfulness caused me great problems when I crossed the quagmire and it became so boisterous that it jumped all over me before shaking itself and thereby splattering me with mud! Eventually, I was forced to pretend to throw things at it in order to rid myself of it and then I had to clean myself up as best I could before keeping my important appointment with the book buyer for Hanley Library.

The topography of The Cloud is such that the occurrence of 9 February on the Cloud Side line took place for over an hour and a half, even without the final sunset being observed! Unfortunately, in order to record the data from this, I had to stand in near zero temperatures in a snow-covered field for the whole of that period and, although I was wearing rubber boots, I only had a pair of thin ankle socks on my feet, owing to the lack of time to put on anything more substantial. Not surprisingly, my feet quickly became numb, which led me to wonder momentarily for the first and only time whether I might be better doing something more sensible like most other people!

On 31 March, there was a bolt from the blue with the publication in the *Leek Post & Times* of an article entitled 'Sun going down on astronomical curiosity.' This summarised the research undertaken on the midsummer occurrence by Kevin Kilburn. Although the astronomical details which it presented were extremely interesting and at times novel, alarm bells sounded because the feature raised the possibility that Kevin, who was then unknown to me, might have recently published, or be about to put into print, sufficient detail on the double sunset phenomenon to make my own long-standing findings obsolete at a stroke. I was obviously worried, but, as it transpired, unnecessarily so.

Some aspects of the article have already been discussed in this book, but various extracts are well worth quoting here:

'One of Leek's most enduring and endeering [sic] curiosities will not last forever, an amateur astronomer has concluded.

The double sunset seen from the churchyard of St Edward the Confessor, at Leek, has baffled locals for some time.

However, six months of investigation by Kevin Kilburn, of Bolington [sic], Cheshire, former president of Manchester Astronomical Society, resulted in an explanation to the phenomenon being published in a scientific journal.

At the centre of Mr Kilburn's research, completed in February, are a number of archaelogical [sic] implications.

Although the present church dates back to the 13th century, Mr Kilburn cites 'circumstantial evidence' as suggesting the site was used as a place of reverence over 3,500 years earlier . . .

Described in literature of the late 17th century, Mr Kilburn observes that the present day sunset differs from that of 300 years ago.

Attributing the difference to the slow reduction of the sun's tilt over thousands of years . . .

Mr Kilburn suggests that a possible fascination with the cycles of the sun and moon, may have prompted our prehistoric ancestors to construct a monument on what they perceived as a 'sacred' landscape.

Thanks to Mr Kilburn's research, double sunset watchers, weather permitting, will be able to view this year's spectacle in the knowledge that they may be standing on a 5,000 year site of worship.

However, although a spot of gardening by the Rev Keith Jones will ensure this year's pilgrimage runs smoothly, trimming overhanging trees which had been obstructing the view, nothing lasts forever . . .'

I commented on the main implications of the article earlier in this book and there is no value in repeating them. Nevertheless, one aspect of the report does need to be considered and that is that it proved to be overoptimistic about the value of the vicar's branch-shearing activities. Although some of the trees in the churchyard were indeed pruned prior to the longest day, this amounted to little more than a trim and it created no discernable improvement in the visibility of The Cloud for the hopeful spectators of the midsummer occurrence. Regardless of this, Kevin erroneously claimed on Manchester Astronomical Society's web page, from 12 April, that: 'Now, thanks to Revd. Keith Jones . . . the trees have been trimmed and the double sunset can once more be seen, weather permitting.'

On 3 April, I returned to Glutton Grange, this time accompanied by Chris Doherty, who successfully filmed a fine double sunset against Parkhouse Hill from the B 5053. While he was doing so, I carefully observed the occurrence and noted that the whole event took 33 minutes to complete, whilst I was rewarded with the full sun reappearing in view for 20 minutes. The only drawback with the precise monitoring location was that the branches of a tree in a field on the opposite side of the road interfered to some extent with the visibility of the final sunset.

Having been given Kevin Kilburn's number, I phoned him on 12 April to elicit the state of play regarding his double sunset investigations and his future plans regarding the phenomenon. During the ensuing conversation, he promised to send me a copy of his article on the occurrence, which had been published in the

Astronomy & Geophysics journal, and he duly did so. He also told me that he was hoping to photograph the double sunset on the summer solstice from St Edward's Church tower and he was confident that, weather permitting, he would be successful. Although I did not say so at the time, I was sceptical about the prospects of this, but decided nevertheless to take a close look at the precise location of the tower in relation to the approximate midsummer double sunset viewing position on the ground. This I did on 14 April and my investigation confirmed that, in spite of its extra height, the tower seemed to be too far to the southwest for the sun to reappear after it had set behind The Cloud.

The following day, a copy of Kevin's article arrived in the post and, although I could detect a number of flaws within it, I was impressed by its astro-geometrical information and calculations in particular. It quickly became apparent that I was in receipt of one of the most revealing documents ever produced on Leek's double sunset, which rivalled Robert Plot's pioneering work of 1686 in importance. Not only did it examine essential scientific aspects of the phenomenon, but it also supplied impressive supporting diagrams and presented brief snatches of the event's observational history, as well as projecting the possible origin of human interest in the occurrence. In addition, there were two sentences which particularly caught my eye:

'Many visitors still go to the churchyard at the summer solstice, but overhanging trees mean that the phenomenon can no longer be seen easily from ground level. The double sunset can be observed from the church tower, weather and atmospheric conditions permitting.'

I was very surprised by these comments. It was clear that Kevin thought that the double sunset could still be seen from the churchyard, albeit with some difficulty because of tree interference, whereas such observations were no longer possible. In addition, he had boldly stated in print that the phenomenon 'can be observed from the church tower' even though this claim remained entirely untested. Consequently, I was perplexed that Kevin, as an experienced astronomer, had made this unequivocal factual assertion before he had actually tested the hypothesis behind it. Therefore, I decided to check his credentials and was given a glowing reference by Cherry Moss, the secretary of Macclesfield Astronomical Society, which reassured me considerably.

One of my occasional mishaps occurred on 4 June when I ripped my jeans and cut my knee while climbing over a wall off Cloud Side following an unsuccessful observation. Undaunted, five days later, I investigated the prospects of the B 5053 to the southwest of Bottom House, which had been recommended to me as a double sunset viewing location by Harry Ball, who claimed to have seen the phenomenon from his garden at Bottom Lane Farm on 7 July 1984 and from near to the Blakelow Common lay-by on 5 June 1999. On the former occasion, he wrote in his nature notebook, 'Only a reddy glow, not a clear disc. Sank behind The Cloud and momentarily reappeared beyond the hill's face.' In the latter instance, he recorded the times of the key stages of the occurrence, with the sun having first set at 9.26, re-emerged at 9.29 and finally set at approximately 9.30. He noted in his diary, 'Only a small proportion reappeared – a hazy smudge.'

It quickly became apparent to me that there was a clear view of The Cloud from a long stretch of the secondary road, from Blakelow Lower Farm almost to

The Green Man, but the hill was rather distant and very small in comparison with the size of the sun. I conjectured that a double sunset would indeed occur from this location, but that the proportion of the sun's reappearance would be small. Unfortunately, I was unable to put my opinion to the test immediately because the 9 June 1999 event was ruined by haze and The Cloud thereafter ceased to be in view from the B 5053 until early July.

On 13 June, I interviewed four people who claimed to have seen a double sunset in order to record their memories for inclusion in this book and to comment on their experiences. Firstly, I met Paul Farrington, of Leek, at The Mermaid Inn, from where he believed that he had observed such an event at around 9 p.m. on the summer solstice in 1996. In advance, both Roy Parker and I had separately checked the panorama visible from the pub and its vicinity and we were puzzled by Paul's claim because we could identify no landscape feature on the horizon remotely likely to produce a double sunset.

Paul explained that he had been sitting in The Mermaid's dining room when the landlord suddenly appeared in a state of excitement and drew the occurrence to their attention. Paul recollected that he had consequently seen the sun set behind The Roaches and then rise vertically before setting for a second time. However, this is an astronomical impossibility. Also, apparently, the chef, who had first noticed the event, asserted that it would not recur for another 700 years! I can offer no obvious explanation of Paul's account, which he genuinely believed to be true and accurate, other than to suggest that he witnessed an atmospheric occurrence which represented an optical illusion, perhaps caused by unusual cloud formations or exceedingly anomalous refraction. Unfortunately, The Mermaid has since changed hands and I have been unable to track down any other independent witnesses to this event.

Next, I called on the aforementioned historian, Cathryn Walton, and together we went to Lowe Hill, from where she had observed a double sunset on an unknown June evening in the early 1980s. She remembered her viewing position as having been opposite the track leading to Lowe Hill Farm and recalled watching the event on a perfectly clear evening for ten to fifteen minutes. She also described to me what had occurred and I quickly realised that her account was authentic because her recollections strongly tied in with the findings which Roy and I had elicited from that site.

My following port of call was the home of Gerald Mee. As I have previously noted, we made a visit to the churchyard, where he outlined the details of various double sunsets which he had seen over the years and wistfully remarked: 'Nobody bothered too much. You tended to think it was always going to be there.' We then drove on to Mount Road. There we stopped and Gerald tried to locate the positions from which he had apparently witnessed the phenomenon several times in the distant past, but he was unable to be very specific. Nevertheless, he confidently stated, 'It gave a second chance if you'd missed it at the churchyard.' Indeed, this was and remains true, but, oddly, Gerald was convinced that he had observed the occurrence from this location around 24 June in the 1940s. The problem with this recollection is that the double sunset is not visible from Mount Road on or near to that date because the sight line still remains at Lowe Hill. The most likely explanation of this riddle is that Gerald indeed saw the phenomenon from Mount Road, but that it was later in the season than he remembered, in July.

After having been treated to a showing of Gerald's video, *Leek: The First Millennium: 1000 Years Of Leek History*, with its historic moving footage of the midsummer occurrence in 1977, I picked up my final witness of the day, the well-known Harold Bode. We went firstly to Lowe Hill, where Harold pointed straight away at the northeastern side of the entrance to Home Farm and said that that marked his initial observation point of the one and only double sunset he had seen from this location, on 21 June 1977, in the company of Nigel Webberley (now a joint-managing director of Webberley Ltd). As the event proceeded, Harold apparently moved his position a few paces to the northeast along the road until he was in alignment with both St Edward's Church and The Cloud. Also, fortunately, he took three photographs of the occurrence, the second of which was published in volume 40 of the *Astronomy & Geophysics* journal in February 1999, along with the incorrect caption, 'Sunset . . . observed from the church of Edward the Confessor, Leek.'

Strictly speaking, for the phenomenon to have real value, it needs to be observed from a fixed point. Otherwise, most people see double sunsets on many days of the year without realising it, as they walk along the street or drive a car, for example, and the sun becomes hidden behind buildings or high ground before re-emerging when a lower horizon appears. Therefore, technically, Harold should not have moved his viewing location, but, of course, unless the exact observation spot for a specific event is known in advance, the spectator will invariably have to make adjustments to his precise position as the sun sets. Harold cannot be blamed for having done that. Also, although his photographs are interesting items, they do not show a double sunset. It can relatively easily be seen from the camera position in the first print that the sun did not go on to set fully, but a part of the disc overshot the northern end of The Cloud. With the second and third photographs, the reverse is true, that the sun had not entirely disappeared prior to having been captured on film.

Further investigation revealed that Nigel Webberley had actually not been present at the event, although his cousin, Robert, had and he confirmed Harold's successful solstitial observation, stating, even on 21 March 2001, 'I remember it vividly.' In 1977, at the time of the occurrence, Robert lived at Lowe Hill House and believes that he observed the event from the farm gate opposite the entrance to his drive, watching the sun set and then reappear. However, this recollection in turn is at odds with the camera evidence that he and Harold had actually stood some distance to the northeast of the leading edge of the viewing window, which, under normal conditions, is actually located southwest of the entrance to Home Farm on the summer solstice.

After visiting Lowe Hill, Harold and I moved on to St Edward's upper churchyard, where he confidently indicated the place, at its northeastern extremity, from which he claimed to have observed a double sunset, with a fractional solar reappearance, on 22 June 1961 and described it as 'Doctors' Corner'. Although I could not fault Harold's recollection per se, recognisable landscape features shown in a photograph which he had taken of the event indicate that it had been shot from near or on the north wall of the churchyard, but some fifty feet to the west of his apparent observation point. It is impossible to decide from the photograph at what stage of the occurrence it had been taken because of the intense light of the sun, which virtually entirely obscures The Cloud, but Harold believes that he moved forward to take the shot in order to avoid trees which partially obscured the view from "Doctors' Corner". Thus the combined effect of his photograph and his memory suggested that the spectators gathered in the northeastern nook of the upper churchyard were having identifiable problems with tree interference even in 1961.

However, I immediately jumped to the conclusion that Harold didn't know what he was talking about because Roy and I believed that we had identified "Doctors' Corner" as being down the slope in the lower churchyard below. Therefore, I queried Harold's use of this term, but he confirmed his statement and pointed out two relevant tombstones which lay at our feet, with both of them containing the word *surgeon* to describe their occupants! Indeed, the flat gravestones, of Eli and Isaac Cope, lay side by side right in the northeastern corner of the upper churchyard in the very place where I'd seen many double sunset observers stand in years past in expectation of seeing the phenomenon.

Further investigation led me to the first volume of Matthew Henry Miller's *Olde Leeke: Historical, Biographical, Anecdotal, and Archaeological*, which revealed detailed information on no fewer than eight surgeons buried in the area that he called "Doctors' Corner". I then verified the precise names of these practitioners through examining transcripts of records of burials and monumental inscriptions kept at Staffordshire Record Office. Finally, as a result of checking the church's card index of burials, I discovered the tombstones of two more of the medics, James Davenport Hulme and Charles Flint, immediately beneath the north wall of "Doctors' Corner", once again in a classic double sunset observation location.

Therefore, the truth of Harold's revelation was indisputable and I was stunned because Roy and I had been working for eight years under the misapprehension that the traditional viewing point of the midsummer phenomenon was located in the lower rather than the upper churchyard. Remarkably, there had turned out to be two "Doctors' Corners", one in the northeastern corner of each of the churchyards! However, as it transpired, the location of "Doctors' Corner" in the upper churchyard, rather than in the lower one well below, much more easily and plausibly explained the gradual shift of the solstitial spectators westwards along the north wall in order to see The Cloud as the trees increasingly blocked their view over the years.

On 15 June, I began to search for a more accessible observation point for the Chrome Hill double sunset and on the following evening, courtesy of Susan Taylor, the secretary to the vicar of St Edward's, I climbed to the top of the church tower to investigate the possibilities of the phenomenon occurring on the summer solstice. Although I controlled my mild vertigo and was rewarded with a splendid view, the sun set into cloud at 9.15 and was not seen again. Nevertheless, I took the opportunity to ask Susan about the double sunset she claimed to have observed from the churchyard in either 1962 or 1963. Her description conformed with the pattern of events with which Roy and I had become familiar and could not be faulted in its reliability. Although she was, not surprisingly, initially unable to remember with any certainty where she had stood that evening, on reflection she concluded that it had been at the northeastern end of the upper churchyard, that is, in "Doctors' Corner". Nevertheless, she was adamant that the whole of the sun had not reappeared after setting behind The Cloud and suggested, almost certainly a little optimistically, that perhaps a 50% re-emergence had occurred.

On the 17th, Roy took a turn up the church tower and saw a perfectly clear sunset on The Cloud, 'about one sun width' back from Cloud End, but, as a consequence, there was no solar reappearance. However, he concluded in his notes that it 'will be very close by 21st'. The same night, I discovered a convenient observation position for the Chrome Hill occurrence in a field immediately northwest of the B 5053 at Glutton Bridge and witnessed the full sun re-emerge and remain in view for approximately 3½ minutes after it had initially set on the summit of the hill.

The next evening, I recorded the essential data from another successful visit to Glutton Bridge and then had to dash to Leek to arrive in time to scale the church tower once more. However, adverse weather conditions struck again at this location as the sun disappeared into cloud shortly before setting and so the prognosis for the solstice remained an open question. Nothing more was gleaned at any site on the 19th because of dense cloud and rain, but the following night proved very revealing.

Twenty-one people gathered in the upper churchyard in anticipation of a rare occurrence and I made sure that I was standing at the most easterly point possible, along the north wall, from which The Cloud could be seen. I knew that this would maximise the chance of the sun re-emerging after it had set behind the hill, although I was well to the west of "Doctors' Corner" and confident that there would be no reappearance. Everyone else, including Kevin Kilburn, was in a less advantageous position to the west of me. The sun set on the back of The Cloud at 9.30.30 (30 seconds after 9.30), too far south to re-emerge, but five or six people close to me became very excited five minutes later, when a bright light appeared off the summit, until I pointed out that it was afterglow, which was subsequently proved as it spread northwards just above the horizon.

Roy was on the church tower at the same time and saw the sun set, slightly under one width of the disc back from Cloud End, at 9.32. Again, there was no reappearance and, although cloud interference off the hill's scarp slope may have been a contributory factor to this, the marginal movement only of the position of the sunset since 17 June convinced Roy that the phenomenon would not be observed on the solstice, the following evening.

Tension mounted on the longest day, particularly because the possible church tower double sunset needed to be put to the test and Kevin was very keen to capture the phenomenon on film. Overnight rain seemed a harbinger of midsummer gloom, but the weather became dry in the morning and sunnier as the day wore on. I was invited into the Radio Stoke studios for a short live interview about the occurrence and its prospects for that evening and afterwards I drove to Glutton Bridge in a vain attempt to monitor the double sunset from that location on this most important of all days. Cloud had formed again and the awaited observations from Leek also seemed in jeopardy.

Regardless of the possible outcome, Susan Taylor escorted a group of about ten privileged spectators, including Kevin, Chris Doherty and me, to the top of the church tower, where we awaited what fate would offer us. I immediately occupied the most northeasterly, and therefore advantageous, position possible, where Chris fixed his camera on his tripod. However, Kevin located himself in the northwest corner of the tower, from which a solar reappearance was even less likely. As it transpired, we all struck very lucky indeed because the sun dropped out of a dense bank of cloud and clearly into view shortly before the event was due to commence. Although there was some cloud interference as it actually set on the dip slope of The Cloud at 9.32, enough of the sun was visible for it to be conclusive that it had disappeared too far south on the ridge in order for it to re-emerge, as was duly observed. There was general disappointment amongst the party and Kevin dejectedly stated that he would considerably have to refine his calculations, which he had computed to an accuracy of one degree, but I was well satisfied with my prediction of the outcome.

Roy was down below, in the upper churchyard, with about eighty other people, but, as we expected, the sun did not return into view after setting on the back of The Cloud from this location. Roy's notebook confirmed that bad weather was not responsible: 'Line of cloud above hill but clear on summit and north side. Good set, no re-appearance.' There were perhaps another twenty spectators on the grass beyond the churchyard wall, in Brough Park, but they were also positioned outside the observation line and had no joy either.

On the 22nd, I took several photographs in and around the churchyard to indicate the problem of the obscuration of The Cloud by the trees, but there were no more visible solar events in Leek until at least the 27th because of adverse weather conditions. Nevertheless, on the 23rd, the *Leek Post & Times* published an article, entitled, 'No joy for the double sunset seekers,' which was sparked by my request for witnesses of previous occurrences to get in touch with me. The report was essentially accurate and the relevant section stated:

'Over 100 people gathered in St Edward's churchyard in Leek on Monday evening, hoping to witness the double sunset.

But they went home disappointed.'

The *Leek Post & Times* further promoted interest in the phenomenon by printing a revealing letter in its 30 June edition:

'Reader Anthony Bode came into the office to inform us that he saw the double sunset from Leek on June 21, unlike the gathering of more than 100 people in St Edward's churchyard.

Mr Bode's successful vantage point was from Lowe Hill, on the outskirts of town.

"Unfortunately, I didn't have a camera with me to record the event, but the double sunset was clearly visible from where I stood," he said.

Mr Bode was among those who ventured unsuccessfully to St Edward's churchyard last year . . .

The vantage point from Lowe Hill is some 40 metres higher than from the churchyard.

"The sun came down through a layer of thin cloud," he pointed out.'

It seemed very likely that Tony's account was accurate because, as I have shown in this book, the double sunset is proven to occur from Lowe Hill and, as the weather conditions were favourable that evening, it is highly probable that the phenomenon was indeed visible from that location. Furthermore, his reference to the sun sinking into view from cloud concurs with the same atmospheric conditions that were experienced in and around the churchyard.

To elicit more details about the circumstances of his apparently successful observation, I visited the site with him on 11 March 2001 and he believed his viewing spot to have been approximately three quarters of the way along the wall from the entrance to Home Farm to the field gate opposite the drive leading to Lowe Hill House. Interestingly, this put his position in between those identified by his brother, Harold, and Robert Webberley at a similar event 22 years earlier and, likewise, it was unfortunately outside the normal midsummer double sunset observation window. In addition, Tony remembered that there had been 'about a dozen' other spectators to his left, or southwest, stretched along the wall towards Home Farm, all of whom he thought had also witnessed the occurrence. He recalled that he had stayed on the same spot throughout the event, because 'It spoils it if you move,' and 'just a few minutes' after the whole sun had set 'perhaps a sixth reappeared'.

However, Tony's recollections of his viewing point and the astro-geographical event that he saw are incompatible, except perhaps under extremely anomalous atmospheric conditions. The extensive primary research that Roy and I have undertaken indicates that Tony was mistaken about the date of the occurrence, his observation position or that the sun fully set on the back of The Cloud during the event. Under normal circumstances, on the summer solstice, the sun does not entirely disappear behind the hill from the spot that Tony recalled, but, instead, a small portion of the disc overshoots and remains in view. The most probable explanation of the consequent mystery is that Tony did not see the whole of the sun set on the first occasion because it seems unlikely that his recollection of the date can have been several days adrift of reality or that his observation position had actually been located some fifty yards to the southwest of where he remembered it.

Nevertheless, on 30 June 1999, the attention of many double sunset followers was focused on the meeting of the Green Dragon Mysteries Society, appropriately held at The Swan, opposite the churchyard, where Kevin Kilburn presented an illuminating talk on his research and findings thus far on the double sunset. Not surprisingly, this had a strong astro-geometrical emphasis and was excellently illustrated through the use of both a slide projector and an overhead projector. Kevin stressed, and if anything over-promoted, the importance of Robert Plot in the history of the phenomenon and went on to make his highly conjectural claims connecting Cock Low with the churchyard double sunset, which were examined earlier in this book. He projected on to a screen impressive photographs of the limited event observed on the 21st and diagrams of what apparently should have been seen had the view from "Doctors' Corner" not been obscured by trees. Indeed, he stressed several times both the key importance of the northeastern corner of the churchyard as an observation position for the double sunset and his new-found knowledge of the critical nature of the dense natural vegetation blocking the visibility of The Cloud. Certainly, in the latter case, he revealed a most pertinent point to his audience.

On 8 July, Chris Doherty photographed a double sunset against Thorpe Cloud, whilst on the same evening I saw the phenomenon for the first time from the line of the B 5053 southwest of Bottom House, in the back garden of Harry Ball's Bottom Lane Farm. I located a viewing position with great difficulty, having scrambled through a barrier of thorn bushes and nettles, but was rewarded with a 6½-minute event, which included approximately a 20% solar reappearance (about 15%, Harry thought) around 9.34. There was further success three days later when Chris photographed double sunsets, both from the southern flank of Parkhouse Hill (shot against Chrome Hill) and the B 5053 slightly northeast of Harry's house.

From 19 August, I began to use my new BSI-approved "Eclipse Over Europe" solar filter, which produced a more precisely defined edge of the sun and, no doubt, was potentially less harmful to my eyes when viewing the disc at its brightest. However, I quickly realised that it was less capable of delineating the last embers of the setting sun than the Roy Parker-approved filters and so I tended to use the two in conjunction thenceforth.

On 16 September, I successfully observed an autumnal double sunset against Parkhouse Hill from the B 5053, whilst five days later Chris captured the phenomenon on film from both Cloud Side and the Toftgreen road. Good fortune continued largely to smile on my efforts to record the few missing pieces of key data and, on 11 October, I monitored an occurrence on the A 523 which produced an approximately 40% solar reappearance to tie in with a similar reading previously noted from this trunk road. Then, a week later, I investigated and dismissed a report of a double sunset being visible in the autumn from the summit of Troughstone Hill, near to Biddulph Moor. I could identify no landscape feature which would create such an event and this was confirmed by Bob Booth, the Biddulph Country Park ranger. Although this erroneous report had proved to be a complete red herring, it still had to be checked before it could be discounted.

In December, Elizabeth Ann Biddulph's book, *Leek's Forgotten Centuries: It's Ancient History Unearthed*, was published. This attractively presented work contained several references to the churchyard double sunset and projected the ancient origin of its human connections, without any hard evidence to support its claim, as I have already argued. In addition, in her section on medieval Leek, Elizabeth stated:

'The Midsummer Fair began three days before the Feast of St. Edward on the 20th of June and continued for seven full days . . . The Fair took place at Midsummer when the light and sun were at their best. After the sun had finally dipped behind 'The Cloud' and everyone had marvelled at the double-sunset, then the minstrels begin to play, hundreds of torches were lit and the townspeople danced and celebrated well into the night.'

Unfortunately, the available evidence indicates that it is most unlikely that there was any actual connection between this medieval fair and the double sunset. The first problem is that two other plausible dates have also been suggested for the annual fair: 15 March, three days before the original and still current feast date of St Edward the Martyr, and 10 October, three days prior to the feast of the translation of St Edward the Confessor (which is presently celebrated by the church in Leek). Nevertheless, 17 June has been offered as an option through preceding the feast date of the second translation of St Edward the Martyr by three days, but this alternative remains speculative. All that is categorically known about the timing of the fair is what was actually written in the original charter, granted in 1207 by King John, which stated: '. . . commencing on the third day before the feast of St. Edward, and to continue for the seven days following'. The second and even more significant difficulty is that in 1207 the Julian calendar was in use and, because of its inaccuracies, the date of the summer solstice had retrograded to 15 June, thereby putting this date two days *before* the possible start of the fair. Consequently, it seems most unlikely that Leek's medieval fair had any specific connection to the double sunset.

Elizabeth also proposed in her book a continuous human link to the phenomenon over an enormous period of time:

'By 1673 Leek was a 'picture-postcard' town, one full of 'good' houses and thatched cottages . . .

The towns-people still came to the medieval church of St. Edwards to drink from the ancient, holy 'leek' or spring and to marvel at the double, Midsummer sunset from the churchyard, as their ancient ancestors had done thousands of years before.'

As I have already shown, it is unlikely in the extreme that there had existed an unbroken chain of human observation of the solstitial occurrence to 1673 (and beyond). Indeed, that particular date was fifteen years prior to the publication of Robert Plot's book, *The Natural History Of Stafford-shire*, which indicated that viewing of the double sunset in Leek had only recently recommenced after an interlude of unknown length. Therefore, it is more than possible that in 1673 the people of Leek did not actually know or did not care that the phenomenon could be marvelled at on the summer solstice. In addition, it is extremely doubtful whether any of the seventeenth century inhabitants of the town were the direct descendants of people living in the vicinity of the site of the churchyard 'thousands of years before'. This is both because of the lack of evidence in support of the ancient occupation of the site and the radically different ethnicity of Leek's Viking or Anglo-Saxon founders from that of much earlier settlers in the Staffordshire Moorlands. Even more importantly, according to Kevin Kilburn's aforementioned calculation, the midsummer double sunset only became visible from the site of the churchyard around 500 B.C. and therefore the 'ancient ancestors' may well not have witnessed the phenomenon on the summer solstice from that location prior to then.

Very little research remained to be done on my double sunset project in 2000, but various loose ends needed to be tied up. I spent two enjoyable sessions with Chris Doherty on 7 and 9 April, photographing The Cloud from the various locations from which the phenomenon can be observed throughout the year for the data section of this book. Then, on the 16th, I visited Woodhouse Green, St Edward's churchyard and the garage forecourt near to the lower churchyard with Kevin Kilburn so that he could make some further astro-geometrical calculations on the occurrence. He seemed particularly impressed with the shape of The Cloud as seen from the southwestern side of Woodhouse Green Farm, but he was markedly unenthusiastic about the location of the latter in a letter to me, drafted the following day:

'As you suggested, from the farm the solstitial sunset line does reappear from behind the hill but the profile needs to be very accurately defined before it can be used for accurate positional and timing predictions . . .

But there is another more important issue. I said that from the corner of the farmyard [the current midsummer viewing point] the geometry would have changed drastically from that in the lane [the observation position which gives the steepest angle of The Cloud's scarp slope, but which, unfortunately, is presently too far south to enable a double sunset to occur] . . . The azimuth of the vertical hill changes by about four degrees and this shows how sensitive to movement the geometry becomes as one gets closer to the hill. It totally overwhelms any changes to the geometry due to the reduction of the obliquity of the ecliptic, by a factor of several thousand to one. Quite frankly, I think you should reconsider placing any weight on historical or future predictions of observations made from Woodhouse Green. They become quite meaningless unless the observation point is meticulously defined. The positional accuracy needed could never be met by the casual observer and if included in your book could actually undermine its authority.

To put some rough figures to this; from a distance of only 1500m [at Woodhouse Green], the angular size of the hill is about seven times bigger than from the church [in Leek] and the hill concavity is half a degree deep. At 47.7 arcseconds per century it takes over 3700 years for the 'observing window', analogous to that I described at Leek church, to cross any defined observing point. By comparison, the angular effect due to reduction of the obliquity of the ecliptic is only about 1/7th that at Leek, and is only about 0.4m/century on the ground at Woodhouse Green. But to make matters even worse, the sun remains the same size, a little over half a degree in diameter. This explains why, as you put it, by 'bobbing about', you and Roy could get any degree of double sunset reappearance you want. This is not good science and would make any, more-detailed, quantitative analysis worthless. I would therefore prefer not to waste too much time on refining the geometry from this location. Mention it, by all means, but I wouldn't regard it as very important. It is only one of several better sites from which to see the double sunset, although they might not be on the solstitial azimuth.

May I suggest doing some accurate geometry of the double sunset from Leek Moor or Leek Lowe? If a map could be included in your book showing the dates on which the LDS [Leek double sunset] could be seen from specific points, this would provide safe observation sites with a longer sight-line and more stable geometry than even that from the church.'

I was rather disappointed that Kevin felt unable to calculate the approximate date on which a double sunset had perhaps once occurred, and might do so again in the future, as observed from the fine viewing point at the southwestern side of Woodhouse Green Farm. However, in retrospect, I could only agree with his explanation of the extreme difficulty of even estimating such a date because of the quite different shapes of The Cloud as seen from the two sites either side of the farm. Nevertheless, I initially found his obvious disinterest in the Woodhouse Green observation location baffling because this site provided arguably the most impressive viewing position of The Cloud's midsummer occurrence. Consequently, I was at a complete loss to understand why he thought that the greatly more distant sight lines at 'Leek Moor' and 'Leek Lowe' were worthy of attention, whereas that at Woodhouse Green was not. What I had not yet realised was that Kevin was more interested in the science behind the double sunset than in the actual event itself. Although I failed to appreciate it at the time, this was confirmed by his comment stressing the advantage of 'the more stable geometry' of 'Leek Moor' and 'Leek Lowe'. In other words, these distant locations enabled easier astro-geometrical calculations because the shape of The Cloud changed imperceptibly even if the viewer moved considerably. Therefore, Kevin actually had a diametrically opposed opinion, regarding the relative merits of observational distances, to that of Roy and me, who favoured a nearer location giving a more impressive visual event.

Kevin's letter also revealed that he did not realise that the numerous double sunset observations which Roy and I had undertaken had been painstakingly recorded so that casual viewers of the phenomenon could enjoy the exciting events from a whole variety of carefully plotted locations. In addition, he had not grasped that the 'bobbing about' which Roy and I practised as the critical moment of a double sunset approached was an absolutely vital technique in the process of identifying the precise observation position from which the maximum amount of the sun's disc would reappear. Our technique, which is described in the next chapter of this book, is effective and accurate, even though it is not regarded by Kevin as being 'good science'. The point is that it works and it has proved to be vastly superior to computer-based orthodox mathematical calculations in the ascertainment of optimum double sunset viewing positions. Neither was Kevin on the ball with his comment that Roy and I 'could get any degree of double sunset reappearance' that we wanted. Actually, we were restricted to only the amount of solar re-emergence that was possible within the observation window at any given locality and, within that zone, we naturally preferred viewing positions from which we could see more rather than less of the sun's disc reappear.

On 16 April, I spent a considerable time on The Cloud, carefully searching for evidence of quarrying and pondering its implications. Six days later, I saw the sunset from Doug Moller's former home, Rockhall Cottage, on The Roaches, which occurred well to the north of The Cloud. Through examining my recorded data from this, in conjunction with an observation I had made from the same location on 25 March, which showed the sun to be setting south of the target, I concluded that a double sunset would most probably take place from Rockhall Cottage (although not from the summit of The Roaches) in early April. However, it became clear that the shape of The Cloud from this site would be likely to produce only a fractional solar reappearance and therefore a double sunset of no great interest.

On 1 May, Kevin Kilburn produced an expanded and updated version of his *Astronomy & Geophysics* article, *Dr. Plot and the Amazing Double Sunset*, for the http://www.leekonline.co.uk website. Not only did this bring both the phenomenon and Kevin's ideas to the attention of a potentially much wider audience, but also it promoted his more recent thinking on the subject:

'The hilltop on which [The Church of] St. Edward the Confessor stands may have been a place of worship for five thousand years. This argument may be strengthened by the name of an old house nearby, called Foxlowe. The placename, 'low', is commonly used in the moorlands to identify prehistoric sites.

. . . At the summer solstice in 1999, blessed by good weather and astro-geometrically ideal, a concerted effort was made to measure the geometry of the double sunset from its classical observation point, the churchyard of St. Edward's. Members of the Manchester Astronomical Society, Macclesfield AS and at least one astronomer from Jodrell Bank endeavoured to document the famous sunset. Photographs and video footage were taken from the churchyard, the church tower and from the field immediately north of the church. Collectively, the evidence showed that although the reappearance could theoretically still be seen from the extreme NE corner of the churchyard, trees planted in the lower graveyard in the 1960s to deliberately obscure a 'pagan' sightline now prevent the reappearance from being seen.

Unfortunately, ongoing reduction of the Earth's tilt is causing the midsummer sunset to move steadily southwards. As recently as 1977 the double sunset was still observable from the churchyard because the present trees were not high enough to obscure the reappearance. Simple geometry shows that the observations of twenty years ago could be repeated if the observer was to move a scant four feet eastwards. There is still room to move before the railings of the vicarage prevent further pursuance of the elusive conclusion to this unique phenomenon. Eventually, after about AD2200, geometry dictates that from its classical observation ground the sun will not reappear beyond the Cloud having once set upon the summit. Sadly the double sunset will then cease to be visible from the churchyard for well over twenty thousand years.'

Unfortunately, Kevin's projected link between Foxlowe, on Market Place, and prehistoric worship on the site of St Edward's Church proved to be a difficult piece of speculation to investigate. The house was certainly known as Foxlowe by 1902, but no categoric evidence has been discovered to prove that it was called such prior to then. Nevertheless, Foxlowe definitely existed as a place, and quite possibly as the name of the house, before that date. This is testified to by three references in the first volume of Matthew Henry Miller's publication of 1891, *Olde Leeke: Historical, Biographical, Anecdotal, and Archaeological*. The first of these occurs during the discussion of the burial of Peter Milner in the northeastern corner of the lower churchyard:

'In the Milner vault next to the Robins-Gaunt tomb and close to the exit to Foxlow, is buried Peter Milner . . .'

Unfortunately, this extract does not make it absolutely clear as to precisely what Foxlow was, although the use of the word *exit* might well suggest the rear access to the house, especially because its grounds stretched down to and well beyond the Milner tombstone. Alternatively, Foxlow may have been a piece of land or an area to the north of the graveyard.

Miller's second reference to Foxlowe is to be found in a feature on Ballhaye Hall:

'The Park is beautifully situated . . . There are four trees still standing on the high ground overlooking Foxlowe.'

As the word *Foxlowe* is spelled differently in this article than in the first, it could be that it does not refer to the same feature. Although the most obvious explanation for the spelling variation is a typographical error in Miller's text, it may be that *Foxlow* means the house and *Foxlowe* a separate area of land. Because the house is situated on the top of a hill, it is definitely not overlooked from any high ground now in Brough Park and once belonging to Ballhaye Park. Even if Miller used the word *overlooking* in the wrong context, then it appears much more likely that he would have stated that the church, as a far more notable building than Foxlowe, was the feature that was being overlooked. Consequently, it seems that Foxlowe in this extract is being described as lying lower down than the 'high ground' overlooking it. Although it is not at all clear where this lower area was sited, in this scenario it cannot have been on the same hill top as the church, if on raised ground at all.

Miller's varied spelling occurs a third time in his book, on this occasion in his

Chronological Table:

'1854 William Cumberlidge killed at Fox Low.'

In this instance, the text seems to suggest that the incident occurred *at* a place rather than *in* a building, but no clue is given to indicate its whereabouts. Nevertheless, it reveals that the name of Foxlowe or its equivalent was in existence in the mid-nineteenth century.

Unfortunately, my research has uncovered no further significant references to Foxlowe, not even on any of the old maps of Leek kept in the town's library or in the sizable collection held by Staffordshire Record Office. Therefore, any link between the name *Foxlowe* and the hill top on which the church stands having been a site of worship 5,000 years ago can only be tenuous in the extreme. This is even more so in the light of Kevin Kilburn's own evidence, which shows that a midsummer double sunset did not occur from the summit of the hill in Neolithic times.

Nevertheless, Kevin was certainly right to say on the website that 'a concerted effort' was made in June 1999 to record the double sunset scientifically from St Edward's churchyard and its vicinity and subsequently it remained possible that the phenomenon could still theoretically be seen from "Doctors' Corner". However, no evidence has been elicited to substantiate Kevin's claim that the intruding trees were planted in the lower churchyard in the 1960s 'to deliberately obscure a 'pagan' sightline'. Kevin believed the source of this information to have been Susan Taylor, the secretary to the vicar, but, when I asked her about it on 5 April 2001, she seemed surprised and could offer no knowledge of such a development. Certainly to plant young trees in the hope that at some point in the future they would obscure the view of double sunset observers on perhaps three evenings a year does not seem a very sensible action to have taken. Indeed, an examination of the lower churchyard reveals that most of it, and not just the area affecting the sight line, is overgrown with trees of several different types, which are apparently randomly distributed. Also, most of the worst-offending specimens are actually located *outside* the churchyard and therefore outside the control of the Church! In addition, the interference of trees in the churchyard is nothing new, as is exemplified by the complaint made in *The Leek Times* on 25 June 1927 about the adverse impact of their unchecked growth upon the visibility of the phenomenon.

Although Kevin was quite right to state that 'the double sunset was still observable from the churchyard' in 1977, the precise viewing point of the successful event of that year remains unknown. Also, it seems less the height of the interfering trees that has caused the obscuration of the occurrence than their density. Furthermore, although Kevin confidently repeated his belief that the phenomenon can still be seen from "Doctors' Corner", vegetation willing, that is a premise which remains uncertain.

Nevertheless, in the light of his experience, Kevin had reduced the final date of the theoretically observable upper churchyard double sunset by 300 years, from 2500 A.D. (projected in his *Astronomy & Geophysics* article in February 1999) to 2200 A.D. In other words, he now accepted that the trailing edge of the viewing window had moved closer to the northeastern extremity of the churchyard than he had originally calculated. Interestingly, his refined figure corresponded much more closely, but still probably not exactly, with the contemporaneously recorded accounts of 1977. Whilst Kevin's original projection had been determined purely by geometry, his new conclusion was based on the memories of particular individuals of their most recently observed event, so that 'witness position is the starting point and geometry calculates the current position from that'. It is most unfortunate that in advisably switching from pure theoretical science to a more empirical approach, Kevin had allowed the dimming memories of witnesses of distant events to prove decisive in determining their precise viewing positions. Thus the error of science had been replaced by the vagueness of human memory!

As it transpired, the two witnesses, Susan Taylor and Harold Bode, whose recollections had proved the focal point for Kevin's new calculations, had previously been interviewed by me to similar purpose. The double sunset to which Susan referred had apparently occurred in 1962 or 1963 and she had the greatest difficulty in eventually deciding that she had witnessed it from the northeastern end of the churchyard, although, not surprisingly, she was unable to be more specific than that. However, Harold had no hesitation in deciding that he had stood in "Doctors' Corner" when he had observed the event of 22 June 1961, but he was most surprised when I informed him that the photograph he had taken had in fact been shot from a spot some fifty feet to the west! It is therefore clear that the memories of witnesses to occurrences forty years previously cannot be relied upon to be specifically accurate as to where precisely they had stood in observing them. Furthermore, whilst Susan conjectured that perhaps half the sun had reappeared after setting, Harold was adamant that there had been no more than 'a glitter'. Therefore, either their memories varied significantly or they had seen the phenomenon from two different points, unless, of course, there had occurred extremely unusual atmospheric conditions on one or both occasions. Consequently, the natural vagueness of this witness evidence means that the precision of Kevin's new calculations has to be open to serious doubt.

I added further to my knowledge of double sunsets through undertaking a successful observation on the B 5053 to the southwest of Bottom House on 30 May, which showed that such events occur from this location from late in that month. However, I learned nothing of note from an article entitled, 'Double sunset rises for tourism,' which was printed in *Sentinel Sunday* on 4 June. This was based around the laudable suggestion of Doug Pickford that, 'The town [Leek] should do more with its double sunset and the district council should promote it as a tourist attraction.' Although Doug repeated the generally accepted myth that the occurrence 'only happens on the summer solstice', he commendably argued that it 'could be mentioned in tourist leaflets and at tourist information centres'.

The same article contained an incredible response to this request from a spokesman for Staffordshire Moorlands District Council:

'The council has not featured the double sunset in its tourism literature as it does not consider the phenomenon sufficiently spectacular to draw visitors to the district or to enhance the reputation of the Moorlands.

Nevertheless, consideration will be given to including the spectacle in next year's What's On Diary.

It should also be pointed out the council's tourism officers are aware of the phenomenon and are able to tell visitors where to watch.'

If these tourism officers did indeed know where to see a double sunset, they had certainly kept it very quiet because their information had never been published in a newspaper to my knowledge, nor did my research uncover a single person who had been made aware of a suitable viewing location by them. Of course, it was easy to deduce that they must have been directing potential observers to the traditional site in the churchyard, from where the event could no longer be seen. To test this assumption, I personally visited Staffordshire Moorlands Tourist & Information Centre in Leek on 10 May 2001 and discovered that there was no available literature at all on the occurrence, whilst, as expected, the staff simply referred interested people to the churchyard at midsummer. Consequently, it became obvious that the council had no idea as to whether the phenomenon was 'sufficiently spectacular to draw visitors to the district' or not and therefore the spokesman's comments were actually ill-informed rhetoric.

Unfortunately, the *Sentinel Sunday* article itself contained a mine of misinformation, apparently conveyed to the reporter, Rosalind Chimes, by Doug Pickford. Thus, the occurrence was stated as 'dating back more than 4,000 years' and could 'only be seen from the Doctor's Corner in St Edward's Church or from Lowe Hill' and 'nowhere else in Britain'. In addition, the sun was described as appearing 'to rise again from the side of the hill', whilst the recent non-observation of the phenomenon was blamed on 'the earth's tilt', the 'erosion of Bosley Cloud' and 'pollution too over Macclesfield and Congleton', as well as the weather. At least Doug managed to include within this list of red herrings the real reason for the missing churchyard double sunset, that is tree interference, which Kevin Kilburn had stressed the previous June. Furthermore, Doug repeated his erroneous claim that the double sunset had not been 'seen clearly' since the 1950s, but then, incredibly, predicted that the annual nonevent 'could pull in crowds of thousands if promoted well'!

Finally, the feature stated that: 'In pagan times the double sunset was used by high priests to show they had the power to make the sun set twice.' Doug later told me that this was his 'own supposition', but, as there is absolutely no known evidence to suggest that such practices actually occurred, his extraordinary assertion can only be regarded as a complete shot in the dark. Furthermore, as 'pagan times' includes the whole of human history prior to the advent of Christianity, and therefore spans the existence of a number of different cultures in the Staffordshire Moorlands, the heyday of these apparent 'high priests' remains entirely elusive.

On 13 June 2000, I began a series of observations, at a variety of locations, designed to add to my information on midsummer and near-midsummer double sunsets and that evening revisited Lowe Hill. The event from the road was obscured by trees and I concluded that the field immediately to the northwest, which had an uninterrupted view of The Cloud, afforded the prime sight line for this location. Afterwards, I checked out the view towards The Cloud from Leek's Ashbourne Road and deduced that there was a short, but most promising, observation line outside and immediately to the south-southeast of Poplar Service Station.

Four days later, I recorded a fine double sunset behind Thorpe Cloud from just south of my 8 July 1997 viewing point, but the proportion of the sun reappearing remained stubbornly at approximately a third. That same night, I went to St Edward's churchyard to see whether any useful pruning of the interfering trees had been undertaken, but, as expected, it hadn't and consequently the view remained as obscured as ever. Therefore, I decided it would be completely unproductive to visit that location on the summer solstice.

On 18 June 2000, for the third night running, I observed a double sunset from the A 523 lay-by above Rudyard Reservoir, essentially because I was seeking more precise details from this site than Roy Parker and I had recorded previously. I had already risked being killed by maniacal ton-up motorcyclists at this location on the two previous evenings and had had my concentration shattered by a near-deafening blast of Eddie Cochran from a parked car on the first occasion and by an overenthusiastic football commentator screaming from the radio in a tractor in the field below on the second. This time, I arrived at my approximate viewing point with not a moment to spare, having collected more data at Woodhouse Green en route. I was surprised to see a man with a camera with an impressive telephoto lens crouching some fifty yards south along the lay-by. Although I thought he might well be Kevin Kilburn, the figure was too distant to recognise and I didn't have time to investigate because the occurrence was about to begin.

An absolutely splendid double sunset followed and the sun was so unusually bright that I was obliged to use two filters in order to observe it. As I was recording the data in my file afterwards, the unknown photographer began to drive off in my direction and, as he approached me, I realised that it was Kevin. So I flagged him down and we had a long discussion about the phenomenon. He told me that his map calculations had pinpointed the spot where he had just stood to be the ideal viewing point for the occurrence, but that, in the event, he had not seen the sun reappear at all. The reason for this was that he was standing too far south and I was delighted to know that my 'bobbing about' method had proved decisively superior to Kevin's 'good science' computations. Nevertheless, it was an absolute mystery to me as to why he had stayed rooted to the spot throughout the occurrence, with no actual prospect of the sun re-emerging, when a move to the north along the lay-by would definitely have put him within the observation window. I could well understand that he would have wanted to take his photographs from a fixed point, but it was clear at least several minutes before the sun initially set that he was standing in an absolutely hopeless position, which would still have given him time to make the necessary directional adjustments.

That same evening, Roy Parker tasted success at Lowe Hill from the field immediately to the northwest of the road, although his viewing position was on its extreme southwestern boundary, adjacent to Home Farm, which put him a little back from the leading edge of the observation window. Nevertheless, he noted that the sun started to set at approximately 9.30, disappeared at 9.33, re-emerged a few seconds later, reached its acme of about a third of the disc at 9.35 and reset at 9.37.

As the solstice approached, the weather deteriorated, although on 20 June *The Sentinel* kindly printed my appeal for first-hand double sunset recollections from its readers, which, unfortunately, prompted just a single response. The article itself proved to be a peculiar mishmash of contradictory information, owing to the fact that my piece written by Rob Cotterrill was combined at the editorial stage with a second feature compiled by Rosalind Chimes following an interview with Doug Pickford. Unfortunately, the article got off to a bad start through its headline, 'Pagan myths about Leek's unique double sunset are exploded in a new book.' This ironically reinforced the very myth of the specialness of the Leek phenomenon, which was the antithesis of what I was seeking. Also, it suggested that the myths which were being exploded had been developed in pre-Christian times, whereas they were actually considerably more recent ones primarily promoted by one of the main contributors to the article, Doug Pickford!

The feature quoted me accurately as saying, 'The book looks at the double sunset mystery and why it hasn't been seen for so long and is aimed at exploding a number of old myths.' However, many of those myths were stated elsewhere in the article as facts, with essentially the same claims made by Doug in *Sentinel Sunday* on 4 June being faithfully regurgitated. The piece then rather optimistically predicted that, 'The recent heatwave should guarantee a clear sky this year – so sunset-seekers should be rewarded with a spectacular display.'

Whatever the shortcomings of the article, I was grateful for the prepublication publicity which *The Sentinel* had given me and fortune further smiled on me the following day when the *Leek Post & Times* printed a feature about my impending book under the headline, 'New thoughts on double sunset.' This had resulted from a telephone interview with the newspaper's reporter, Andrew Shipley, and my information was transcribed with commendable accuracy. I did not reveal the key details which I had uncovered during my research, not wishing to undermine the sales hook of the finished book, but I did confidently predict that the double sunset would not be seen from St Edward's churchyard that evening. Of course, I knew that I was safe to make that public pronouncement because my extensive research had conclusively shown that the available observation positions of The Cloud in the churchyard were off line and therefore it was impossible for the sun to reappear from those places.

That evening, Doug Pickford was interviewed about the same subject on Radio Stoke. Unfortunately, he aired with convincing enthusiasm his usual mythistory, but stated even wilder claims than he had done previously. Thus he made the extraordinary assertion that the double sunset 'is not known anywhere else at all in the northern hemisphere', although how he came to be an expert on the astro-geography of half the entire world was a complete mystery in itself. Furthermore, having presented his normal list of reasons to explain the lost phenomenon, he amazingly concluded that, 'The whole world is against it!' Finally, he claimed that, 'It can be viewed from two places in Leek, the churchyard and Lowe Hill bridge.' As Doug's luck would have it, the double sunset could then be observed from neither of these locations and even The Cloud itself could not be seen from the latter!

Having listened to this programme, I drove to my usual viewing site at Glutton Bridge for the Chrome Hill occurrence, but my effort was ill fated because the sun disappeared into dense cloud about two minutes before the event was due to commence and then it started raining. Therefore, I recorded no midsummer data at this location and so I moved on to the A 523 lay-by above Rudyard Reservoir. Although I was not initially very hopeful of any success here either, the sun dropped out of the cloud shortly before the occurrence started, so this time my luck was in. I observed the sun start to set at 9.22, then disappear behind The Cloud and begin to re-emerge from the scarp slope at 9.26.30 before around 45% of the disc (the maximum possible under normal conditions) came into view at approximately 9.28.30. Soon after that, the cloud swallowed the sun once again (as it did at Lowe Hill, to ruin Roy Parker's observations entirely) and nothing more was seen, although I reliably calculated the final sunset, from information gathered on the previous evenings, as having been at 9.33.30.

I was surprised to be joined at this event by Geoff and Lesley Channon, who had introduced themselves to me after Kevin Kilburn's talk at The Swan in Leek the previous June. They had used their initiative to try to find a new location to view the phenomenon and I lent them one of my filters to help them see it clearly. However, shortly afterwards, I almost knocked them over as I moved rapidly in their direction in order to get to the optimum viewing point! The conversation which followed was intriguing because Geoff claimed to have witnessed a double sunset on the 18th from the road from Milltown Way to Pickwood in Leek. After I had recorded my data at the lay-by, he took me to the approximate site of his successful observation and it became immediately apparent to me that his claim was in all probability correct because The Cloud was not only visible on the horizon, but could also be seen either side of an alignment through St Edward's churchyard. Nevertheless, he freely admitted that he had moved from his original viewing position after the sun had set and he had only been able to return to approximately the same spot when he realised that the sun had reappeared as he was walking away.

The following day, a clear colour photograph of the sun setting on the dip slope of The Cloud on the solstice was printed in *The Sentinel*, along with a short accompanying feature:

'A crowd gathered outside St Edward's Church in Leek last night to witness the town's unique double sunset.

But clouds got in the way and the natural phenomenon could not be seen clearly.

Local people have witnessed the sunset since pagan times but it has not been seen clearly in Leek for more than 15 years.

Sunset follower Tony Smith, of Leek, said: "The sun sets behind the hill known as Bosley Cloud and then appears to rise again from the side of the hill and sets again.

Unfortunately the weather was not so good last night, but the sunset can be viewed the two days either side of [the] summer solstice, so there is still time to see it." '

Unhappily, the article contained misinformation as well as fact and therefore only added to the confusion surrounding the double sunset. For example, Tony was wrong to blame the weather for the non-reappearance of the sun, as could be ascertained by studying *The Sentinel's* photograph. This showed the sun setting too far to the south (or left) of the summit of The Cloud in order for it to have re-emerged from the scarp slope, regardless of the weather conditions. Indeed, on 11 March 2001, I uncovered virtually conclusive evidence to this effect when the newspaper's photographer, Dave Randle, pointed out to me, without any hesitation, the spot in the churchyard from which he had taken the shot. This was on the north wall, some 170 feet to the west of the eastern extremity of "Doctors' Corner", a position from which the sun does not reappear and which he had selected as much by accident as design:

'I wasn't sure where to go to take it. These people were all set up here and I assumed they'd been here before, so I walked amongst them and then chose the best vantage point for the equipment I'd got.'

A further problem with *The Sentinel's* feature was that it was astronomically impossible for the phenomenon to have been observed from the churchyard for 'two days either side of the solstice' because even the best available viewing point was off line on the longest day and became increasingly so beforehand and afterwards. Furthermore, when Tony suggested that the sun 'appears to rise again' after it had initially set, he gave quite the wrong impression of what actually happens. Finally, it was a mystery as to what was meant in the article by the event not being 'seen clearly' because it had clearly not been seen at all!

Although I was out researching that evening and the following one, there was no further occurrence until the 24th when I witnessed a double sunset from the location off Milltown Way in Leek, which Geoff Channon had showed me. From the road, I observed the sun set behind the apex of The Cloud and immediately reappear from the scarp slope slightly below at 9.32.30. The sun descended into cloud shortly afterwards and so the maximum amount of reappearance could not be ascertained. Unfortunately, owing to poor weather conditions, it wasn't discovered on any other occasion that summer either. Nevertheless, because of its position a little nearer to The Cloud than Lowe Hill, the proportion could be reasonably estimated as slightly more than the one third re-emerging from the latter site.

Nothing else really definite was discovered from the Milltown Way area because the view on the 26th was obscured by trees and then, incredibly, there was no further sunset at all at any location until 16 July, by when the Milltown Way observation line had become unproductive, with the sun setting well too far south on the dip slope of The Cloud to reappear. However, from seeing the position of the sun shortly before it started to set on the 11th, I estimated that the phenomenon could be witnessed at this site only until early July at the latest. Nevertheless, by ascertaining the approximate viewing point on 26 June and measuring the distance between that and the observation position on the 24th, I calculated that the occurrence would probably be visible on the summer solstice from either the road off Milltown Way or the field to the southeast of it.

At the end of June, I received a letter, dated the 27th, from Doreen Watts of Madeley, in response to my appeal for double sunset recollections in *The Sentinel*. Her reminiscence was particularly instructive in indicating just how unclear the concept of the phenomenon presented in this book can be to anyone not specifically familiar with it:

'One sunny afternoon my husband and I decided to go on a picnic up in the hills . . . Leaving Meerbrook we took the wrong turning going higher and higher up in the hills . . . where we were lost. But what we did see was the most gorgeous sunset, pink and gold against the black outline of the hills. Going farther on we were surprised to see the sky [and] it was lovely to watch the sun set again. I thought I was in heaven.'

Technically, Doreen and her husband had observed a double sunset, no more and no less so than had been the case with any of the other authentic accounts described in this book. In other words, they had seen the sun set twice on the same day. However, the occurrence that they had witnessed was not of the particularly unusual type created by a single landscape feature viewed from a fixed point. They had moved their position considerably by driving along in their car and weaved in and out of shadow as a result of the changes in topography on the way. Although doing this can make for an interesting experience of the type that Doreen enjoyed, it is a relatively easy circumstance to engineer and is far more commonplace than the extraordinary fixed position phenomenon.

The complete absence of sunsets in late June and early July unfortunately meant that I had to estimate when the occurrence would have been seen from Ashbourne Road in Leek. On 11 July, I noted that the position of the sun, as observed from here prior to disappearing into a bank of cloud, was too far south along the ridge of The Cloud for it to re-emerge after setting. However, I deduced that I had missed the occasion by only a few days, which suggested that the viewing site had been productive in early July.

Five evenings later, I had a further disappointment, in my usual field at Glutton Bridge, when I discovered that the phenomenon had already ceased to be visible from this location too. I saw the sun set, but no part of the disc re-emerged from behind Chrome Hill and I estimated that the sight line from here had terminated perhaps several days or a week before. However, my misfortune was still not over. I drove from Glutton Bridge to Bottom House in the hope of identifying the date of the final visible double sunset of the year occurring from this location, but I perceived that I was a day, or maybe two, too late. The observation line had moved to the northeast of the A 523/B 5053 crossroads, from where The Cloud could no longer be seen.

Finally, I had some success, on 20 July, when I witnessed an occurrence behind Thorpe Cloud from a short distance north of my 8 July 1997 viewing point. However, only a tiny fraction of the sun reappeared after setting because the shape of the hill had become decreasingly conducive to a double sunset as the observation position tracked gradually northwards after the solstice. Nevertheless, I achieved the object of my exercise because I was trying to elicit the time period of the sight line and that evening was towards its outer limit. Indeed, the event was already not worth watching as a spectacle and I estimated that there would shortly have been no re-emergence at all as the form of the hill continued to deteriorate.

Poor weather persisted in dogging my efforts to glean missing and extra pieces of information about the double sunset phenomenon that summer, but, on 8 August, at Cloud Side, an unusual incident occurred. I was crouching, quietly making notes by the side of the road, with my back to a field. All of a sudden, I felt a gentle push at the base of my back, which rocked me forwards, and I assumed it to have been delivered by a small dog that I'd noticed in the field a few minutes earlier. However, when I turned around, a light brown horse was staring at me and had obviously been trying to attract my attention, no doubt in order to encourage me to feed it. Unfortunately, I had nothing to offer it except a fuss, which didn't engage its interest for long and it duly trotted off down the hill to join its companion!

From late August, my main efforts were directed at throwing more light on the apparent double sunset visible from Rockhall Cottage and the lower slopes of The Roaches. Unfortunately, just like in the spring, definitive evidence proved elusive. On both 23 August and 3 September, I observed that the sun was still overshooting the summit of The Cloud from this location, but yet another extremely poor spell of weather and a small number of commitments prevented me from achieving any further success until 22 September. By then, the viewing point had shifted to approximately the junction of the Upper Hulme and Meerbrook roads, well to the northwest of Rockhall Cottage. Nevertheless, I estimated the likely event at Rockhall as having occurred at least a week before and very probably several days or more prior to that.

On 8 September, I investigated the potential of the road linking Knotbury End with the A 53 as a location for the observation of a double sunset, as Doug Moller had claimed it was. However, I was perplexed because I could identify no landscape feature which looked even remotely likely to produce the phenomenon. Consequently, I wrote to Doug, which prompted his reply of the 19th:

'I was coming home by car. Now from the A 53 half way down that steep hill, I saw the sun dropping out of sight, but when I got home I saw the sun setting down over by the Congleton road . . . I have only seen it a couple of times but it did definitely happen.'

I did not doubt that what Doug had written was true and it clearly provided the explanation that I had been seeking. My scepticism regarding a fixed spot double sunset in the locality had been vindicated because he had obviously moved his viewing position and also had probably witnessed the sun setting behind two separate landscape features as a result of doing so.

Also in September, Tim Cockin's tome, *The Staffordshire Encyclopaedia*, was published and it naturally contained an entry on the double sunset. Like the vast majority of writers on the subject, Tim had not seen the phenomenon for himself and was thus dependent on secondary information, which was mostly unreliable. Nevertheless, he listed a sizable number of reference sources, correctly stated that "Doctors' Corner" was the traditional observation point and accurately noted the impact of the trees in the churchyard on the view. Also, he rightly pointed out that, 'It is a present misconception that the double sunset can still be seen from a raised position 50 yards to the W of Doctor's [sic] Corner,' that is through the few remaining gaps in the trees from which The Cloud is still visible from the churchyard. He then appropriately explained that, 'This position is too far to the W for the sun to reappear from behind the Cloud.'

However, Tim incorrectly suggested the last successful event from this location to have been in 1958, on the basis of Doug Pickford's unsubstantiated claim, and mistakenly ascribed the existence of the occurrence to 'the extremely steep *western* escarpment of the Cloud', which is, in fact, a north-facing feature to the northwest of Leek. Also, he stated that the sun, after reappearing, set for the final time precisely 'two minutes later', whereas the specific interludes, which actually depend upon exactly where the spectator is standing, are currently unknown. In addition, he cited 'c 1962/3' as the date of an apparently successful churchyard observation, but the names of the relevant witnesses were unknown to him, whilst little sense could be made of his statement that, 'The phenomenon can be seen at certain other places near Leek on three successive days sometime in a fortnight either side of June 21.' Furthermore, he wrongly identified 'Lowe Hill bridge' as a viewing point of the occurrence, alongside the bona fide site at Leek Moor and the very likely ones at The Roaches. Finally, he was unable to identify any of the 'Several double sunset 'enthusiasts' from the Leek area,' who he claimed had, 'from the 1960s, measured the distance the sun moves in its daily progress, advancing and receding, around the Cloud.'

On 22 October, I undertook my final double sunset observation of the millennium, in the field immediately southwest of Toft Green Cottage where I had been pestered by bullocks on 21 October 1995. The beasts were again present in numbers and proved a nuisance once more, rounding off their inquisition into my presence by slobbering liberally on the solar filters which I left on the ground as markers for my positional measurements!

Thereafter, I turned my attention to more pressing matters, but resumed work on the project in February 2001 and quickly became absorbed in the time-consuming task of tying up numerous loose ends before publication. On the 13th, I rang Tony Smith, the web master of the http://www.leekonline.co.uk site, which featured the double sunset, and he described his experiences observing the phenomenon from the churchyard:

'I've seen it about four times in my life. The last time was in the 1970s when a blurry image of the sun set and part of it reappeared some minutes later, but I can't remember seeing the entire orb reappear. In the sixties, I think, I remember looking around, while waiting, and seeing the doctors' names.'

I found Tony's account to be perfectly legitimate and his comment about the names of the medics strongly suggested that he had made at least one of his successful observations from the traditional spot, "Doctors' Corner". However, the most interesting aspect of his statement was his recollection of the time span between the initial sunset and the reappearance of the disc, which broadly tallied with the occurrence shown on Gerald Mee's *Leek: The First Millennium* video and indicated that Tony had seen only a small solar re-emergence well down the scarp slope of The Cloud.

On 11 March, I paid a pleasant visit to Leek to record the accounts of four further witnesses of midsummer sunsets. I have already discussed the experiences of Dave Randle in photographing the failed occurrence from St Edward's churchyard on 21 June the previous year and Tony Bode in apparently observing a double sunset from Lowe Hill on the summer solstice of 1999, but the latter's recollections to me of his earlier visits to "Doctors' Corner" are also well worthy of attention:

'When I was a kid, in the 1930s, I used to come up here with my father and it would be crowded. I saw it easily four or five times, but, in those days, you used to come up, see the double sunset and not think much about it. I also saw it after the war. It was certainly before these trees [in the churchyard] grew. They're self set and they've been allowed to run riot. You now see people all along here [the north wall of the upper churchyard, well west of "Doctors' Corner"] trying to get a peep at it. Well, they're changing the angle!

I've seen it come down on the back of the top [of The Cloud] and then out after a few minutes on the right-hand side, about a third of the way down, but I can't swear to that. You don't see anything like a full disc. You see less of it than on Lowe Hill, possibly only an eighth.'

It was immediately clear to me that Tony's comments were not only fundamentally on the ball, but indeed rather perceptive. It was interesting that he thought the interfering trees had planted themselves and he had never heard of the theory of the Church conspiracy to obscure the double sunset. Also, it was obvious that he realised the implications of the gathering of spectators well to the west of "Doctors' Corner" – that they were congregating in an area from which the phenomenon does not occur. Intriguingly, Tony's description of the occurrences that he had previously witnessed indicated that his viewing positions in the northeastern nook of the upper churchyard were in the trailing end of the observation window. This is specifically suggested by the fact that he had had to wait for some time before the sun reappeared and, when it did so, it was already a fair way down the scarp slope. If he had been standing on the leading edge, the sun would have re-emerged almost instantaneously after setting and considerably higher up the northern face of the hill. Furthermore, I drew a similar conclusion from his comment that less of the sun could be seen to reappear from "Doctors' Corner" than from Lowe Hill, which is over a mile more distant from The Cloud. From the same point in their respective viewing windows, the opposite is true, whilst Roy Parker had recorded several occurrences from the garage forecourt, below the churchyard, containing approximately 25% solar reappearances.

I also met Brenda and Roy Beniston, of Leek, on 11 March and went with them to the churchyard where they related their memories of seeing the double sunset in the 1950s. Brenda was fairly confident that the event had occurred on the summer solstice in 1953, 1954 or 1955 and, because Roy, who lived in Walsall, had been with her, she was sure that it must have taken place on a Friday or a Saturday night. Roy's 'instinct' quickly decided that their observation point had most probably been by the railings just north of the large stone tomb in "Doctors' Corner", but Brenda was not so sure:

'I've got a feeling that there was a tomb. What is so off-putting is all these trees. You could see the outline of the skyline so clearly, but standing here . . .'

Nevertheless, her memory of the event itself was graphic:

'It was thrilling and spectacular. It was a nice clear evening. [As it set] everywhere was darkening as though it was going to be dusk. It came through brightly, but it wasn't the whole thing and, as soon as it came, it started to go again.'

Roy then added his own recollection of the occurrence:

'There was no haze. I've got a picture of a vivid red ball. When it came out of the other side, it didn't have that yellow edge round it. The sun dipped down behind the saddleback and went down at such an angle that I couldn't see how it would come out of the other side, but, after quite a long time, I would say 10 minutes, about two thirds of it came down below the pinnacle. It certainly wasn't the whole sun.'

There was no doubt in my mind that Brenda and Roy had indeed witnessed a double sunset, but a calendar check revealed that the summer solstice did not occur on a Friday or a Saturday in any of Brenda's projected years. As luck would have it, the coverage by the *Leek Post & Times* of the phenomenon during the three years in question was quite thorough, but no successful sightings were reported. In 1953 and 1955, the newspaper recorded failed events on the evening either side of the solstice, as well as at midsummer itself, whilst in 1954 the occurrence on the longest day was ruined by 'heavy low clouds'.

I found Brenda's uncertainty about their observation point to be instructive, especially because her recollection was not surprisingly thrown out of gear by the trees which now prevent the phenomenon from being seen from the churchyard.

In addition, both Brenda and Roy rightly remembered that only a part of the sun had re-emerged, although the latter's estimation of the proportion was almost certainly overoptimistic, as was his calculation of the length of time that the sun had first disappeared from view. However, a degree of error of this extent, or even more, was only to be expected considering the period of time that had passed since Roy had observed the event.

Before we left the churchyard, Brenda mentioned that she possessed a badge depicting the double sunset, which had been sewed onto the rucksack of her daughter, Jane. Brenda believed that she had bought it, as one of a pair, at a small shop in Leek around the mid-1960s. Naturally, I went to see it and found it to be broadly shield shaped, with both the horizontal and vertical axes almost two inches long. The blue base material appeared to be canvas, onto which had been embroidered several colourful images. The most notable of these was a yellow sun straddling a black peak, which was clearly intended to represent The Cloud, even though artistic licence had made its summit somewhat pointed. A single word, *Leek*, appeared in red at the bottom of the badge, which seemed to me to have been hand crafted. Two of Brenda's friends (Ray Poole and Ray Lovatt) have independently suggested that the badges were made by the textile manufacturer, Brough, Nicholson & Hall Ltd, although I have been unable to confirm this categorically despite my appeal for further details to Leek Library and to the public, through the *Leek Post & Times*.

Undaunted, on 15 March, I phoned Nigel Pickford, who had seen a double sunset from the churchyard around 1979, according to Kevin Kilburn's 1999 *Astronomy & Geophysics* article. Unfortunately, Nigel's recollection was rather vague, which he openly admitted, but he thought in retrospect that the successful occurrence which he had witnessed had been 'probably in the mid-1960s', whilst the date that he had given to Kevin had been 'off the top of my head'. He added that he had recently returned to the churchyard to revisit his observation point, which he remembered as having been near a seat, but, in the event, he had been able to find neither. Nevertheless, he recalled having seen the sun set and reappear, although he was unable to remember whether the whole disc or just part of it had re-emerged.

Although I learned nothing substantially new from Nigel's account, I noted that his missing seat may well have been one of those shown on Gerald Mee's aforementioned photograph of "Doctors' Corner", taken not later than the 1950s.

In April 2001, I hoped to ascertain more precise information about the highly probable Roaches double sunset, but my efforts were largely thwarted by an atrocious spell of weather and the closure of the relevant footpaths owing to an outbreak of foot-and-mouth disease. However, on the 11th, I was able to observe from the road below Rockhall Cottage that the sunset was already well to the north of The Cloud and estimated in my notes that it had overshot the hill, from vantage points on the lower slopes of The Roaches, 'at least several days ago, perhaps a week, maybe even more'. Thus the mysterious double sunset managed to keep one of its remaining secrets a little longer! However, I did resolve an outstanding question that day when I climbed the stairs of the St Edward's vicarage, courtesy of Reverend Matthew Parker, to discover that even the top floor of the building was nowhere near high enough to enable the phenomenon to be seen above the trees in the churchyard.

The following month, the double sunset received further publicity in the form of an article, entitled *A Feast For The Eyes – Times Two*, contributed to the May edition of *Peak District Magazine* by Kevin Kilburn. It largely was a rejig of his earlier work, but also contained several new pieces of information, the first of which stated:

'In medieval times there was a Midsummer Fair at Leek, perhaps to celebrate its unique position to view the double sunset.'

Unfortunately, this suggestion lacked firm evidence to support it. First and foremost, I have been unable to uncover any source material which indicates a direct connection between the double sunset and Leek's medieval fair, except for the aforementioned and unsubstantiated reference contained in Elizabeth Ann Biddulph's 1999 publication, *Leek's Forgotten Centuries*. In addition, the primary purpose of fairs in the Middle Ages was to sell goods and services and for the hiring of labourers and there is no indication in the charter granted by King John that Leek's annual event deviated from the norm, let alone was based on the double sunset. Furthermore, as I have already argued, it is most unlikely that this eight-day fair was even held on the summer solstice.

Kevin then went on to say:

'For decades during the 20th century it [the double sunset] was regularly reported in the Leek newspaper whether or not it was actually seen, depending on the weather. Then, in the mid 1970s, the phenomenon mysteriously stopped.'

Unfortunately, it is not true that the double sunset was 'regularly reported' in the *Leek Post & Times* prior to the mid-1970s. On the contrary, it featured most irregularly and even the newspaper's intermittent coverage near petered out after 1961. Also, the lack of local press attention thereafter is not necessarily commensurate with an absence of double sunsets and can just as easily be explained by other factors, for example, perhaps by a change in editorial policy. In addition, as both Kevin and I have previously argued, the phenomenon itself did not mysteriously stop, but human observation of it from the churchyard most certainly did, very probably after 1977.

Surprisingly, Kevin's article ended by stating that, 'Within the next century . . . Leek's famous double sunset will end forever.' This contradicted both his 1999 *Astronomy & Geophysics* article and his leekonline website feature, which estimated that the occurrence would cease to be visible from the churchyard for 'more than 10 000 years' and 'well over twenty thousand years' respectively. The latter figure appears to be the most accurate, being roughly the amount of time that it will take the angle of tilt of the earth's axis to reach its minimum and then return to its current point. Indeed, the impending period without an astronomically visible double sunset from the site of the upper churchyard has been calculated by Richard Stephenson as approximately 22,000 years. However, Kevin explained to me that his objective in stressing the finality of the event was to point out that, although the phenomenon will occur again in due course, 'Leek itself will no longer be there' when it does!

Kevin's article was supported by one of the colour photographs that he took from the church tower on 21 June 1999, which showed clearly that the sun was setting too far south on the dip slope of The Cloud in order to reappear. However, the accompanying caption stated:

'Sunset at the solstice, June 21, photographed from the roof of the tower of St

Edward's Church. The disappearing sun briefly emerges from within the concavity of the northern side of the hill known as the Cloud – six miles away in this image – before setting on the more distant horizon.'

Unfortunately, this implied that the photograph depicted the beginning of a double sunset, which it certainly did not.

Also in May 2001, Roy Parker told me that, by chance, he'd bumped into Tim Duffin, a caretaker at Moorlands House, who had become interested in the phenomenon as a result of the (unsuccessful) efforts of Roy and me to observe an occurrence from the building in 1997 and 1999. To our surprise, Tim had been keeping a careful eye on the sunsets visible from the office block and claimed to have witnessed the phenomenon from room 2034 on the first floor on 15 June the previous year. Consequently, I called on Tim at work on 10 May and he took me to the east-northeastern end of the room, where he'd primarily stood, and he enthusiastically recalled his experience:

'I'd been watching it for several nights, setting just prior to the tip and then on the 15th it actually set on the tip and reappeared just off the side, perhaps 5% down from the top, after about three or four minutes. It appeared more and more as it worked its way down the edge. It was so beautiful and bright orange and red. As it set first time, the room went dull and within five minutes the room started filling with orange again. As it was coming down, I moved down the building [to the east-northeast] to see what difference it made, but I couldn't see that it made a vast difference as to what was coming out, so I went back to the original room. It was so bright all the time, I was squinting, looking through my fingers. As it appeared towards the bottom, it was more or less the full globe and I watched it set in the hollow, more or less right at the base of it. I was quite gobsmacked by it and I just wanted to tell somebody, so I rang my wife and said, "I've just seen the double sunset for the first time!" '

There was little doubt in my mind that Tim had witnessed the phenomenon – indeed Roy had predicted, following his observations in 1997, that the double sunset would be observable from the building a short time before and after the summer solstice. The general pattern of events which Tim described was very familiar to me and it was clear that his original viewing point had been advantageously near to the leading edge of the observation window. However, unless there had been an extremely anomalous amount of refraction, the full sun cannot have reappeared after setting. Indeed, my own observations had revealed that only approximately 45% of the disc can be expected to re-emerge from the summer solstice viewing location on the lay-by of the A 523 above Rudyard Reservoir, which is three miles closer to The Cloud. This discrepancy seemed to be explained firstly by the fact that Tim had been unable to see the sun with any precision because of its intense brightness, which in itself had perhaps suggested to him that the whole disc or thereabouts had reappeared, even though it had not. In addition, he had moved his observation position between the first sunset and the maximum re-emergence and therefore he may well have inadvertently returned to a more advantageous spot. Nevertheless, he thus became the first known person to have witnessed the phenomenon from this location.

On 28 May, the occurrence received further public attention, through a talk, entitled *The Mysterious Double Sunset*, which I gave to Leek And Moorlands Townswomen's Guild at Milward Hall in Salisbury Street, Leek. Although it was well received, its preparation had caused me some difficulty because I needed to present an enjoyable and informative lecture, without revealing any of my key discoveries regarding the phenomenon prior to the publication of my book. I therefore skirted around the danger zone, assisted by aids such as my solar filters and a circular stained-glass sun, and simply hoped that my efforts would not be recognised as circuitous! In the event, fortune smiled on me because the *Leek Post & Times* reported on 13 June that I had given 'a most interesting talk about this fascinating Leek phenomenon'!

Interest in the double sunset continued to build up, much earlier than it had done in previous years, and, on 29 May, I received a phone call from Rosalind Chimes of *The Sentinel*, who interviewed me for an article that she was writing on the occurrence. This was duly printed on the 31st, but, because I kept the essentials of my research under wraps once more, the feature not surprisingly contained a mixture of fact and myth, much of the latter being a repetition of claims made in *Sentinel Sunday* on 4 June 2000. Nevertheless, Rosalind kindly promoted both my forthcoming book and the double sunset 'guided viewing sessions' that I planned to hold around the summer solstice in the event of good weather. The report also contained a number of valid comments made by Kevin Kilburn and was accompanied by a second showing of Dave Randle's colour photograph of the midsummer 2000 setting sun, as seen from St Edward's churchyard.

I resumed my double sunset observation research on 4 June and, three evenings later, discovered that the short viewing line on Ashbourne Road, Leek, had already ceased to be productive, but only very recently. Co-incidentally, that night, Roy Parker reported exactly the same situation with regard to Mount Road, which he believed had continued to yield an occurrence until at least the 4th. However, on the 8th, I successfully observed the Chrome Hill double sunset from my usual site at Glutton Bridge and estimated that the phenomenon had been visible from this location for at least several days. Then, two nights later, clear weather enabled Roy and I to ascertain that the occurrence had not yet come into view either at Lowe Hill or in the vicinity of Milltown Way. Unfortunately, poor conditions thereafter prevented us from discovering the first observation date of the occurrence from both these locations, but it must have been soon after 10 June.

I rang Tim Duffin on 14 June, with the intention of checking the double sunset from Moorlands House myself, but he reported that the previous evening he had seen approximately 10% of the sun overshoot the northern edge of The Cloud from the same spot that he had witnessed a double sunset on the 15th the year before. Therefore, I was apparently already too late! However, these two events were incompatible because, as viewed from an identical place under normal circumstances, the phenomenon could not already have ceased to be visible on 13 June 2001, but still have been occurring on 15 June 2000. Consequently, I carefully probed Tim's memory and was satisfied that his account of his recent observation was accurate, not least because it had been made with the aid of one of Roy's solar filters. In addition, because the sun had been 'so bright all the time' during Tim's previous viewing, it seems inconceivable that he mistakenly believed that the disc had set and reappeared from behind The Cloud. Therefore, the most plausible explanation appears to be that he had inadvertently entered the wrong date in his diary when he did so 'some time after' the event and, indeed, this is the conclusion that Tim himself has come to.

On 19 June, after I had been interviewed for a second time by Rosalind Chimes, *The Sentinel* printed a further double sunset article, which generously publicised the 'guided talks' that I had planned for the three evenings around the summer solstice. Because I wanted to keep an element of surprise for the occasions, the feature simply stated that interested people should assemble at St Edward's churchyard, the traditional observation site, but that I would 'then be taking everyone on a short walk to another viewing point, where I hope the double sunset will be seen'. The article also stated that I believed that 'the natural phenomenon may be witnessed this year – if the weather holds out,' which I was able to predict with confidence because my planned location was the tried and tested Lowe Hill.

The following day, an article in the *Leek Post & Times* kindly reiterated the key details of my impending guided observations, but it also stated that, 'The phenomenon dates back to at least the 13th Century,' as a result of the dubious claim that, 'a midsummer fair was held in Leek at the time of the summer solstice.' According to the newspaper, it was then that the occurrence 'was noted', but no evidence was produced to substantiate this belief. In addition, the feature firmly announced that, 'The viewing window [of the double sunset] . . . is no longer within the grounds [of St Edward's churchyard],' although in reality this was a highly debatable claim.

That same evening, I pinpointed a precise observation spot at Glutton Bridge of the Chrome Hill phenomenon and then dashed to St Edward's churchyard in eighteen minutes to greet the waiting crowd, some fifty of whom decided to accompany me to Lowe Hill for the anticipated event. However, the sun disappeared into a thick bank of cloud just after 9.20, to the great disappointment of the 75 or so expectant spectators, and even I thought that the prognosis was near hopeless. Nevertheless, a small portion of the sun amazingly burst back into view approximately a minute before the completion of the first set on the back of The Cloud, which I saw and timed at 9.33.30. The sun then reappeared virtually instantaneously, rolled down the scarp slope of the hill and finally set at the foot of the incline, but I was unable to record any further precise details because of my involvement with the excited observers. Unfortunately, I was technically the only person there who actually saw a double sunset because I had mistakenly assembled the crowd in an erroneous position almost immediately to the northeast of the entrance to Home Farm, but, when the sun was setting, I realised that a thin crescent was going to overshoot The Cloud and so I rushed southwest along the road to identify successfully the ideal observation point on the leading edge of the viewing window. This spot was by the farmhouse wall on the grass verge, just to the southwest of the entrance to Home Farm, precisely two thirds of the way from the telegraph pole to the first split-trunk sycamore tree, but the hill was only visible from a crouching position.

On the summer solstice, media interest in the phenomenon not surprisingly peaked and got off to an early start with a morning feature on Radio Stoke. Unfortunately, this was riddled with myths, errors and vague statements and must have utterly confused its listeners. The presenter, Richard Baynes, firstly interviewed Doug Pickford, who claimed that the double sunset was still visible from "Doctors' Corner" in St Edward's churchyard, but that successful observations had become 'reliant on the wind moving the branches of the trees'! However, the foliage was so dense that only the arrival of a hurricane actually offered any hope of the occurrence being seen from this location.

Richard then stated that, 'Up here on Mount Road, on the outskirts of Leek, there'll also be a good crowd tonight waiting to see the double sunset. There's a good clear view of Bosley Cloud from here and there's no trees or other obstructions.' Richard then introduced his next guest, Chris Brown, a Leek-based complementary therapist, who supported this statement: 'I've been advised by people who know infinitely more about this than I do that Mount Road itself at Leek would give a vantage spot and also Morridge.' Unfortunately, there was just one snag, which hadn't been realised, and that was that the phenomenon is not visible from either of these areas around the summer solstice. Chris was then asked whether it was still possible to see the occurrence from St Edward's churchyard and he replied: 'Scientifically it isn't going to happen again.' The reason given for this was that, 'The angle of the sun was now altered . . . due to the tilt of the earth on its axis,' but the actual problem was the complete obscuration of The Cloud from the observation site by trees, as Kevin Kilburn had pointed out in 1999 and afterwards.

I was then inexplicably introduced on the programme as Jeff Wheeler and I failed to throw much light on the situation because of my determination not to reveal any new information prior to the publication of my book. Nevertheless, my research enabled me to state confidently, 'I'll categorically predict that it won't be seen from the churchyard this summer.' Richard then rightly added that I wouldn't 'explain precisely why', which he perceptively deduced from my woolly elaboration which followed. He was therefore left to conclude inaccurately that, 'Unless you can be in two places at once, it sounds as if The Mount is the place to be to try to see the double sunset this year.'

In the evening, the phenomenon featured strongly on the BBC TV regional news programme, *Midlands Today*, the highlight of which was the screening of impressive footage of the latter stages of the occurrence filmed by cameraman, Ian Hickman, from Lowe Hill the previous night. Also of note was an impressive computer graphic illustrating the double sunset sequence on a highly distorted representation of The Cloud, with a near-vertical scarp slope, out of which reappeared a somewhat larger proportion of the sun's disc than was normally possible. The feature was generally informative and largely accurate, although it was mistakenly stated that the initial sunset had not been witnessed the night before. In addition, I was interviewed live in St Edward's churchyard by the programme's science correspondent, David Gregory, and the regional weather forecaster, Shefali Oza, and thereby commented on the traditional nature of this observation site and the future prospects for viewing the phenomenon.

I then made a futile visit to Glutton Bridge, where dense cloud entirely ruined the Chrome Hill event, before returning to the churchyard to direct the gathered crowd again to Lowe Hill. This time, around a hundred spectators were present, but we struck unlucky because the sun remained obscured by the elements until it appeared approximately halfway down the scarp slope of The Cloud, well after the initial sunset. Afterwards, I returned home to be interviewed on the Radio 5 programme, *Late Night Live*, as media interest in the occurrence showed no signs of abating. On this occasion, I was primarily required to outline the essence of the double sunset, presumably for a geographically widespread audience unfamiliar with the phenomenon.

The following morning, Richard Baynes presented an enthusiastic and accurate report on Radio Stoke of the solstitial event, as seen from Lowe Hill. Regardless of the lack of an initial sunset, he said that he had been 'genuinely impressed' and described even the incomplete occurrence he had witnessed as 'a fantastic thing to see'. In support of his observations, he played an extract from my running commentary of the event, which he had recorded the previous night and in which I had mistakenly stated the time to have been an hour earlier than it actually had been! For good measure, Richard also alerted the listeners to the fact that, weather willing, the phenomenon could still be seen that evening, the 22nd.

A report of the midsummer occurrence was additionally carried by *The Sentinel* on 22 June, following my interview with Samantha Lawton. Although the previous two nights' developments were described with some accuracy, the article also included the well-worn myth that 'Leek is the only place in Britain where the sun appears to set twice,' whilst the phenomenon was amazingly described as a 'once in a life time sight'!

That evening, I again undertook a successful observation of the Chrome Hill occurrence at Glutton Bridge, from an almost identical position to that recorded on the 20th, but commencing approximately fifteen seconds later, at 8.35. Then, once more, I drove to the churchyard and advised the spectators to adjourn to Lowe Hill, where an even larger crowd of perhaps 125 people was disappointed as the sun permanently vanished into cloud at 9.31, shortly before the occurrence was due to begin. I continued to monitor this location until the 27th, without further success, but interest remained so strong that 26 spectators gathered in anticipation on the 24th, although none was present on the subsequent three evenings.

On the 29th, I observed a cloud-interrupted double sunset from the east-northeastern end of room 2034 in Moorlands House, in the company of Tim Duffin and his wife, Rachel, during which perhaps 20% of the sun's disc reappeared. Although Tim was confident that the whole of the sun had set before re-emerging, I retained slight doubts because the initial disappearance had been partially obscured by the elements. Nevertheless, the re-emergence of a smaller portion of the disc than was theoretically possible suggested that Tim was right.

That same evening, Roy Parker struck more lucky on Pickwood Vale Recreation Ground in recording a complete occurrence, commencing at 9.27, and then we both switched our efforts to the short viewing line on Ashbourne Road. We were successful here on 5 July, despite considerable haze on the horizon, and I observed the sun set and almost instantaneously reappear at 9.30, before swelling to over 20% of the whole disc, from a spot 3½ strides to the south-southeast of lamppost FL77. Unfortunately, we had no further joy at this location because of poor weather conditions, although I did find my Glutton Bridge field site to be still productive on the 10th, but almost exhausted and with only a partial solar reappearance. I also achieved success five evenings later when I drove to the B 5053 at Bottom House and observed this site's final visible occurrence of the year, commencing at 9.22.30, from directly opposite the northeastern side of the entrance to the car park of The Green Man.

All that then remained to be done prior to the publication of my book was to try to produce some definitive evidence of a double sunset from the lower slopes of The Roaches, but, unfortunately, I was foiled by an almost complete lack of clear skies for over a month! Nevertheless, on 9 September, I saw sufficient flickers of sunlight through dense cloud to ascertain that the viewing point of the anticipated phenomenon was located in the gap between Hen Cloud and The Roaches. However, I was able to glean little more until 1 October when the elements again ruined the event, but not before I had noticed that the observation line was nearing the slopes below Roach End. Therefore, to my considerable frustration, I had still only succeeded in recording a rough time span for the highly probable, but yet empirically unsubstantiated, Roaches double sunset.

Nevertheless, by October 2001, not only had the essential mystery of the vanishing double sunset been resolved, but also much data connecting the occurrence had been researched and recorded, whilst a large number of observation locations had been identified for a variety of events involving four separate hills within a relatively short distance of Leek.

7 The Double Sunset Conclusions

As has already been noted and shown, the double sunset is a transient phenomenon, constantly subtly changing on its relentless journey from the past to the future. Its current features are the products of past astronomical events, but are at the same time simply aspects of ongoing processes which are propelling the occurrence into a predictable future determined by cyclic forces. However, the future prospects for the double sunset can only be clearly projected from knowledge of the mechanics of the phenomenon in the past and the present.

Although the viewing window of the midsummer occurrence tracked southwest to northeast across approximately the whole of St Edward's upper churchyard from around 350 B.C. (according to a calculation based on Kevin Kilburn's aforementioned map) until recently and possibly until today, the double sunset is no longer visible from the churchyard nor its immediate vicinity. This fact is testified to particularly by the observations and reports of 1977 and 1999. The essential reason for the current nonevent is that The Cloud cannot be seen from potentially successful viewing positions in "Doctors' Corner" in the upper churchyard and the path following the southeastern and eastern perimeter of the lower churchyard. The responsibility for this entirely lies with the trees which have grown considerably in recent times and consequently virtually completely obscured the view of the hill beyond. Thus Kevin Kilburn hit the nail entirely on the head, during his lecture at The Swan on 30 June 1999, when he said: 'Chop the trees down and you've got your phenomenon back.'

In theory, a less drastic, but still effective, solution than that proposed by Kevin would be carefully to prune selected trees only, in order to open a summer solstice observation window to The Cloud for interested spectators. However, that would be extremely problematic in practice because no one is clear any longer as to where precisely the ideal viewing position and indeed the full observation zone are located. Obviously, there is only one way to find out and that is by pruning the trees in a guesstimated manner, hoping that not too much damage is done before a successful hole is produced. Even this creeping approach would be fraught with difficulty as it might take several years for each visual avenue to be investigated because of the unreliability of the weather. It seems doubtful that such a patient approach would actually be maintained for long and so, sadly, Kevin's extreme proposition may be the most realistic option after all, should the town wish to regain its unusual churchyard phenomenon. Nevertheless, it is not a solution that I favour and it could well be that such an action would be opposed by other local environmentalists. Furthermore, should all be revealed in due course from the churchyard, the intriguing double sunset mystery will be replaced by the scientifically-tamed and explained double sunset occurrence.

Should it be ascertained that the trailing edge of the midsummer viewing window has already moved beyond "Doctors' Corner", public spectators will not be able to proceed any further east in pursuit of the setting sun because access is blocked by the wall separating the upper churchyard from the grounds of the vicarage. Instead, they will be forced advantageously east-northeast and then north-northeast down the path outside the lower churchyard. This will point them towards the garage forecourt where Roy Parker reliably observed double sunsets on 17 and 24 June 1992, on the latter occasion from his stepladders, and 24 June 1993. Unfortunately, these pre- and post-solstice events cannot really be recommended to the readers of this book because the viewing line here suffers from tree interference with, and obscuration of, the phenomenon. The future holds an outlook for this location similar to that of the churchyard in that the observation positions on any evening will shift extremely gradually, but this time to the northeast along the wall in front of the garages because that is where the best sight line exists.

A better bet around the summer solstice for the double sunset spectators is Lowe Hill. This site has the great advantage over the churchyard and its environs in that it offers a fairly unobstructed view of The Cloud. Also, as the sunset is relatively late in the evening as seen from here, the sun is frequently observable with the naked eye. Another benefit of this location is that the likelihood of the phenomenon being seen in any year is great because the line of the quiet minor road leading from Home Farm to the bridge over the A 523, and that in the field immediately to the northwest, give opportunities stretching for over a week either side of midsummer. Prior to the solstice, the viewing position progressively moves towards the farm and afterwards it returns in the opposite direction. Double sunset devotees can even continue their observations beyond the road bridge, along Mount Road, from the direction of the A 53, up to early June and, on the return leg, from approximately a month later. Although Roy, in particular, has done a considerable amount of work in identifying observation points at Lowe Hill and along Mount Road, there remains much to be done in order to locate precise viewing spots from which people in the future can know with reasonable certainty that they will be able to see the occurrence in favourable weather. Nevertheless, the observation positions on this line will gradually move broadly northeastwards over an extremely long period of time.

However, there is one major disadvantage with Lowe Hill as a double sunset viewing location and that is that it is further away from The Cloud than the churchyard and more recommended places still closer to The Cloud. The first problem with this is that, all other factors being equal, the greater the distance the spectator is positioned from the hill, the larger the sun becomes in comparison and therefore the less of its disc can reappear after initially setting. For this reason, Lowe Hill produces a smaller amount of solar re-emergence than do locations more proximate to The Cloud and it will continue to do so in the future. Far worse than that, as the distance from The Cloud increases, there is a greater chance that the occurrence will be ruined by mist or haze, as has been borne out by recent observations. Furthermore, the field immediately to the northwest of the road, which provides part of the viewing line, has no public right of access.

Just to the north of Lowe Hill is the short observation site on Ashbourne Road, south-southeast from Poplar Service Station. Although this gives a relatively clear view of The Cloud, it does so for such a brief period not around the summer solstice that it cannot be considered particularly noteworthy. The nearby alternative off Milltown Way and on Pickwood Vale Recreation Ground is, however, more commendable, despite some obstructions of the sight line. Although this location probably yields a double sunset at midsummer and is essentially productive for over a week either side of then, very little data has yet been obtained on it and therefore future observers here will be acting as pioneers in a relatively unexplored situation.

However, a better alternative for the hopeful spectator is provided by the A 523 northwest of Leek. The midsummer viewing point from this sight line is just over four miles nearer to The Cloud than is Lowe Hill and three miles closer to it than is St Edward's churchyard. Consequently, The Cloud appears as a much more impressive landscape feature as seen from the trunk road to Macclesfield and a larger portion of the sun can be expected to reappear from here after initially setting than from more distant locations. In addition, the hill remains clearly in view along most of the road from the phenomenon's midsummer viewing point at the side of the A 523 lay-by above Rudyard Reservoir to its furthest position north on the shortest day, just south-southeast of St Mary's Church in Bosley. Roy, especially, has conducted a series of observations from this sight line on and around the summer solstice, whilst I identified the midwinter viewing point, as is shown in the data section of this book, which follows. Also recorded and included are two interesting places along the road from which sizable solar reappearances occur within range of both equinoxes.

However, much observation needs to be undertaken along the road in order to link reliably the few viewing positions which Roy and I have so far identified. The main reason why we did not persist for longer on this apparently advantageous sight line was that we considered it to be highly dangerous. Unfortunately, the A 523 suffers from extremely fast traffic and suicidal drivers, particularly of motorbikes, desperate to overtake at even the most dangerous locations. Although the lay-by above Rudyard Reservoir, in particular, is a handy spot for double sunset spectators to stand, there are long stretches of the road with little room at the side where pedestrians can relax and concentrate on their observations. Another disadvantage of viewing the phenomenon from here is that on average the sun is brighter as it starts to set than it is from more distant observation sites, because the event begins at an earlier time, and therefore the necessity of using a solar filter is greater. Nevertheless, should this trunk road become a major sight line for double sunset enthusiasts, the long-term future will see an exceedingly slow movement of their viewing spots to the northwest.

My recommended off-the-hill double sunset sight line for keen spectators is that from Woodhouse Green to Toftgreen, which follows the closest possible positions to The Cloud throughout the year, being at no point more than about a mile distant. This location has the immense advantage of the hill appearing quite large in comparison with the size of the setting sun. Consequently, considerable solar reappearances can be expected on most occasions, whilst the phenomenon can be seen at all times, from mainly accessible places, given favourable weather conditions. In addition, from the northern section of the line, on and for a period either side of the winter solstice, an impressive double sunrise occurs, with a full solar re-emergence. Furthermore, in such close proximity to The Cloud, the prospect of the ruination of the event by haze and mist is not particularly great, whilst all the viewing positions are set in essentially quiet and peaceful countryside, where it is a delight to relax and engage in the fundamentally harmless pursuit of double sunset watching. For all these reasons, a detailed series of observation points and potential sunset and sunrise outcomes are given for this location in the following data section of the book.

There are few real disadvantages to double sunset viewers with the

Woodhouse Green to Toftgreen line. The most significant is that the event, as seen from here, occurs at a relatively early time of day and therefore the sun often has to be tracked through a filter for at least part of the occurrence because of its brightness. Also, purists might dismiss it because it does not include the traditional site of St Edward's churchyard, whilst Kevin Kilburn argues that the astro-geometry of the phenomenon is much more difficult to calculate from such close proximity to the hill. In addition, parts of the observation line, including the recommended position on the summer solstice, are on private land and have no public right of access. However, probably of greater significance to many potential observers living in North Staffordshire is the fact that the location is further in distance from their homes than is Leek, whose residents will need to make a short car journey to reach the recommended site. Nevertheless, each time they get there, they will not have to move very far from their previous viewing point because of the closeness of the observation line to The Cloud. Also, for what it's worth, their very distant descendants will find, for exactly the same reason, that they remain extremely close to the observation spots formerly used by their long-departed ancestors.

I have also included extensive data in this book on the Cloud Side observation line because this presents spectators with considerable opportunities on and around the summer solstice and for much of the year to see the sun fully, or almost fully, reappear after it has initially set behind The Cloud. It does so primarily because, at such a short distance from the summit of the hill, the key features of the landscape are large in comparison with the size of the sun. As the viewing line is immediately below the main body of the hill and on its eastern flank, its solar events are not commonly spoiled by mist and haze. Indeed, on occasions, especially in the winter, both the observation positions and the summit of The Cloud rise above the dense fog that lingers on the Cheshire Plain. Also, the proximity of the viewing points to the top of the hill result in very early events, which mainly occur before the sun has lost its strength and begins to vanish in the evening gloom. In addition, the observation line that I selected and have recorded details from is entirely rural and essentially tranquil, although a short walk across a private field is needed in order for several of the double sunsets to be seen, including that on the summer solstice.

Fundamentally the same criticisms which I raised regarding the Woodhouse Green-Toftgreen line can also be applied to the Cloud Side location, except even more so. Because all the occurrences from here take place relatively early in the day, the sun is usually blindingly intense and almost invariably needs to be viewed through a filter. In addition, not only does this line exclude the historical observation site of the churchyard at Leek and require a car journey to be reached by almost everybody, but it can also be faulted for not being off the hill. Cloud Side runs along the eastern slope of The Cloud and therefore it can be argued that the double sunsets which occur from this location are not independent from the hill itself. In other words, at a certain point of proximity to The Cloud, for example when standing right under the summit, the concept of the phenomenon becomes virtually meaningless and little different in practice from an observer watching the sun re-emerge from the side of his house after first setting behind the roof. Having said that, I do not feel that Cloud Side comes into that category. Certainly, as far as the few residents on the road are concerned, once the sun has sunk below the ridge of The Cloud for the day, it *has* actually set, however early that may be. Therefore, the event from Cloud Side is just as real as the ones from more distant locations, which may be favoured by purists. Furthermore, because of the nearness of the line to the summit of the hill, immense amounts of time will need to pass before the broadly northerly long-term movement of any of the viewing positions will become even slightly noticeable.

The only other noteworthy location which has been discovered to offer a double sunset involving The Cloud is the B 5053 southwest of Bottom House. Unfortunately, this viewing line has few advantages. It is unproductive on and around the summer solstice and has only a short observation period each year, from late May to early June and in July. Also, it is some 11½ miles away from The Cloud, which is rather dwarfed by the size of the sun at this distance. Therefore, the amount of solar reappearance, in comparison with that seen from the more proximate locations, is unimpressively small. In addition, as the furthest of the positions from The Cloud, the chances of the ruination of its events by haze and mist are greater than elsewhere. Furthermore, car transport is needed by the vast majority of people in order to reach this rather isolated location, whilst, ironically, speeding vehicles do not make this the most pleasant of viewing lines.

Finally, The Cloud is visible from the lower slopes of The Roaches and it is most probable that a double sunset occurs from this area for a period around the equinoxes, although, as yet, this remains empirically unsubstantiated. No doubt actual occurrences visible from this location on fine evenings will appeal to climbers and walkers, but any such events will almost certainly be less impressive than those observable from the A 523, a sight line much closer to The Cloud.

As was stated earlier in this book, The Cloud is not the only hill in the area which produces a double sunset. I have personally discovered three others, all of which are composed of Carboniferous Limestone and lie just inside the western boundary of Derbyshire: Chrome Hill, Parkhouse Hill and Thorpe Cloud. In my view, Chrome Hill is the most significant of these, both in terms of the excellence of its event and in that it yields a full and lengthy solar reappearance on the summer solstice. Unfortunately, the most impressive occurrence behind Chrome Hill is seen from the steep southern flank of Parkhouse Hill and therefore cannot be recommended to the readers of this book. Nevertheless, an interesting alternative is viewable on the longest day from a field to the northwest of the B 5053 in Glutton Bridge. Although its precise observation point has not yet been ascertained, it can be estimated relatively accurately from the viewing position recorded on 22 June 2001.

However, from this location, which is on private land, the Chrome Hill occurrence can only be seen for a short period of time each year, around midsummer, because the peak soon becomes obscured by Parkhouse Hill from an observer moving to the north. In addition, the relatively early sunset here means that the event commonly needs to be watched through a filter, whilst this peaceful rural area is situated at an even greater distance from the main centres of population in North Staffordshire than are the observation points for the double sunset involving The Cloud.

The Parkhouse Hill phenomenon has the advantage of being viewable from the verge of the B 5053 at Glutton Grange, just under a third of a mile to the north-northeast of the recommended Chrome Hill position, although care still needs to be taken with regard to passing traffic. For a short period in late March and early April and again in early to mid-September, the sun fully re-emerges for a considerable time after initially setting behind the hill, during a more outstanding event than that observable from Glutton Bridge involving Chrome Hill. Unfortunately, either side of the aforementioned periods, the phenomenon cannot be viewed because Parkhouse Hill becomes obscured, by its eastern flank as the spring progresses and by the immediate foreground as autumn deepens. Therefore, this occurrence is not observable on the summer solstice, unlike those visible from most of the other sight lines listed in this chapter. Also, as the event begins comparatively early in the evening, it usually requires the aid of a filter to be seen and, like the Chrome Hill phenomenon, is not placed in close proximity to the major urban centres of North Staffordshire.

The last and least important of the three limestone features to create a double sunset is Thorpe Cloud. Although the occurrence produced by this hill takes place on the summer solstice and for around a month before and afterwards, from an uninterrupted series of points along an extensive viewing line, the maximum amount of solar reappearance is small in comparison with that visible during the more impressive events observable from elsewhere on the longest day. Also, I have recorded data on this occurrence on only five occasions and so further fieldwork needs to be undertaken for a comprehensive knowledge of its various aspects to be accumulated. Again, a filter is very likely to be required as once more this event commences well before the sunset time scheduled on the Cheshire Plain, whilst its location is not the most immediately accessible to Staffordshire folk, but at least it is positioned in peaceful and impressive countryside near or on a public footpath.

In order for a spectator to gain the optimum reward from observing any of the fixed position double sunsets outlined and recorded in this book and indeed any further such events, the most careful viewing techniques need to be applied. Turning up and hoping for the best is likely to produce limited success only, if that. Because of the high incidence of cloud and haze in the skies of the Staffordshire Moorlands and the Peak District, double sunsets are not seen on average with any great consistency and therefore when opportunities present themselves, they need to be seized. The specific techniques recommended are intrinsically those developed by Roy Parker and me by accident and through subsequent fine tuning, as a result of both successful and unsuccessful experiences. Because we discovered no guidelines in print about how best to observe double sunsets, we simply developed our own practices, which may not satisfy conventional scientists, but the optimisation of the viewing potential of the phenomenon for the interested spectator is actually something of an art form and our techniques do work in reality. Indeed, a major advantage of our methods is that the only specific piece of sophisticated equipment that is required in order to achieve success is the human brain!

Initially, the observer needs to identify the approximate position of the double sunset anticipated. With regard to the events produced by the four hills discussed in this book, precise information is given on a representative sample of occurrences, which will hold absolutely or nearly true in any subsequent observations in the near future. Otherwise, locations accurate to within yards can usually be deduced from the data given on proximate double sunsets in time, especially those involving The Cloud, which I have naturally presented in the most detail. It is rather obvious, but most important, that the spectator should arrive at the selected place in plenty of time because unexpected problems might occur, such as an interfering tree directly on the sight line, a farmer to be negotiated with, interruption from an interested local resident or a chance passer-by, an inquisitive herd of bullocks or even the failure in the autumn to remember that the clock has been put back by an hour!

Once a rough viewing position has been located, then the build-up to a precise occurrence can begin. Roy and I have always attempted to seek observation points exactly on the leading edge of the viewing window because these specific spots will produce the maximum amount of reappearance after the sun has set initially and therefore give a more impressive event than from other places further back in the zone. Thus the primary objective is to find the precise observation position from which the sun entirely sets behind the selected feature of the landscape and re-emerges instantaneously. As a general rule, the longer the time interval between the sun setting and reappearing, the smaller the portion of the disc that will re-emerge until, beyond the trailing edge, the sun will not reappear at all. Unfortunately, it is easier said than done to discover the optimum viewing position and it is usually best achieved through practice. It cannot be expected to be obtained on the first attempt and it may be that the novice spectator will have to settle for a somewhat less impressive, but certain, event, rather than risk the sun slightly overshooting the desired point and consequently a double sunset not being seen at all.

When the sun has sunk to a level just above that of the selected landscape feature, the real action starts and events move increasingly quickly, so that the observer needs to have his wits about him and to react rapidly and decisively. If, from the viewing spot where the spectator is located, it seems as if the sun will overshoot the edge of the hill (that is, that it will not fully set), then he will need to move somewhat to the south or west and thereby ensure that the sun does entirely disappear in due course. However, if this change of position indicates that the sun will now set some way back from the edge of the hill, a compensatory further alteration of location will be needed, in the reverse direction, towards, but not as far as, the original observation point. The spectator should also note that if he is watching the phenomenon from a site close to the hill, such as Cloud Side, his necessary degree of movement will be small, but, if he is at considerable distance from the peak, for example, at Bottom House, the distance to be covered by any compensatory action will be much greater and may not even be possible within the time available.

As the occurrence proceeds, the viewer will almost certainly have to continue to refine his position by toing and froing in the same manner, but over decreasing distances until the optimum observation spot is finally discovered. However, it is important to note that this geographical point will not be absolutely identical for a tall person and a small one, such is the precision of the event, especially the closer to the hill the observer becomes. Indeed, the optimum position may eventually be decided by shuffling across tiny amounts of ground and even by swaying backwards and forwards from a fixed spot. The spectator can confirm that he has arrived at this exact point by taking a step to the north or east and then to the south or west. Having undertaken the first stride, a small portion of the sun should be visible at the critical moment of solar disappearance and re-emergence, indicating that the observer has moved beyond the leading edge of the viewing window. Conversely, by taking the second (reverse) step, the spectator should see a little less of the sun reappear than from the optimum point, but this will only be critical in cases where the maximum possible solar re-emergence is very slight.

Having ascertained the optimum observation position, it is imperative that the viewer regards that spot as fixed and remains rooted to it for the rest of the occurrence, or, alternatively, clearly and precisely marks it so that it can be exactly returned to. A failure to do so will mean that the spectator cannot reliably claim to have seen a double sunset from a particular place. At a short distance from the hill in question, the movement of an observer even a few strides northwards or eastwards may create a double sunset, whereas from any fixed point in the vicinity there is no such occurrence. Double sunsets of this nature can be seen by individuals moving around on any evening in favourable weather conditions from an absolutely immense number of places and thus they are effectively of no value. The acid test is as to whether the phenomenon can be observed from a fixed spot.

Once the viewer has identified the optimum fixed position and seen the sun set and reappear, the difficult work has been done and all that remains for him to do in order to enjoy the rest of the event is to stay stationary and observe what happens. The most interesting things then to monitor are the amount of the solar re-emergence and the location of the final sunset.

There is one further consideration for a double sunset spectator and that is whether to use a solar filter whilst undertaking his observations. For reasons of safety, staring directly at the sun with the naked eye can never be recommended, but vast numbers of people throughout the ages have watched sunsets at the end of the evening when the power of the sun has become weak and they have not suffered any ill effects. Indeed, Roy Parker and I are two such individuals and we know of many others as a result of our research on this project. Ultimately, the choice and risk of doing so is up to the specific observer himself. However, he will undoubtedly discover that it is practically impossible to view without the aid of a filter the many double sunsets listed in the data section of this book which do not occur in the late evening and during which the light from the sun can be expected to be intensely bright. Therefore, an observer of these events and others of similar ilk will definitely require a suitable and safe filter.

I am not an expert on solar filters, nor on the safety aspects of viewing the sun, and therefore refer the readers of this book to the advice given by the eminent and famous astronomer, Dr Patrick Moore, to potential observers of the August 1999 solar eclipse:

'The British Astronomical Association advises that the eclipse should be viewed through only special filters such as aluminised Mylar filters that bear a statement saying they conform to the EC directive 89/686/EEC, or through a welder's glass rated number 14, or higher.

Do not use filters that are scratched or if they have pin-holes. Place the filter over your eyes before looking at the sun, and remove [it] only after looking away.'

In conclusion, suitably equipped, the observer should find great pleasure in seeing the double sunset once he has located its viewing position, assuming that the weather proves to be kind, of course!

8 The Double Sunset Observations

This chapter provides detailed information on the locations, times and sequences of forty-six double sunsets and five double sunrises, set against four separate hills in Staffordshire and Derbyshire, which I observed on various specific dates over a period of nine years. My objective in presenting this data is to enable the reader to locate the whereabouts of and to enjoy unusual solar occurrences similar to the ones that I was privileged to experience. There are numerous viewing points of such events, but I have selected for inclusion in this book only those which yielded the most notable and impressive results during my numerous observations.

Double sunsets or sunrises occurring behind The Cloud are visible all the year round from the Woodhouse Green-Toftgreen line and I have included details on these events at approximately fortnightly intervals, to enable the spectator both to enjoy those which are listed and to estimate with reasonable ease and accuracy the times of and viewing positions for successful occurrences on all the days in between them. Nevertheless, it should be noted that the daily shift in time and distance of visible events around the equinoxes is much greater than it is around the solstices. The Cloud Side line is presented in exactly the same manner, but for a period around midwinter, its observation points effectively merge with those around Toftgreen so that its relevant information is identical with that of the latter site. However, because of its greater distance from The Cloud, I chose to provide specific details about the A 523 line on just four occasions during the year: the solstices and two dates near to the equinoxes on which relatively impressive double sunsets occur. In addition, the other three hills known to produce the phenomenon (Chrome Hill, Parkhouse Hill and Thorpe Cloud) do so only for limited periods from their monitored locations and therefore my selected data simply represents the essence of their events.

The key details for each selected location and date are given on a single page, which contains a diagram illustrating the observed solar occurrence and a sketch map pinpointing its viewing position. The diagrams include the following abbreviations: STS (starting to set), S (set), R (reappeared), S + R (set and re-appeared), M (maximum reappearance visible), FD (full disc in view), STR (starting to reset), FS (final set) and c. (estimated data, not precisely recorded). The times of all the events witnessed are rounded off to the nearest 30 seconds and conform to Greenwich Mean Time and British Summer Time as appropriate.

The associated sketch maps are intended to enable the observer to locate the viewing points of the selected events (marked as *VP) and those in between as easily as possible and therefore depict only the landscape features essential to this purpose, whilst, for the same reason, the scale is distorted as necessary. Also, the relevant distances are recorded in paces (each equivalent to about 2½ feet) to enable the lay spectator to discover approximate observation points with relative ease. Indeed, the precise viewing spots of all occurrences alter according to the height of the observer, especially at locations close to the hill, so that no exact measurement can apply to everyone, whilst further inconsistencies are created through the impact of variables, such as leap year. Furthermore, the maps will inevitably decline in accuracy because of the ravages of time and are already doing so, but, hopefully, they will remain a useful guide in the foreseeable future.

A 523 LOCATIONS

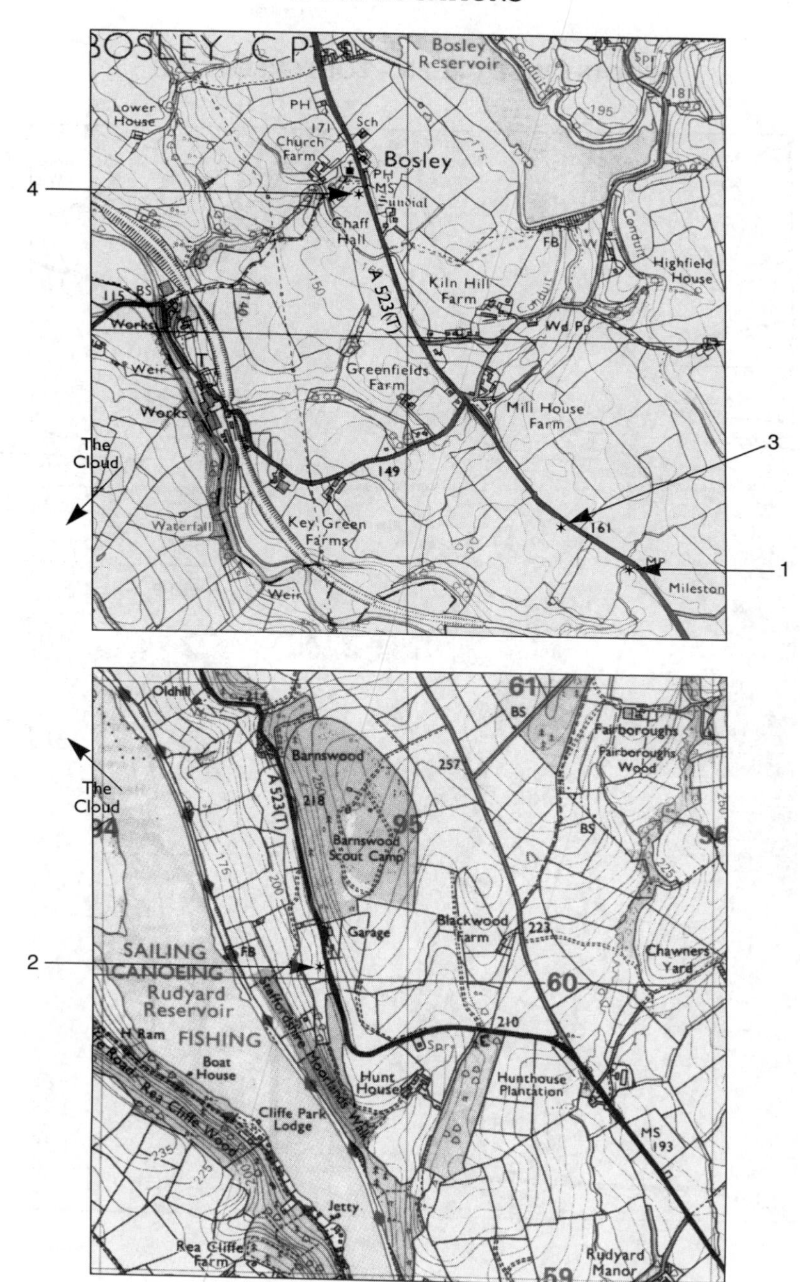

WOODHOUSE GREEN - TOFTGREEN LINE

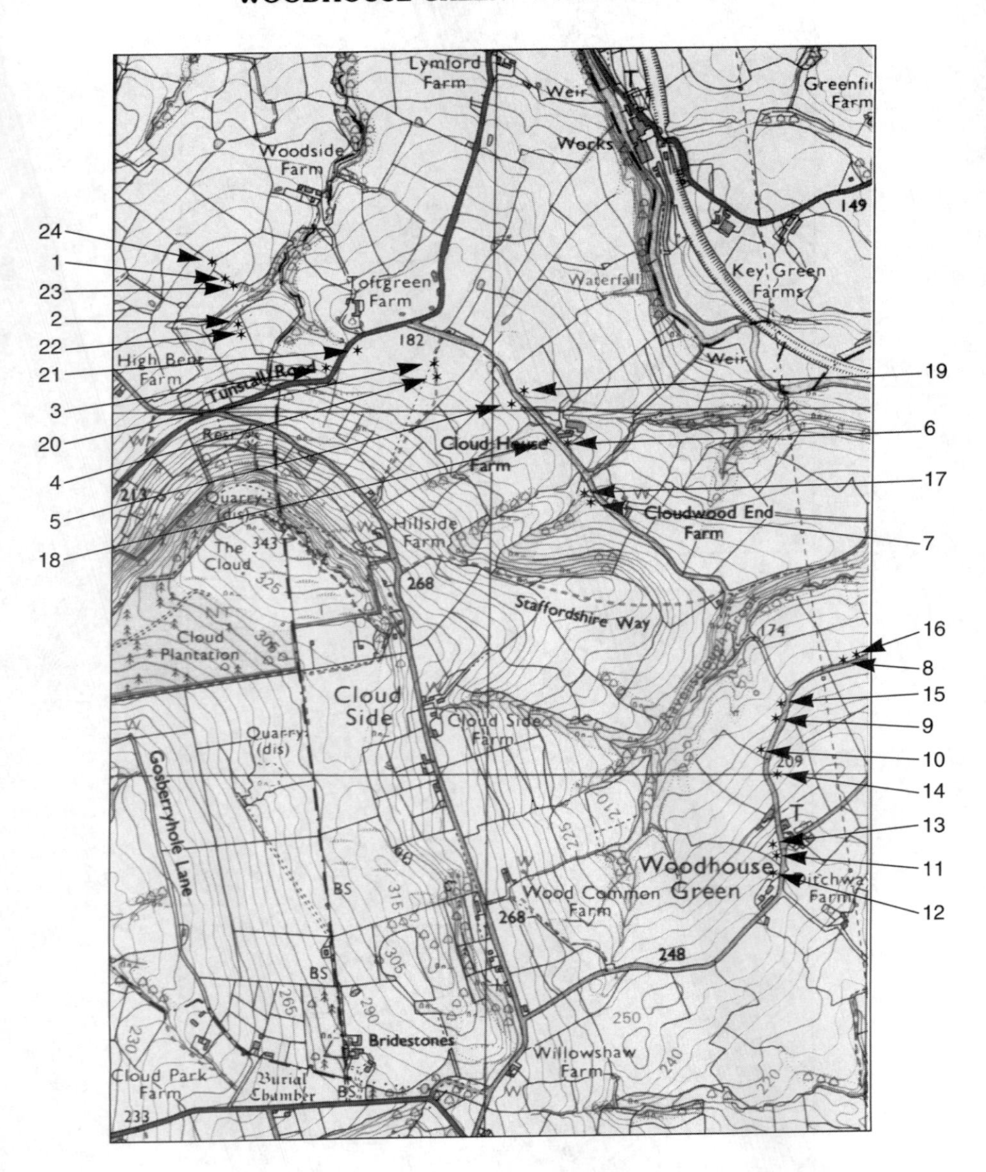

CLOUD SIDE LINE

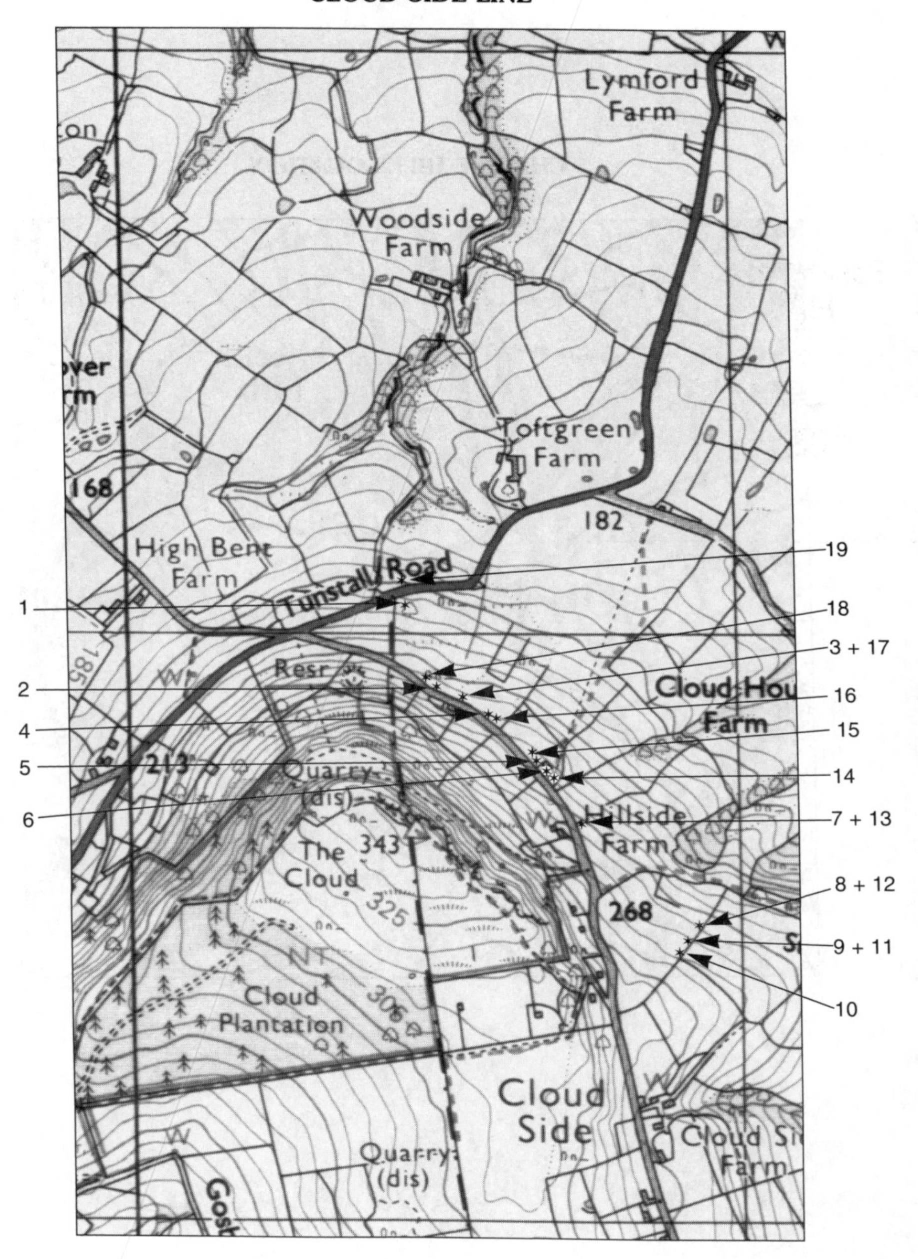

CHROME HILL LOCATION

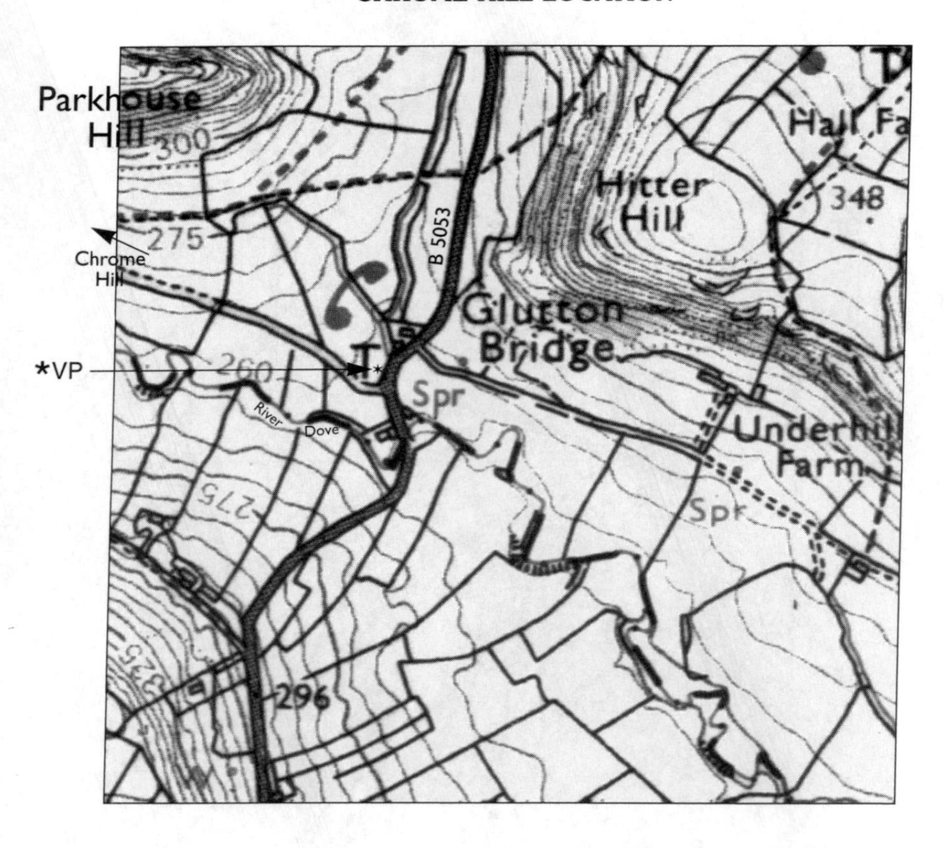

PARKHOUSE HILL LOCATIONS

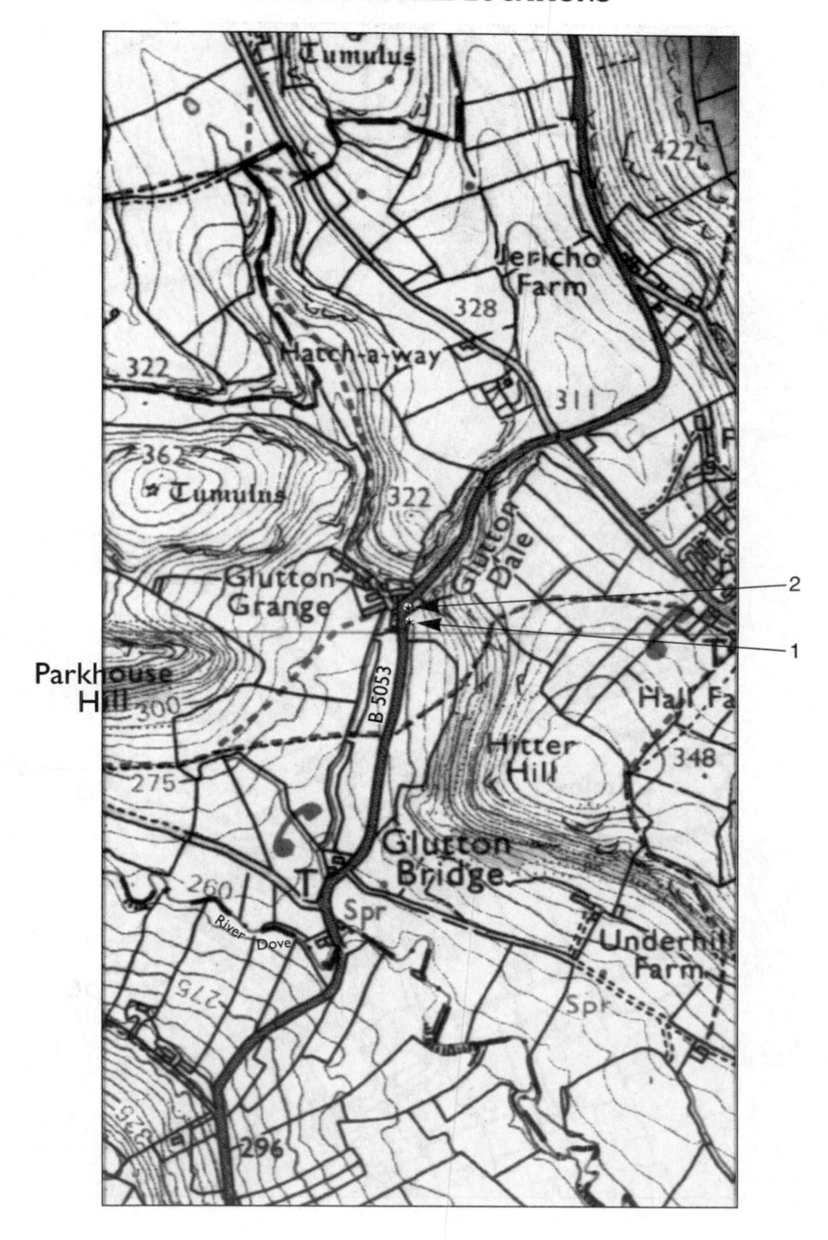

THORPE CLOUD LOCATION

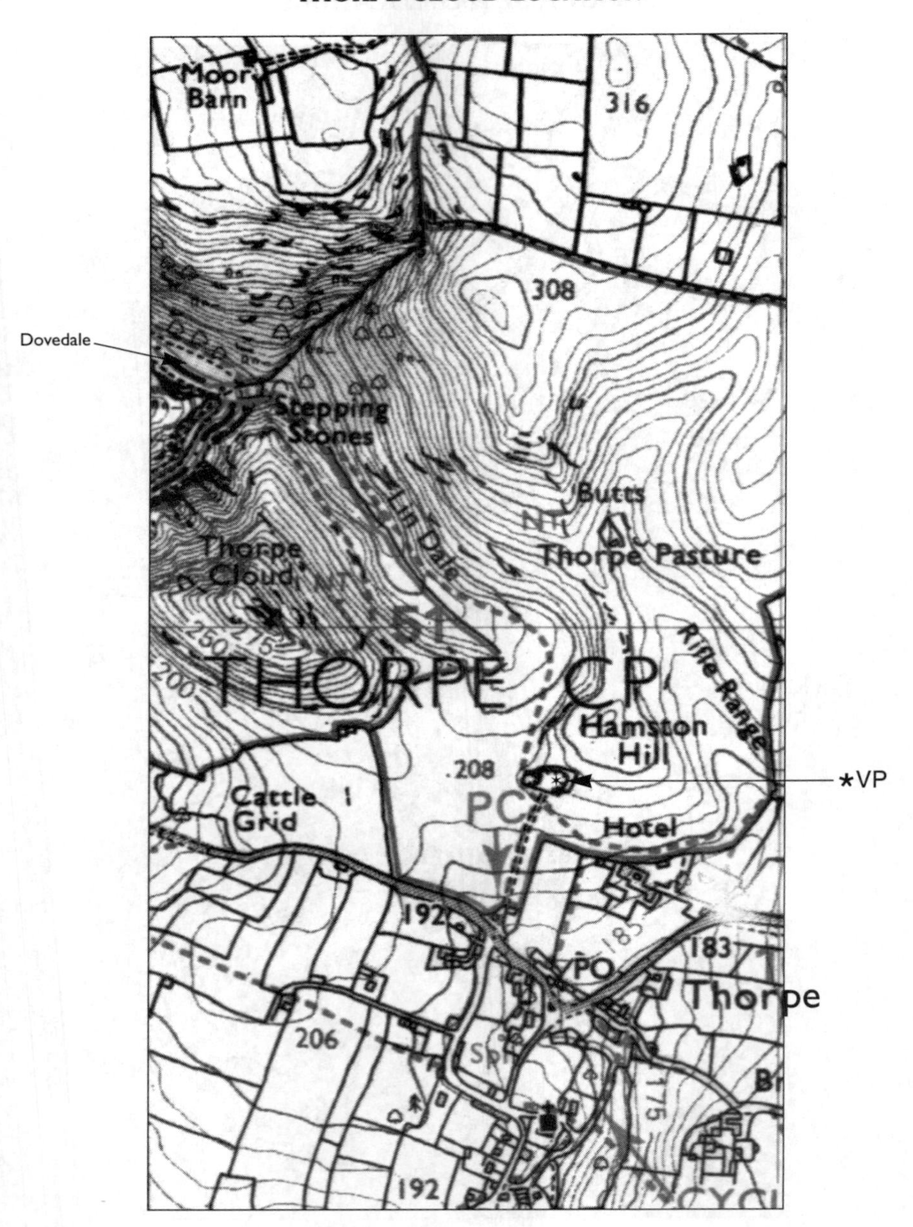

A 523: No. 1, 8 MARCH 1997

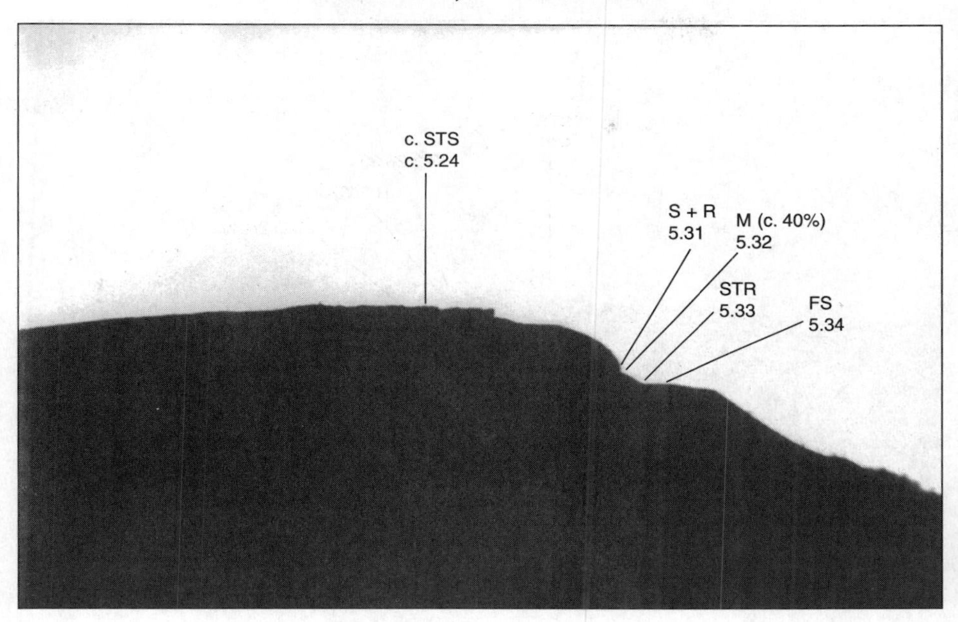

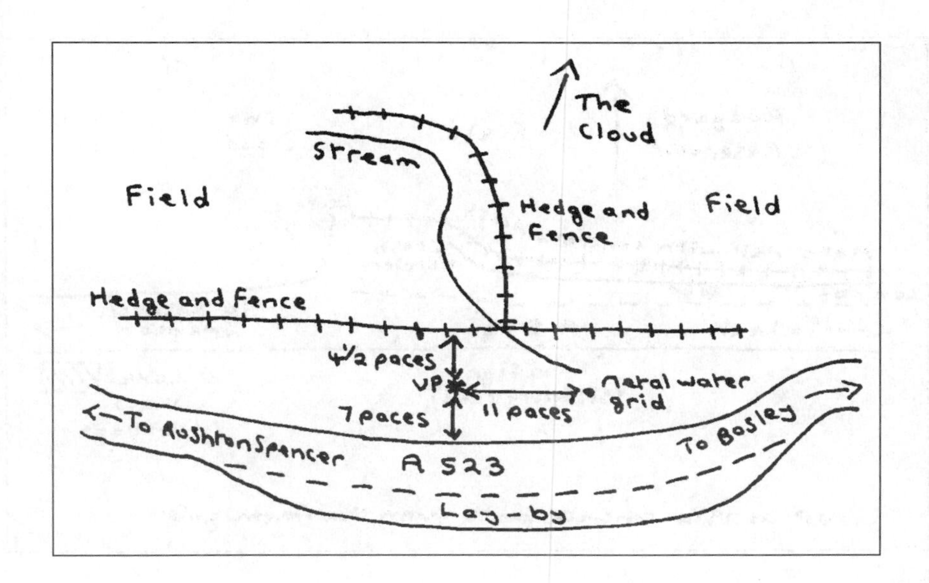

A 523: No. 2, 21 JUNE 2000

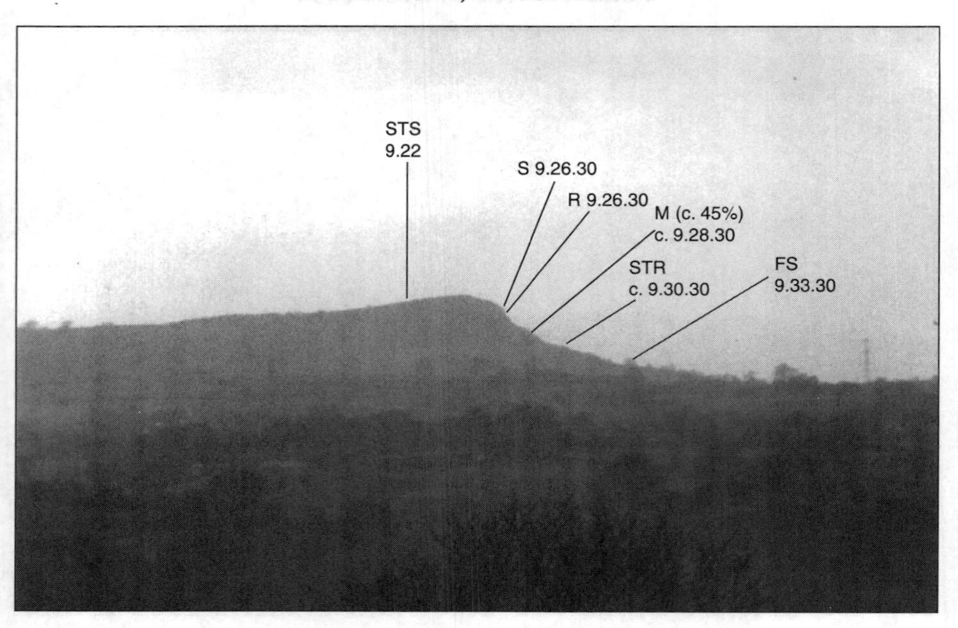

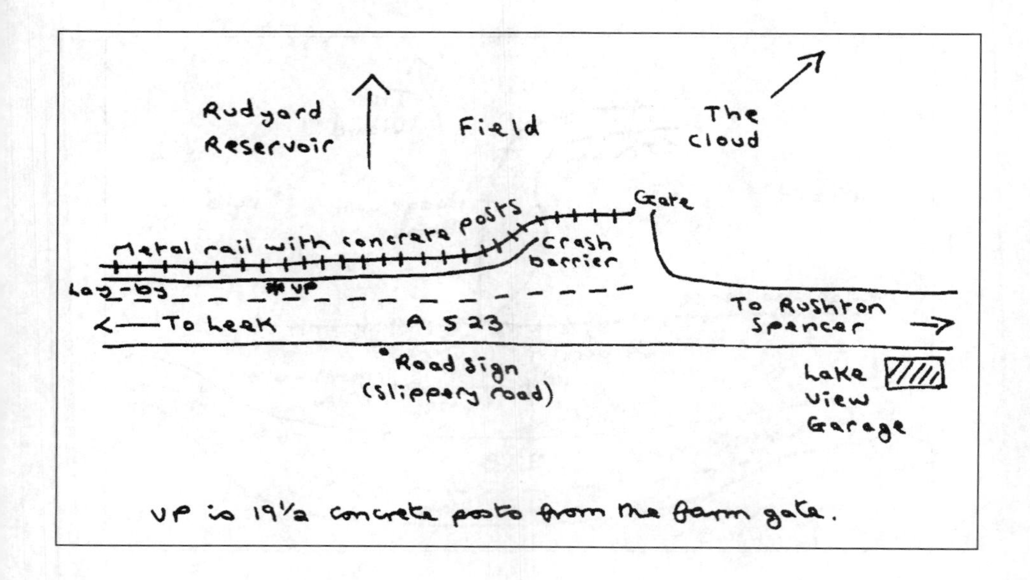

A 523: No. 3, 11 OCTOBER 1999

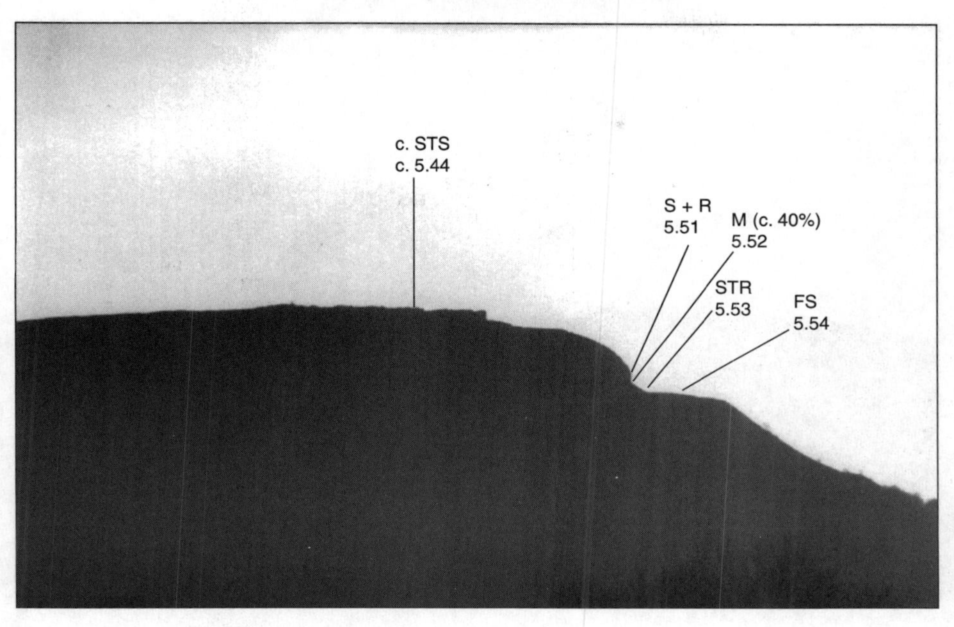

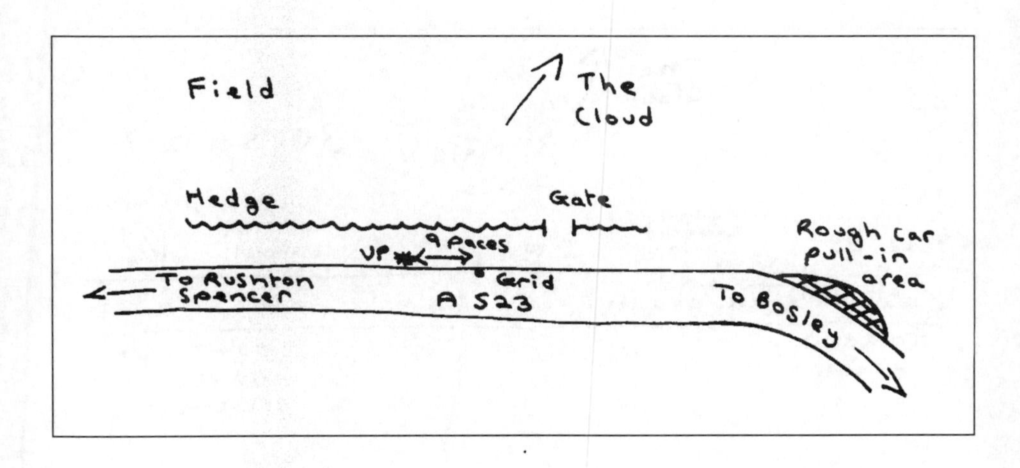

A 523: No. 4, 21 DECEMBER 1996

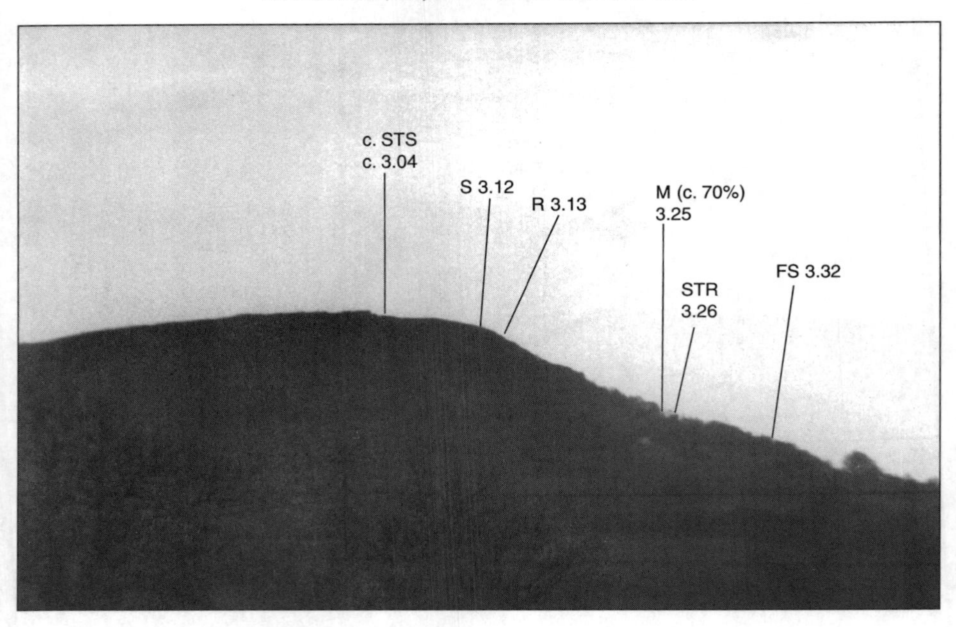

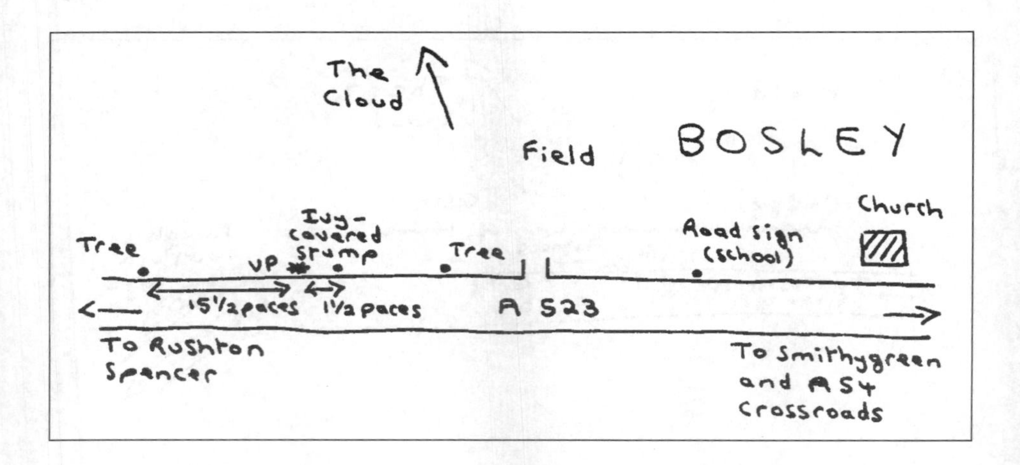

WOODHOUSE GREEN - TOFTGREEN LINE: No. 1, 8 JANUARY 2000

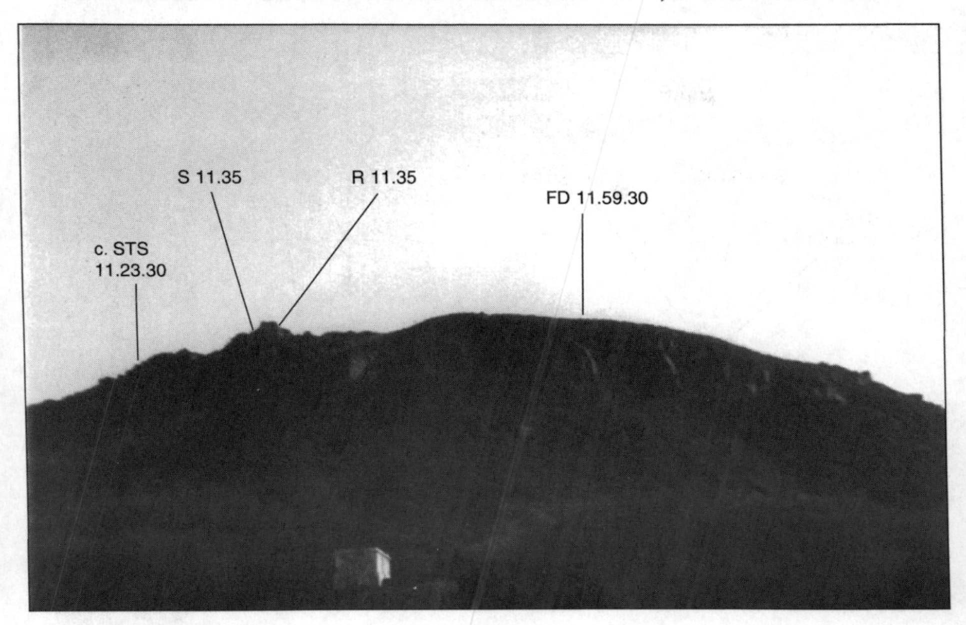

A second sunrise!

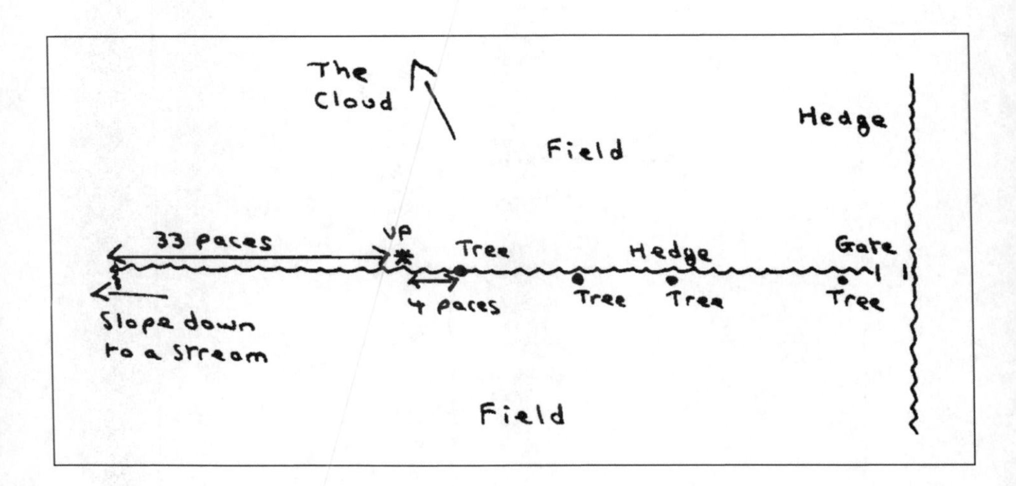

WOODHOUSE GREEN - TOFTGREEN LINE: No. 2, 23 JANUARY 2000

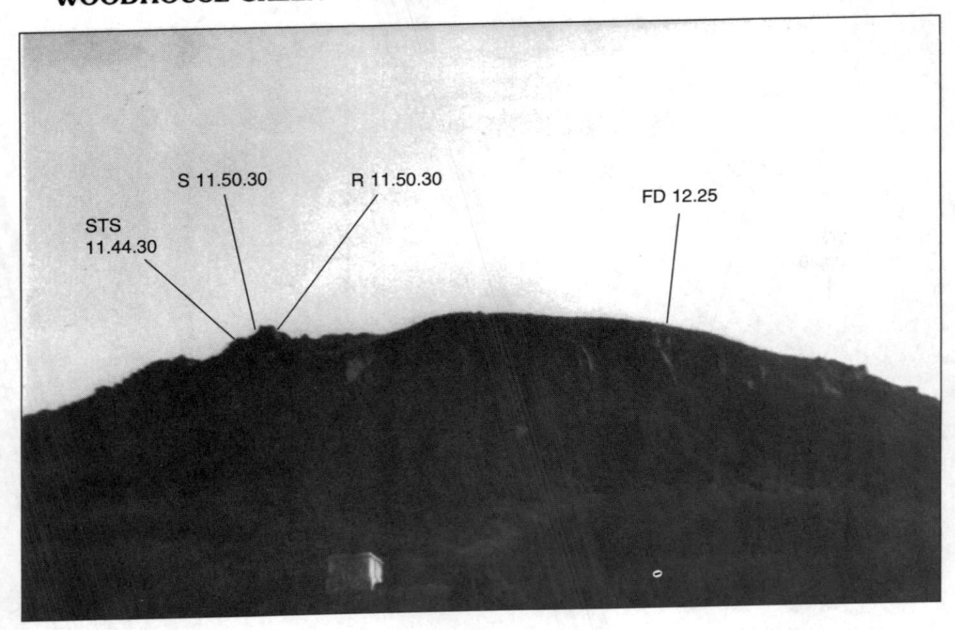

A second sunrise!

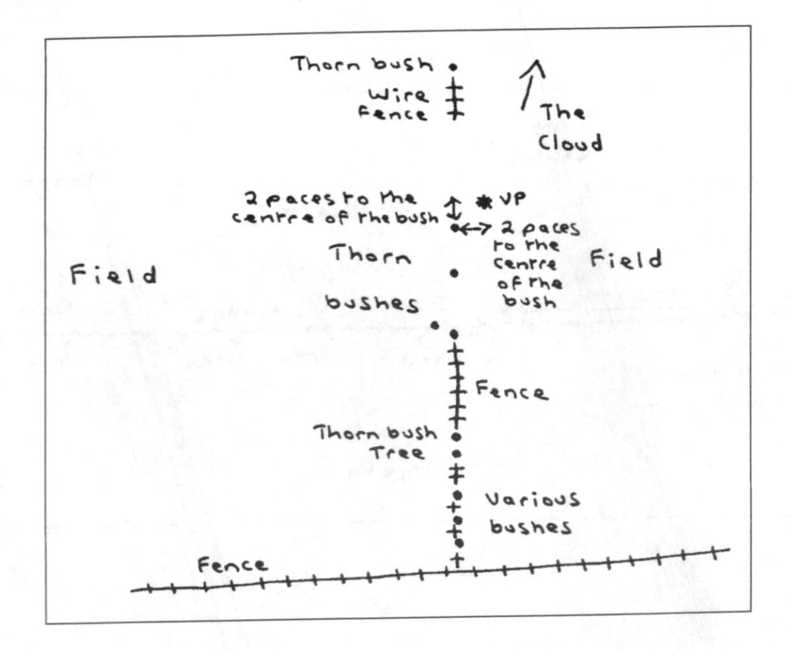

WOODHOUSE GREEN - TOFTGREEN LINE: No. 3, 7 FEBRUARY 1997

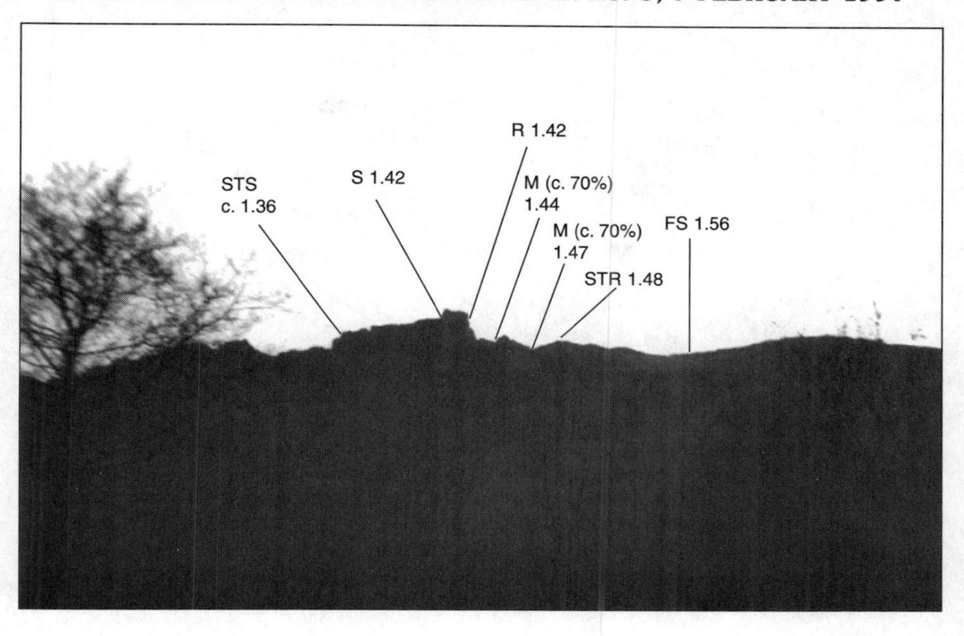

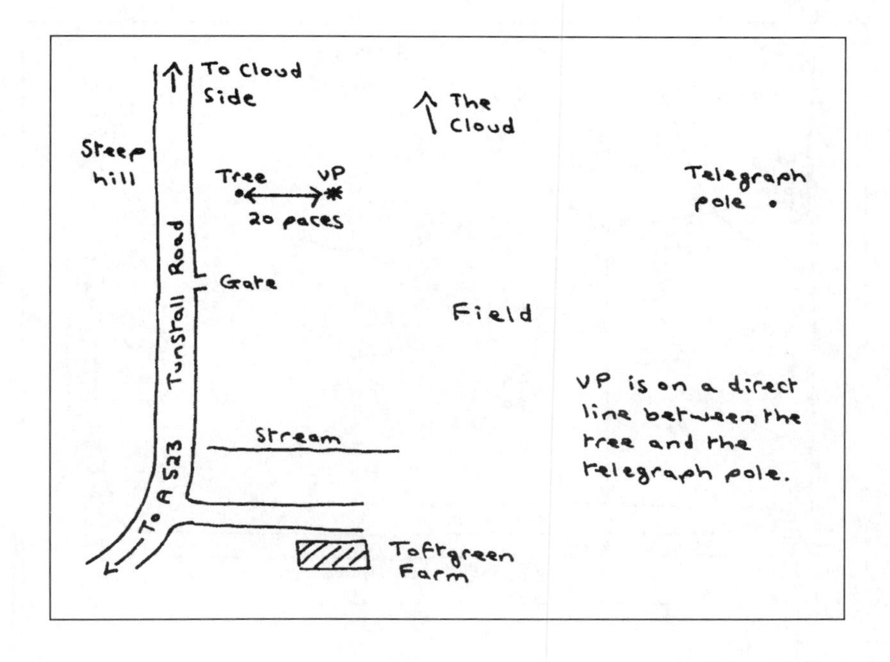

WOODHOUSE GREEN - TOFTGREEN LINE: No. 4, 22 FEBRUARY 1998

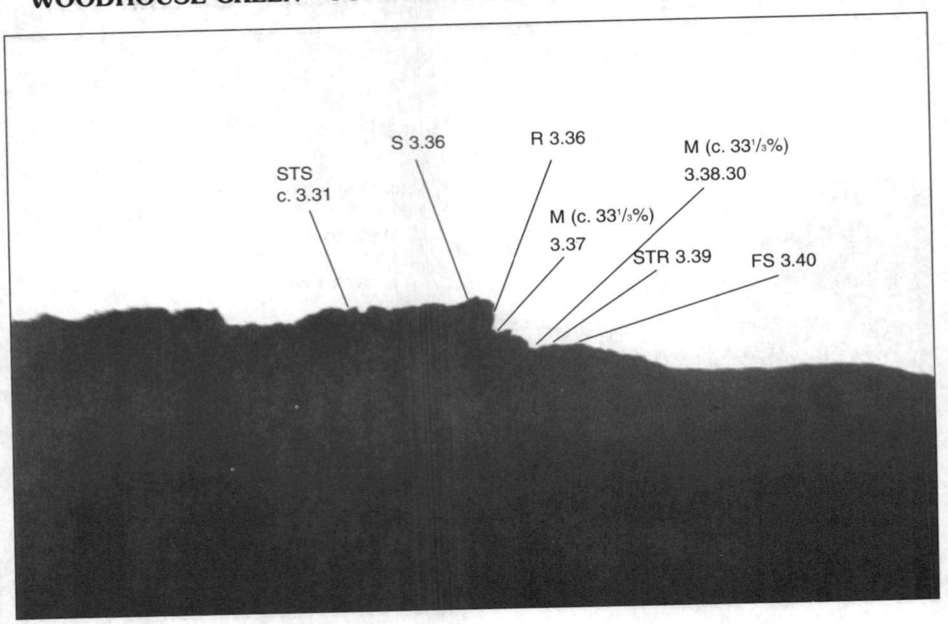

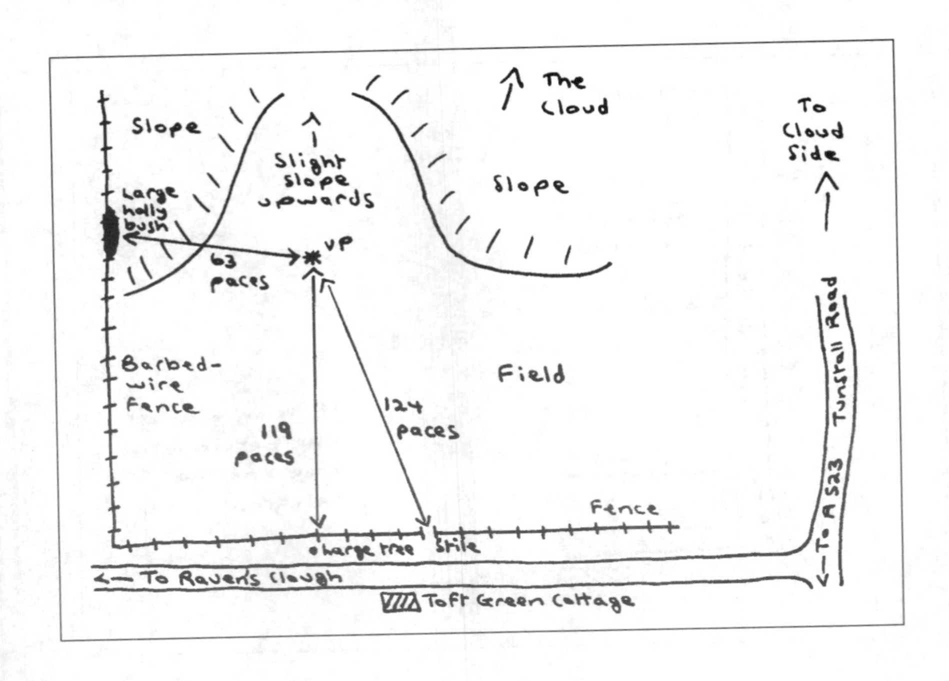

WOODHOUSE GREEN - TOFTGREEN LINE: No. 5, 8 MARCH 1997

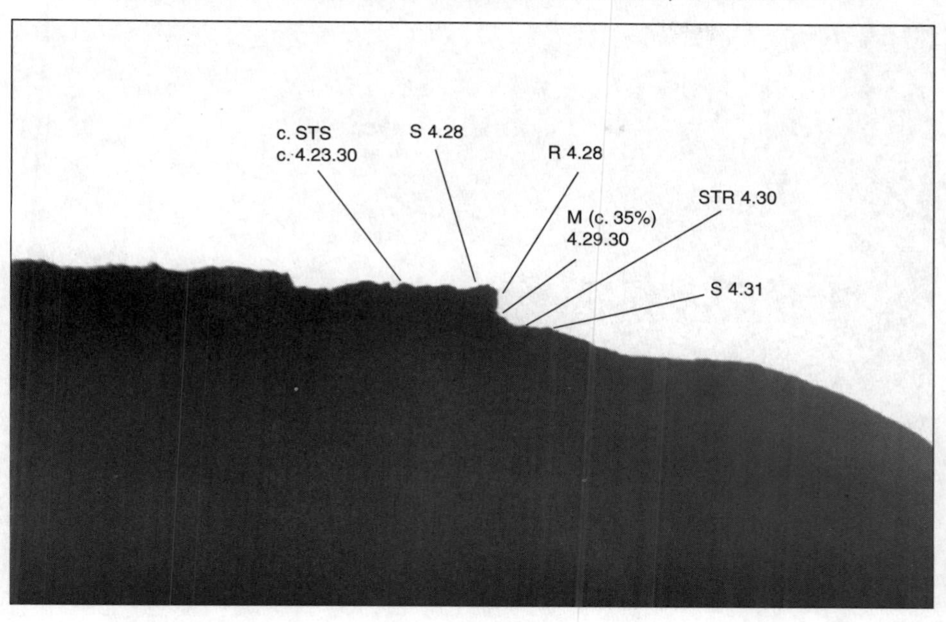

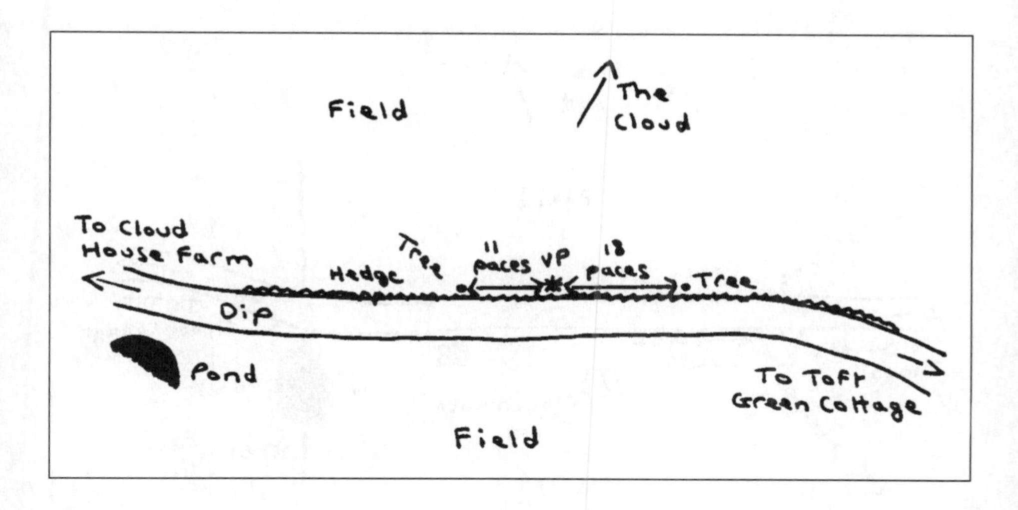

WOODHOUSE GREEN - TOFTGREEN LINE: No. 6, 23 MARCH 1995

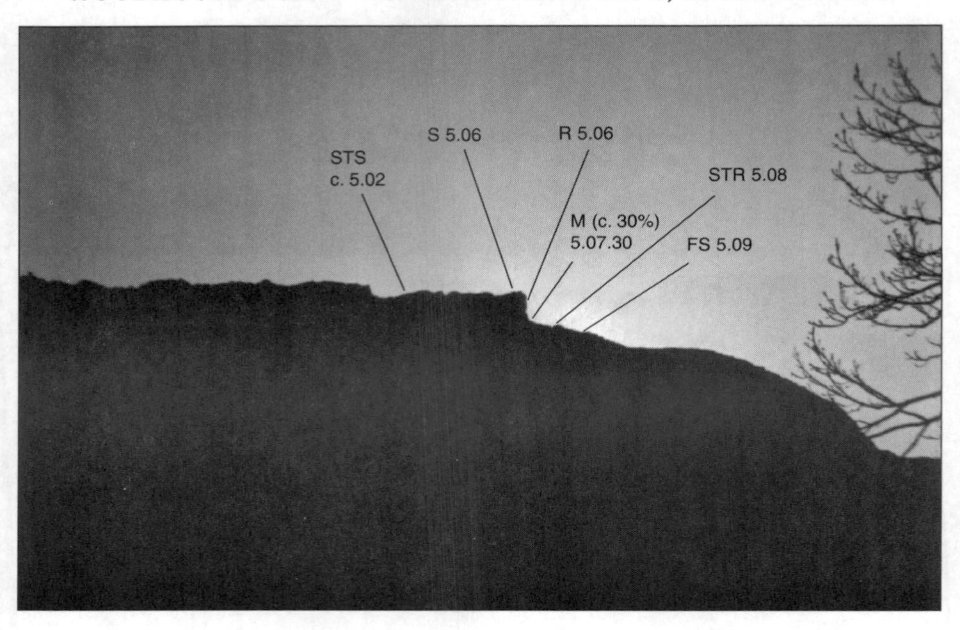

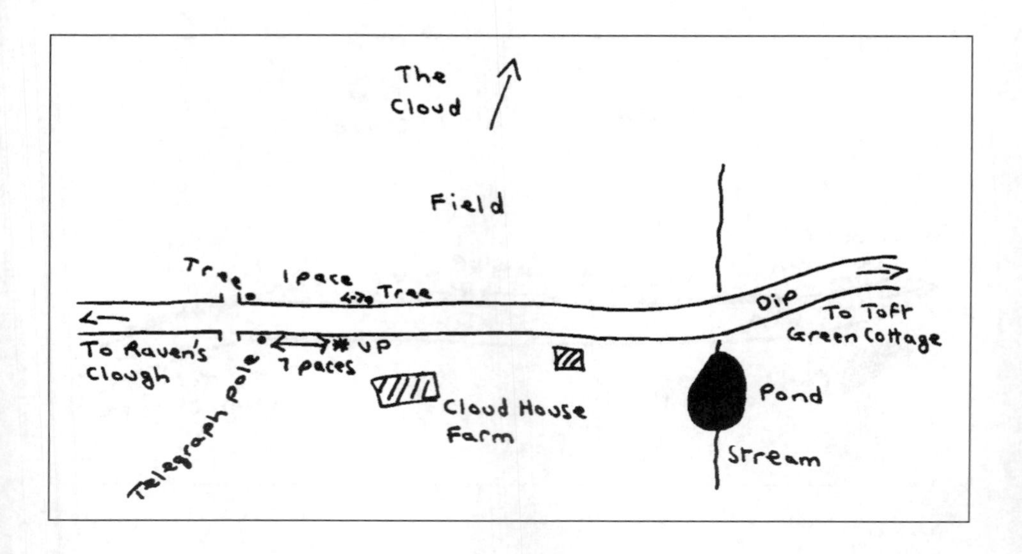

WOODHOUSE GREEN - TOFTGREEN LINE: No. 7, 6 APRIL 1995

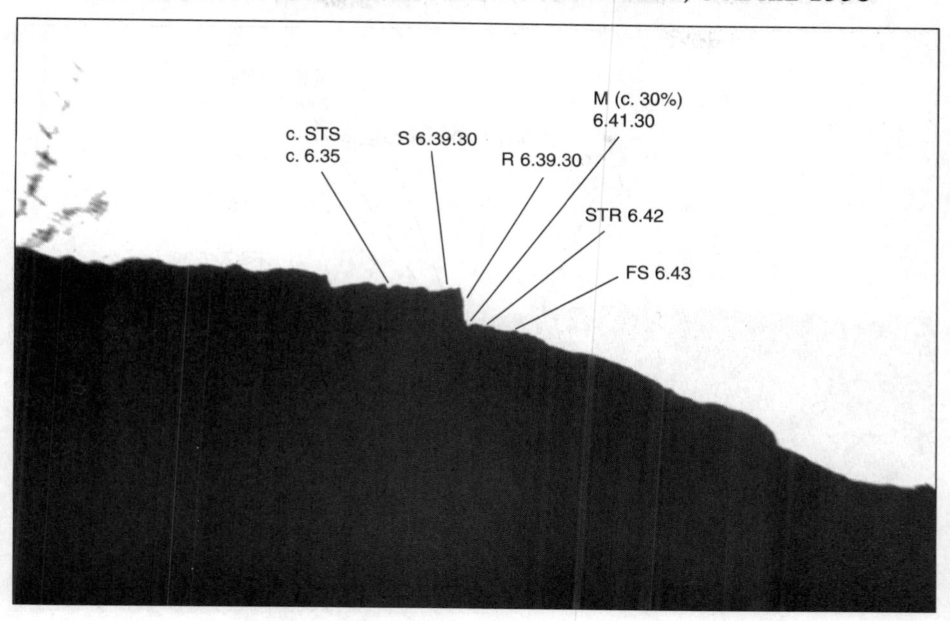

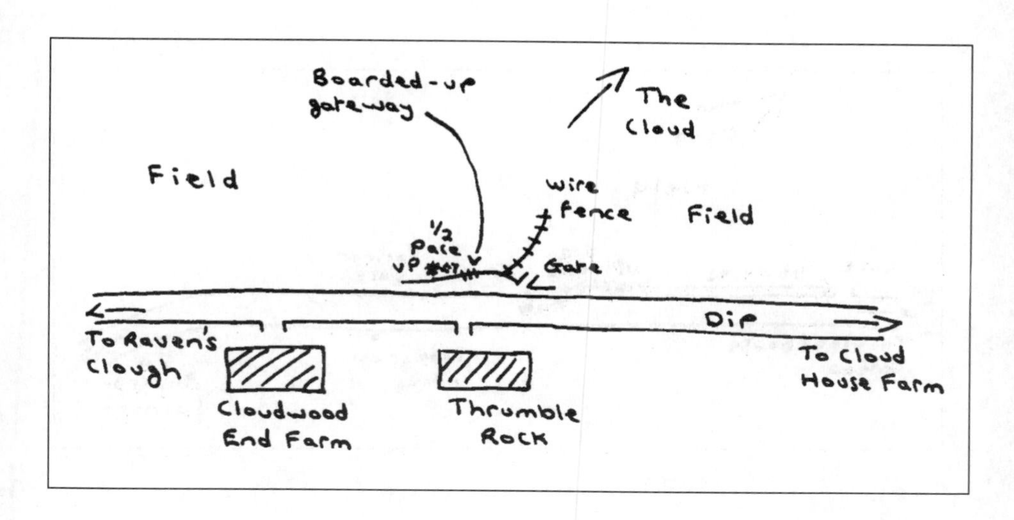

WOODHOUSE GREEN - TOFTGREEN LINE: No. 8, 24 APRIL 1999

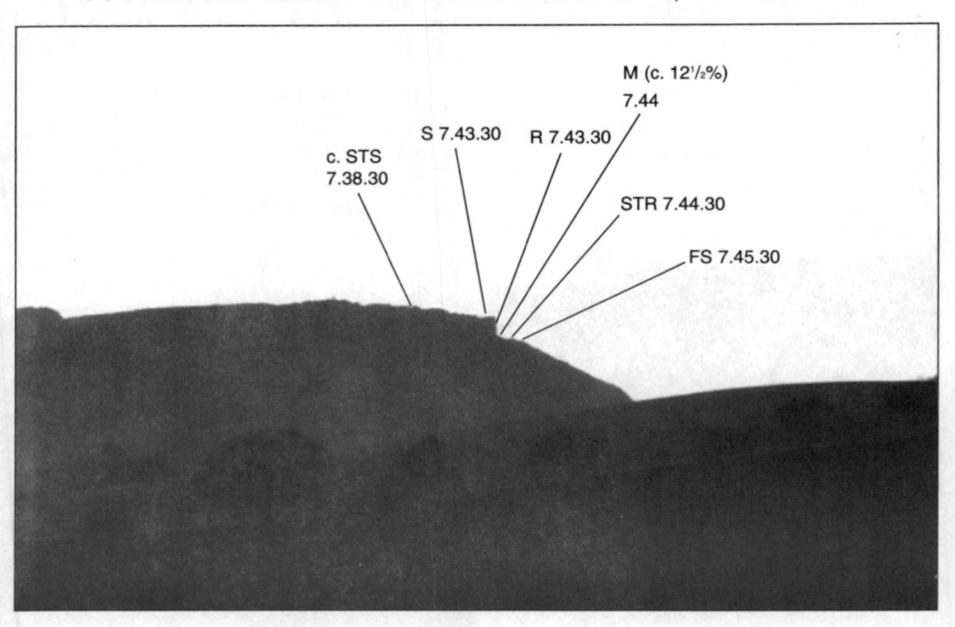

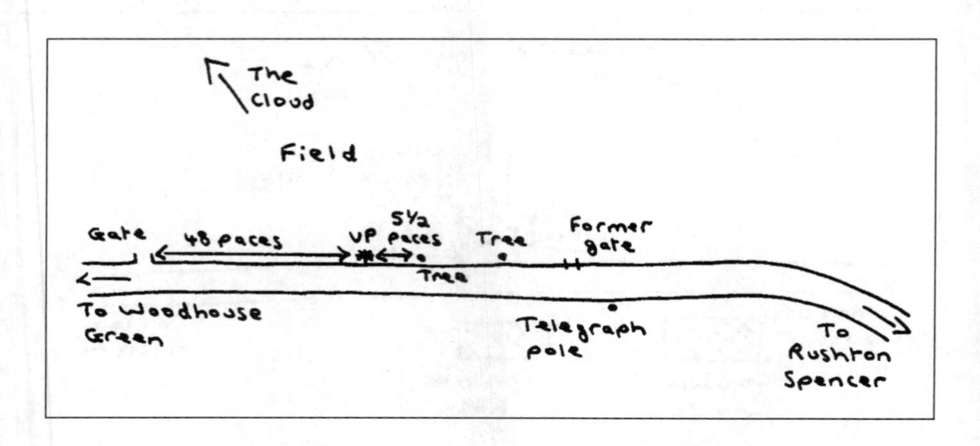

WOODHOUSE GREEN - TOFTGREEN LINE: No. 9, 9 MAY 1998

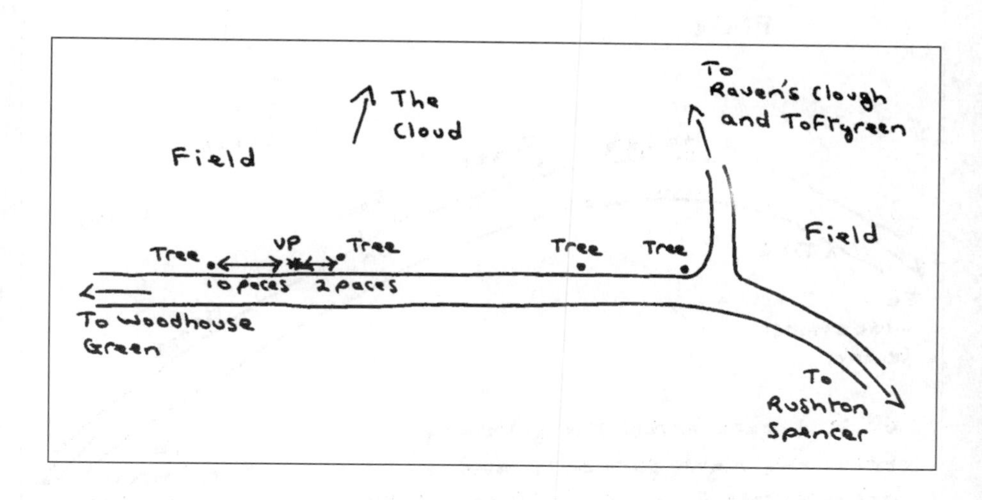

WOODHOUSE GREEN - TOFTGREEN LINE: No. 10, 18 MAY 1998

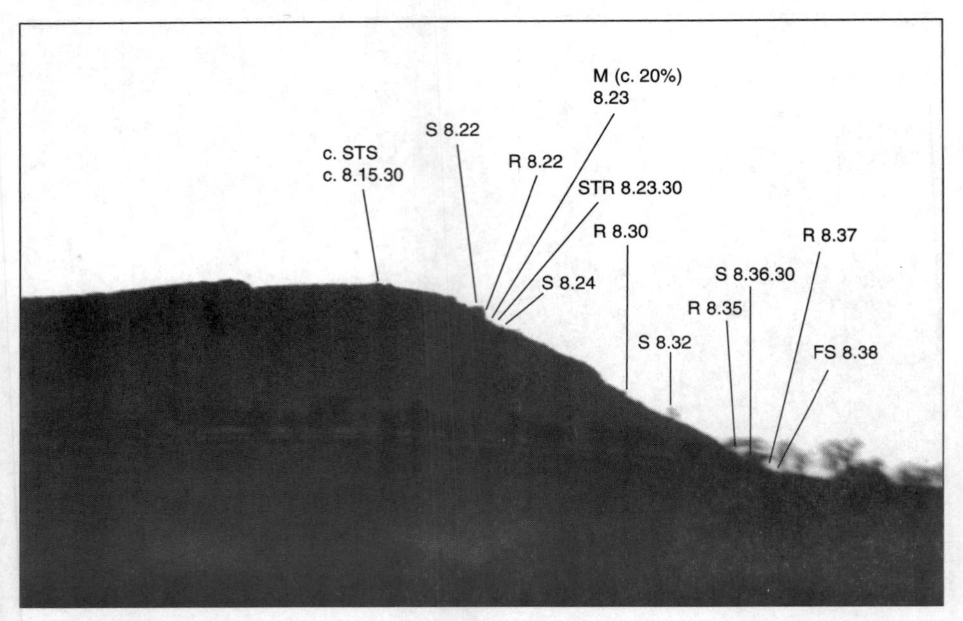

A quintuple sunset!

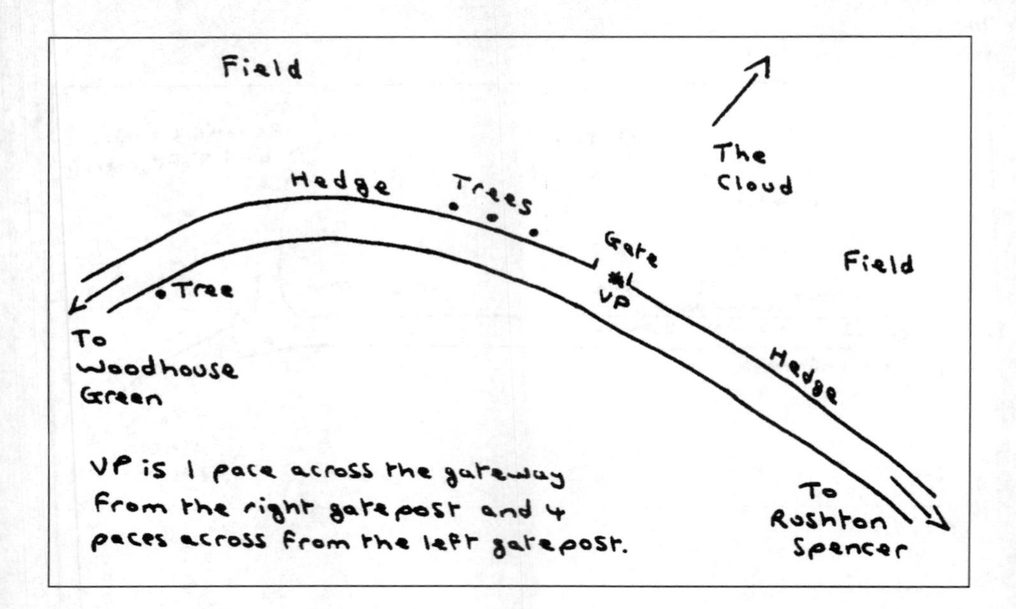

WOODHOUSE GREEN - TOFTGREEN LINE: No. 11, 8 JUNE 1999

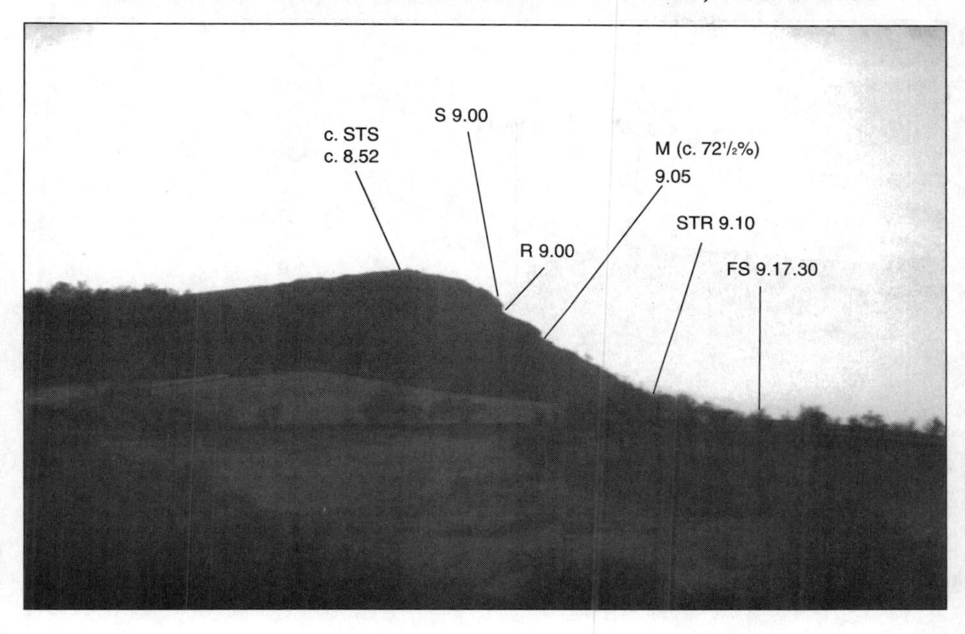

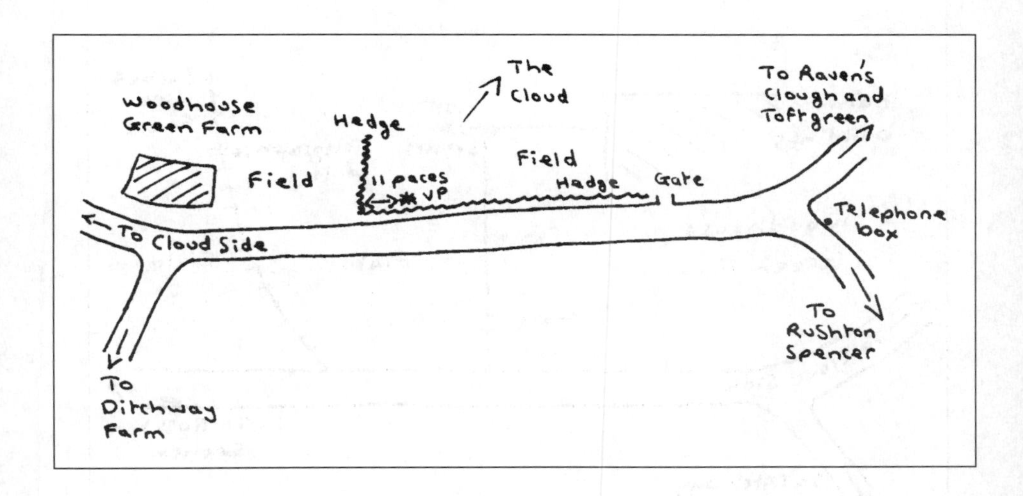

WOODHOUSE GREEN - TOFTGREEN LINE: No. 12, 21 JUNE 1998

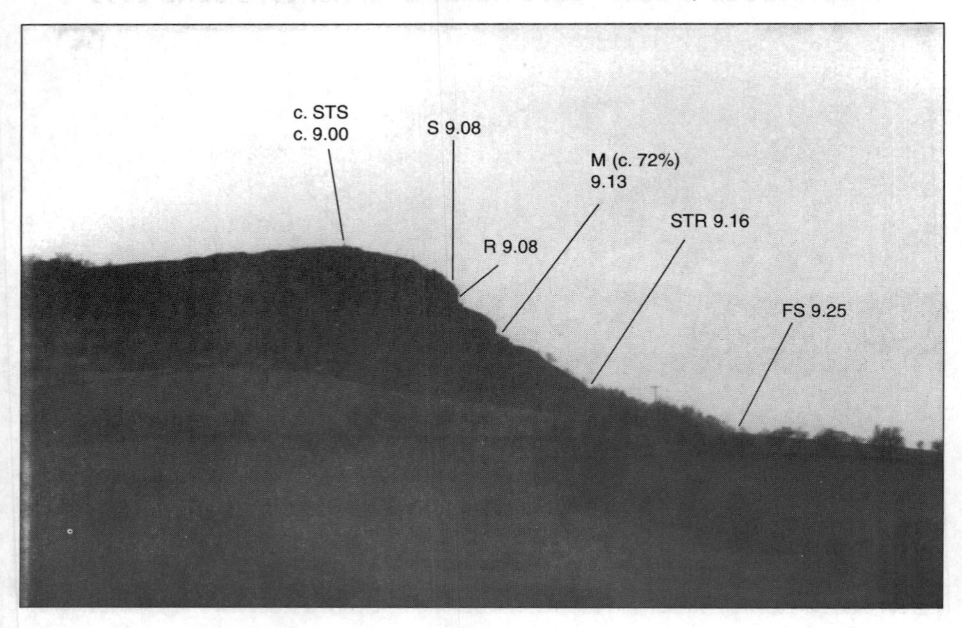

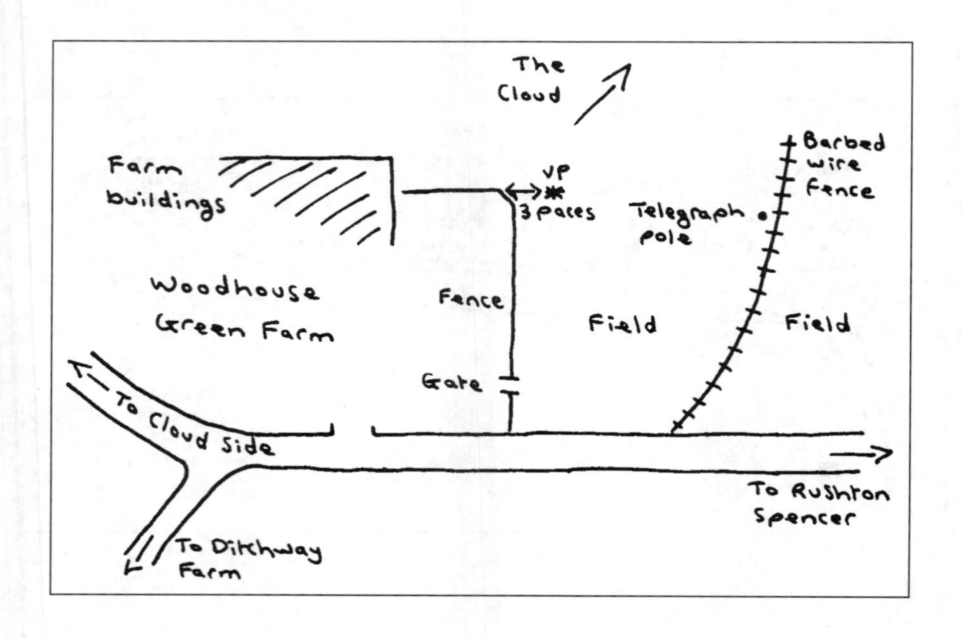

WOODHOUSE GREEN - TOFTGREEN LINE: No. 13, 6 JULY 1997

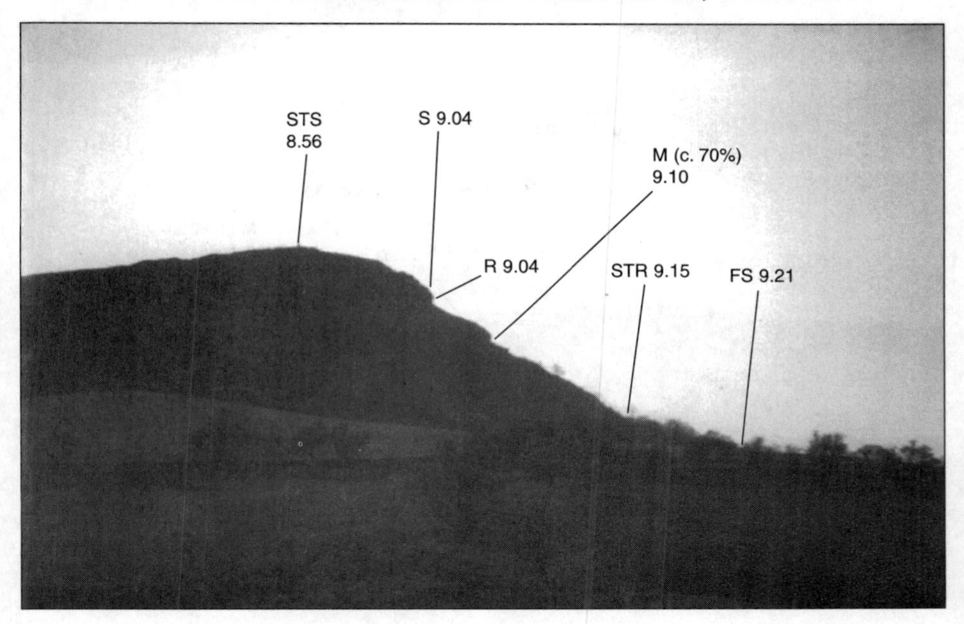

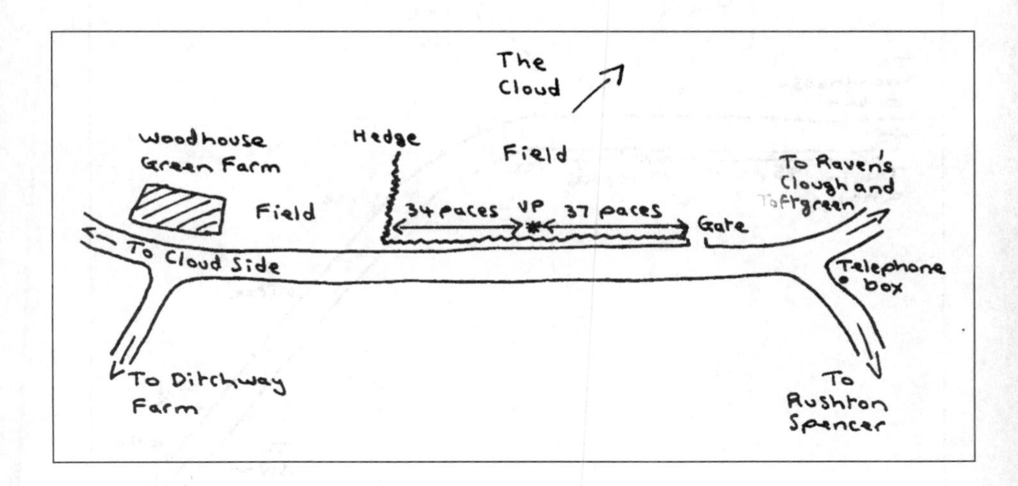

WOODHOUSE GREEN - TOFTGREEN LINE: No. 14, 20 JULY 1996

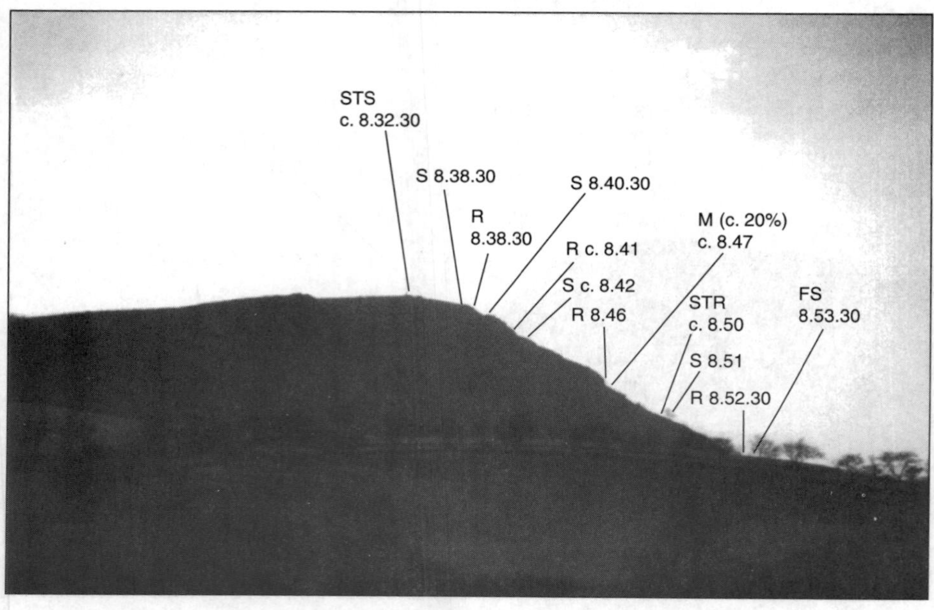

A quintuple sunset!

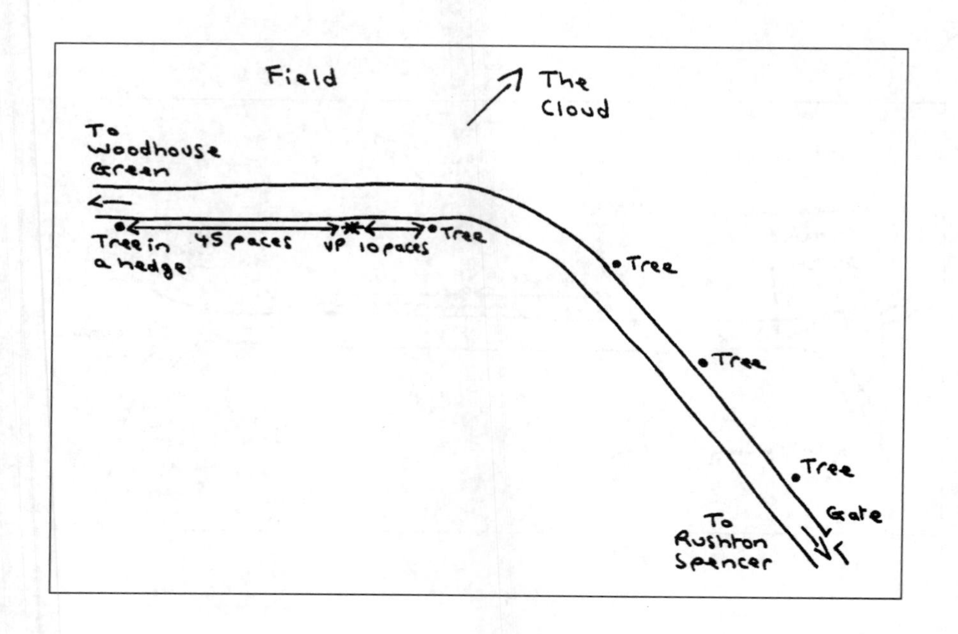

WOODHOUSE GREEN - TOFTGREEN LINE: No. 15, 5 AUGUST 1994

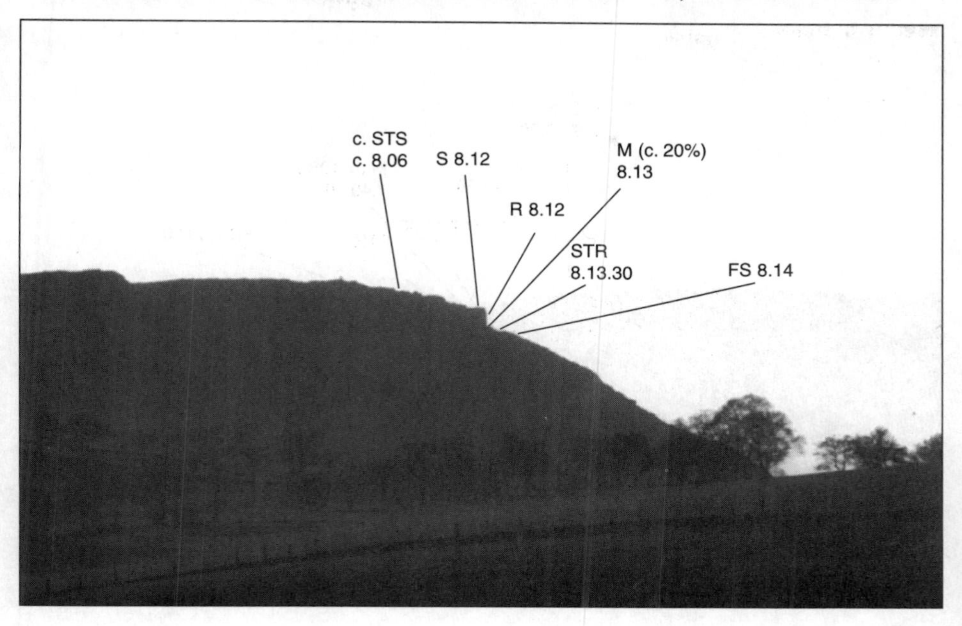

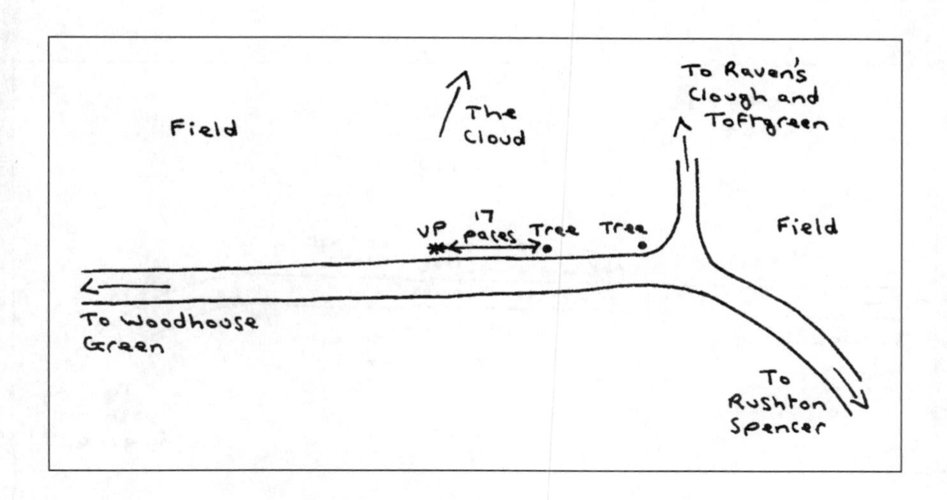

WOODHOUSE GREEN - TOFTGREEN LINE: No. 16, 18 AUGUST 1996

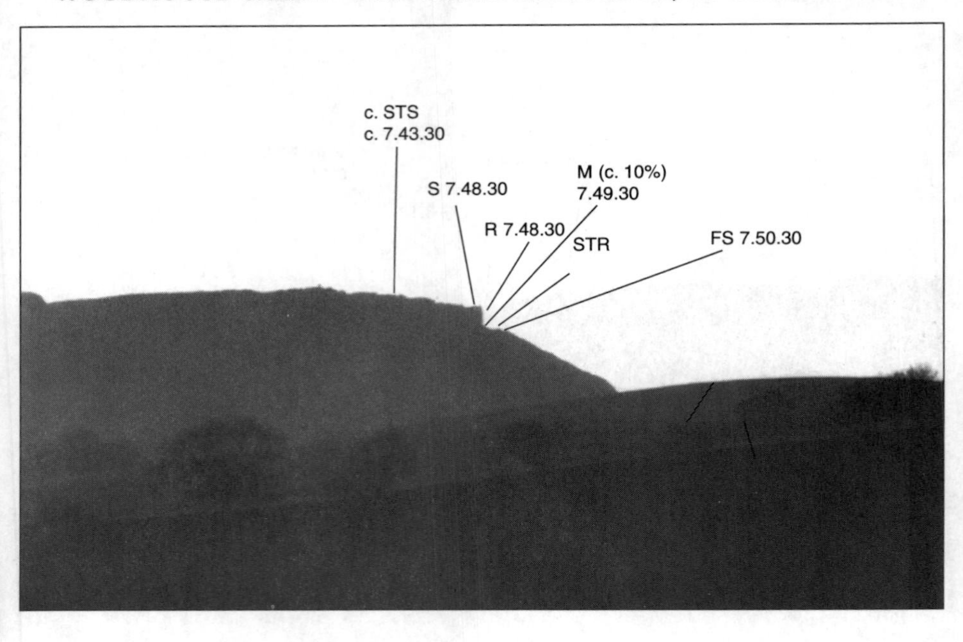

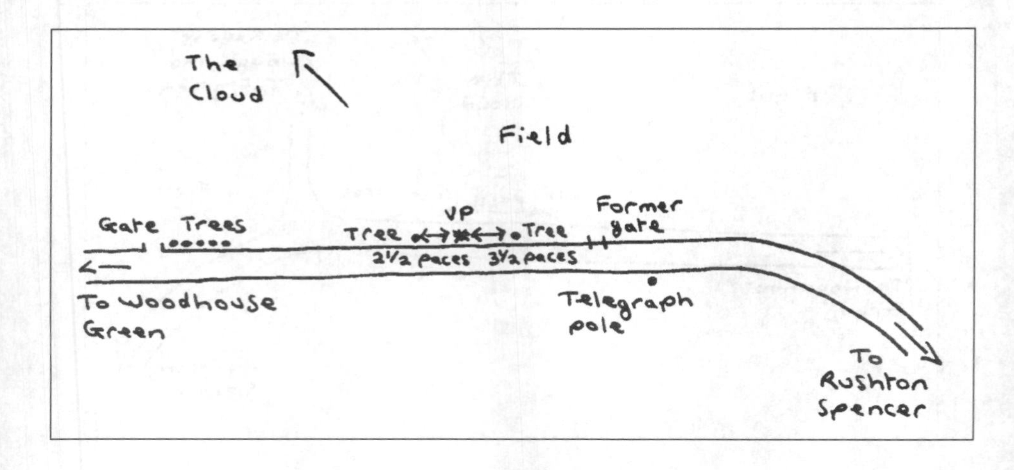

WOODHOUSE GREEN - TOFTGREEN LINE: No. 17, 8 SEPTEMBER 1996

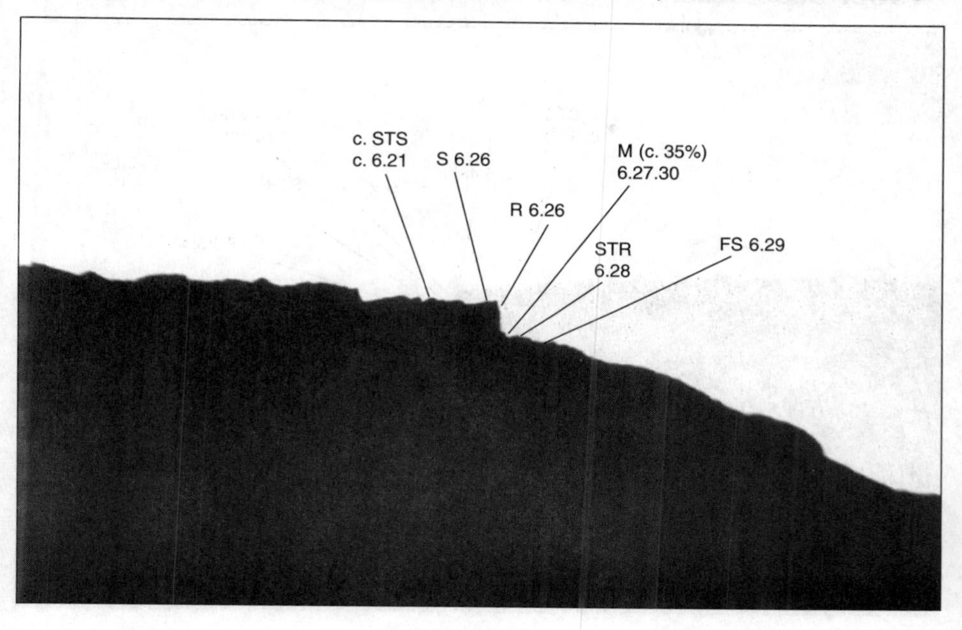

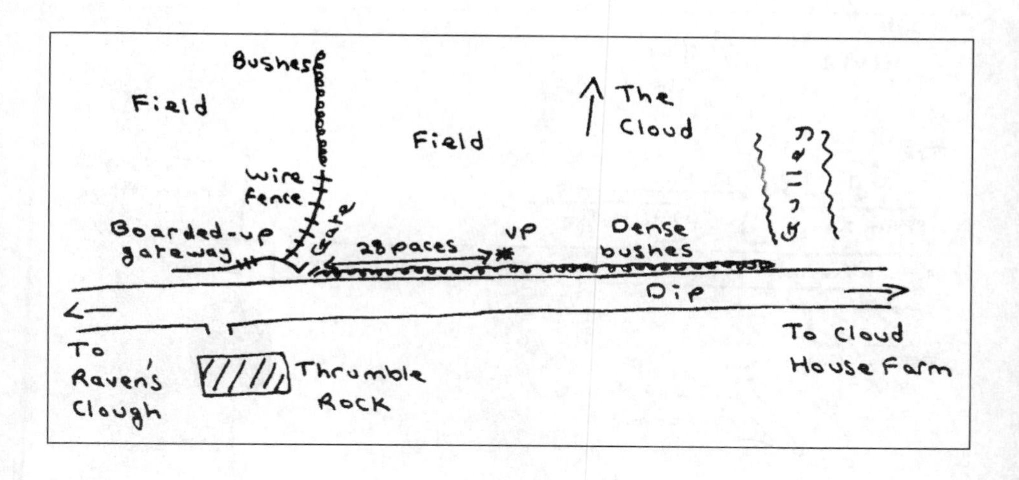

WOODHOUSE GREEN - TOFTGREEN LINE: No. 18, 23 SEPTEMBER 1995

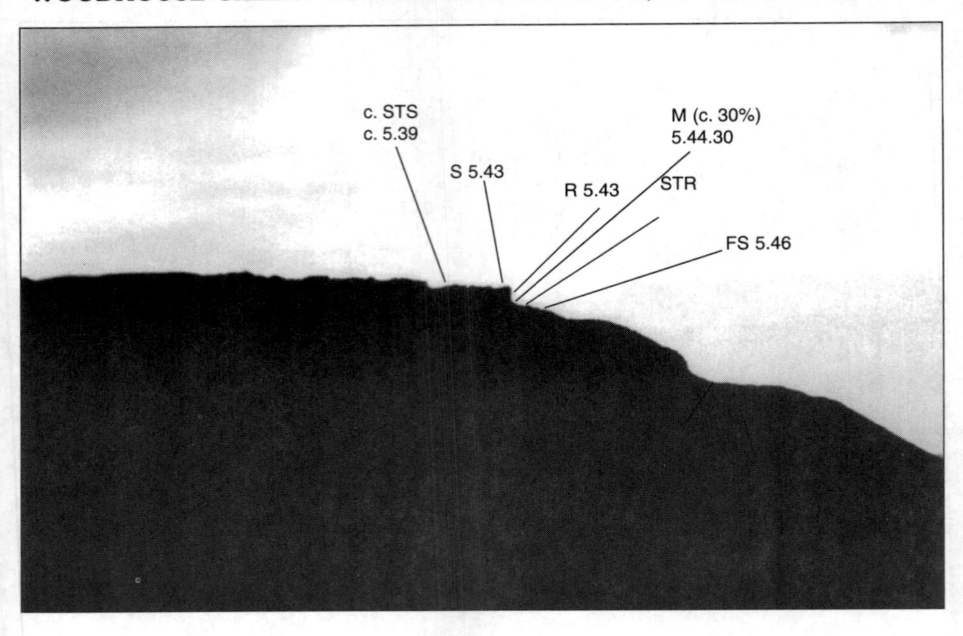

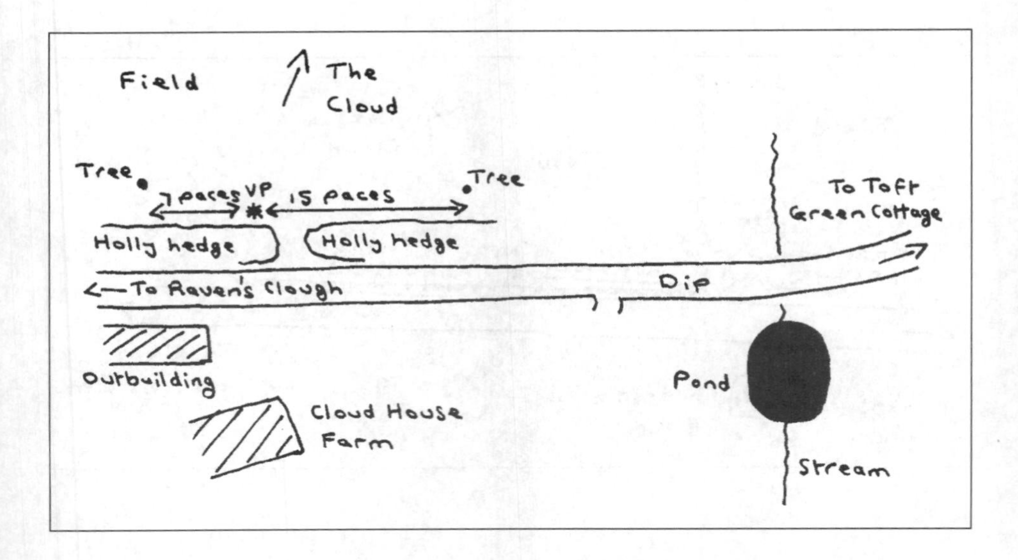

WOODHOUSE GREEN - TOFTGREEN LINE: No. 19, 5 OCTOBER 1996

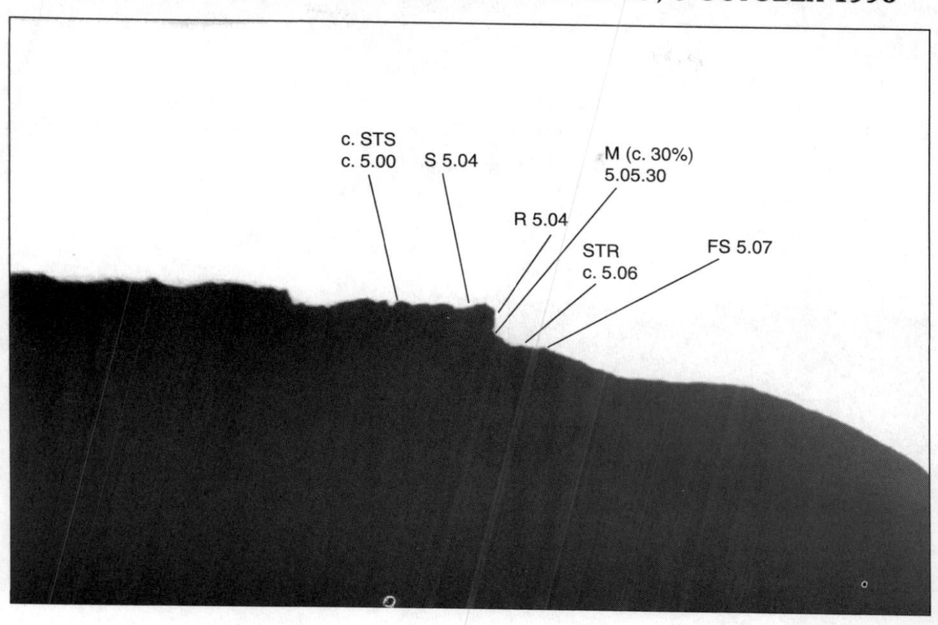

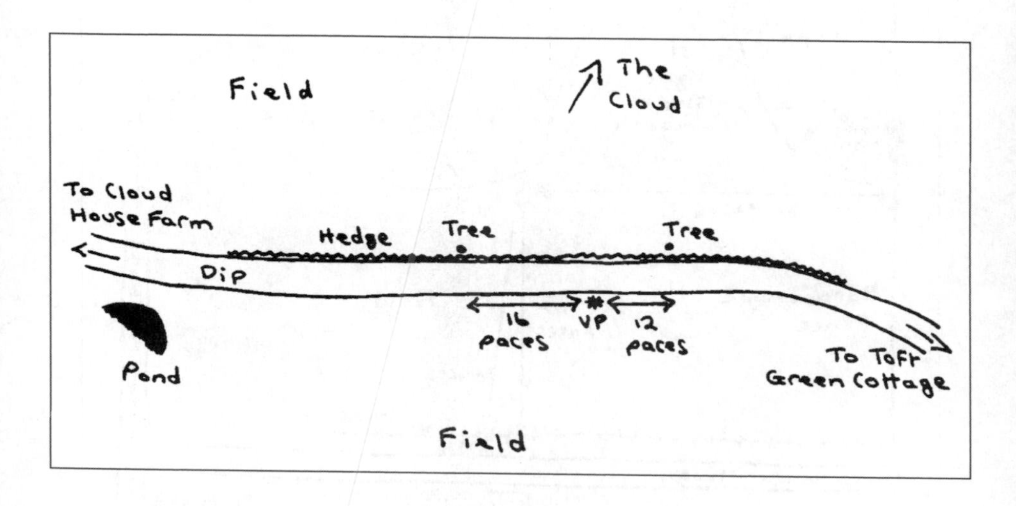

WOODHOUSE GREEN - TOFTGREEN LINE: No. 20, 21 OCTOBER 1995

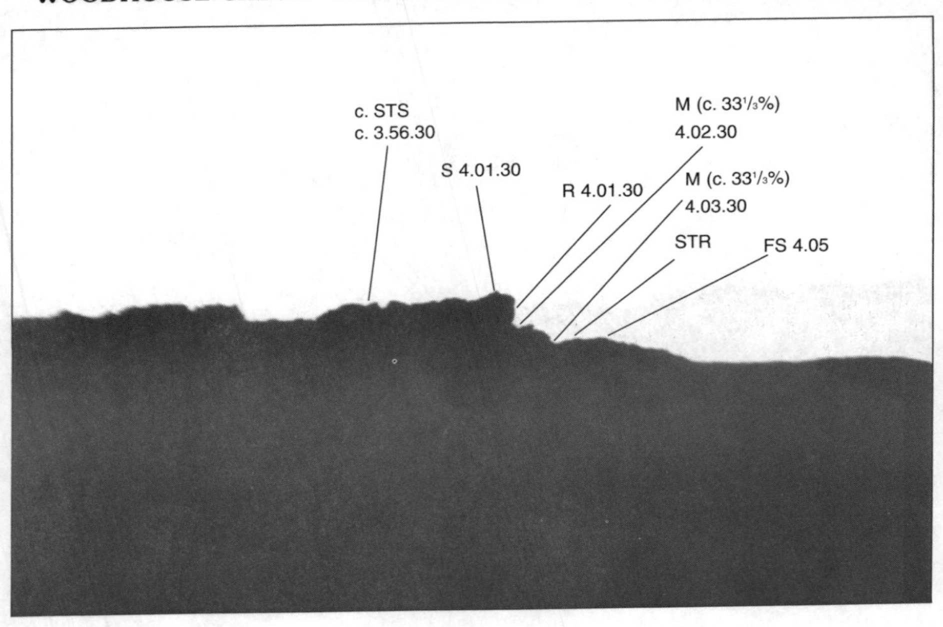

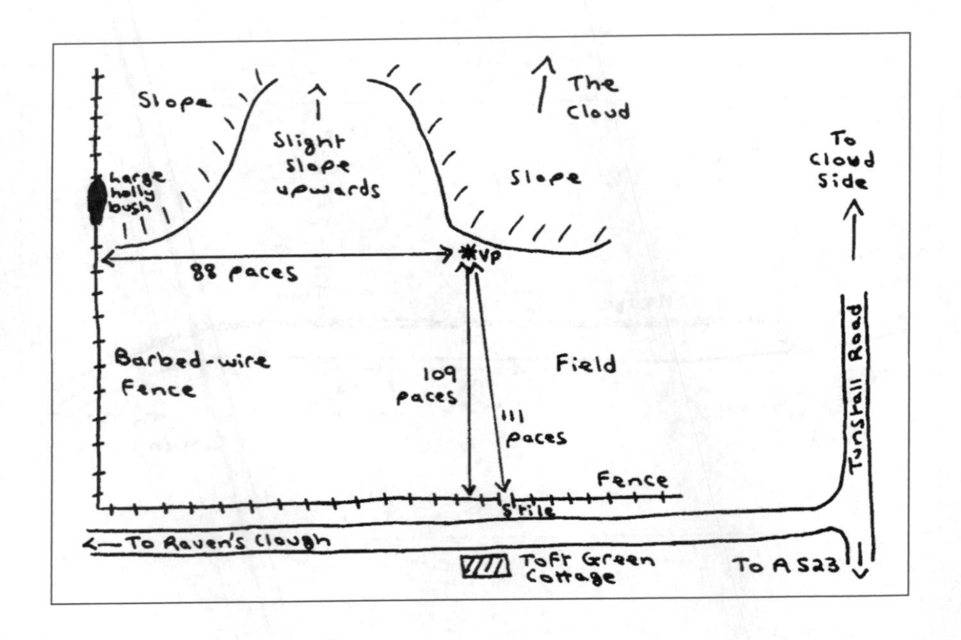

WOODHOUSE GREEN - TOFTGREEN LINE: No. 21, 5 NOVEMBER 1995

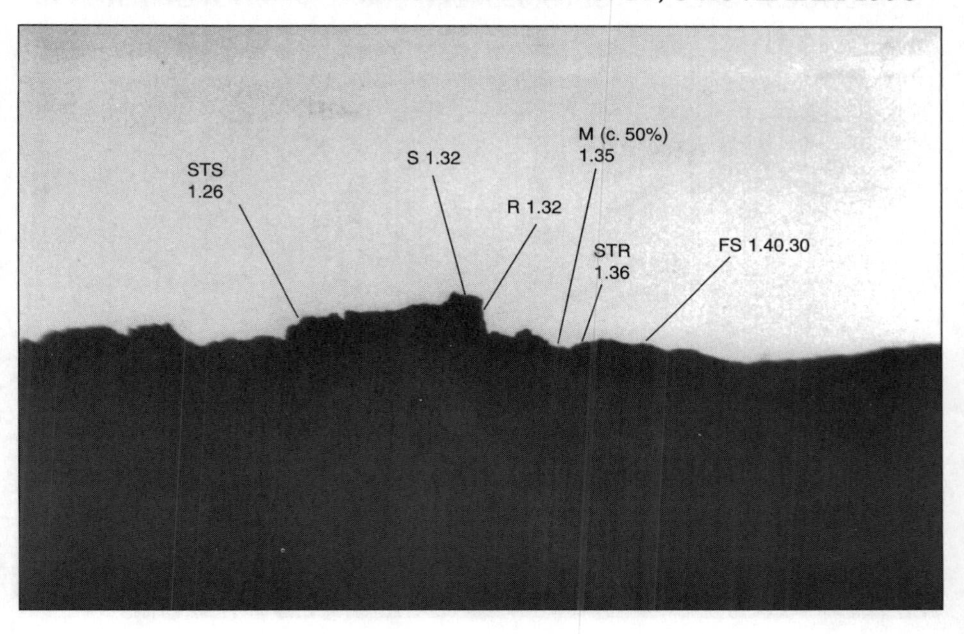

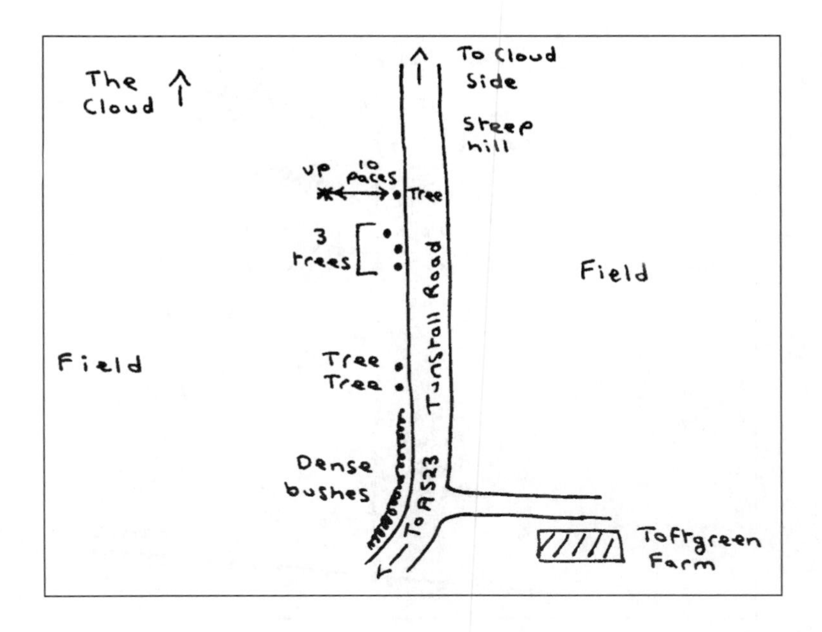

WOODHOUSE GREEN - TOFTGREEN LINE: No. 22, 19 NOVEMBER 1999

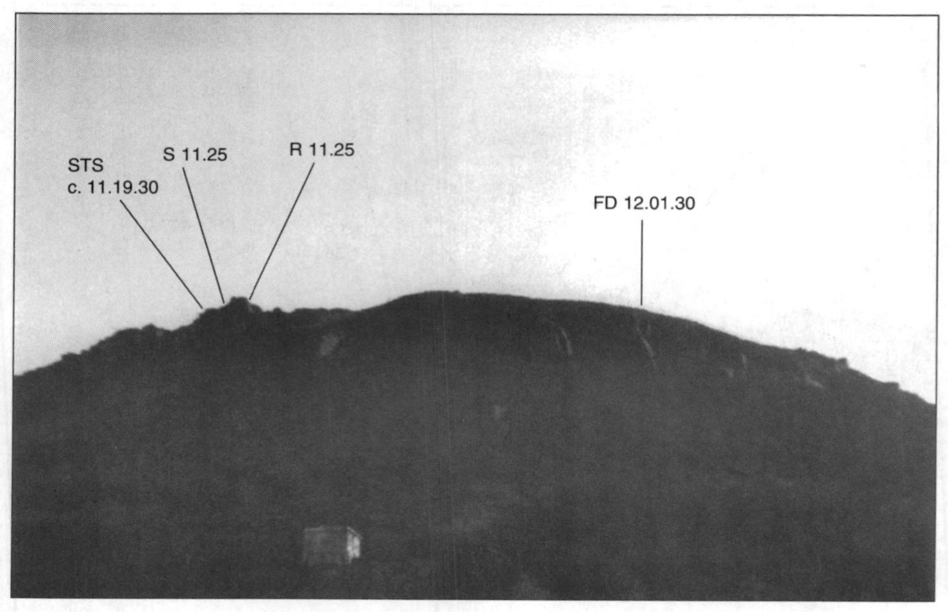

A second sunrise!

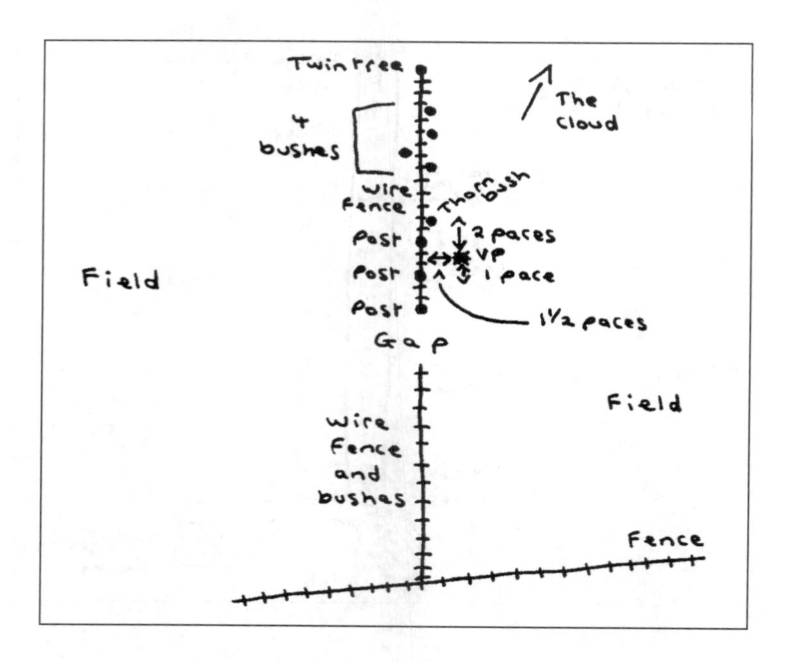

WOODHOUSE GREEN - TOFTGREEN LINE: No. 23, 4 DECEMBER 1998

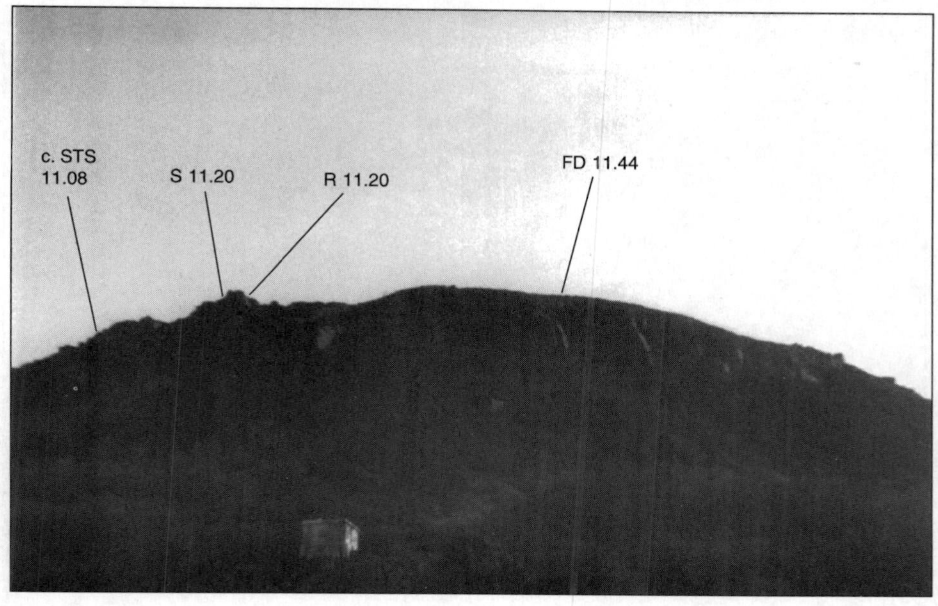

A second sunrise!

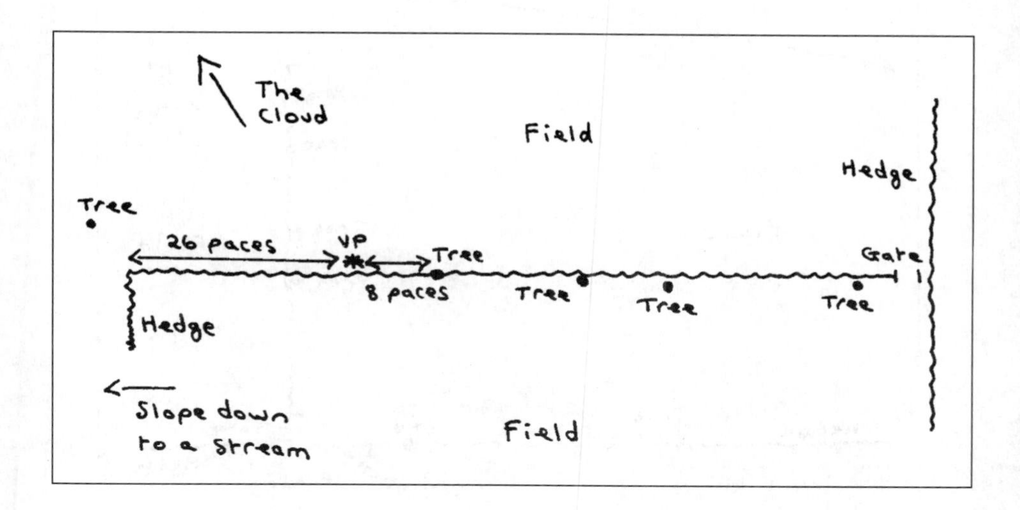

WOODHOUSE GREEN - TOFTGREEN LINE: No. 24, 21 DECEMBER 1996

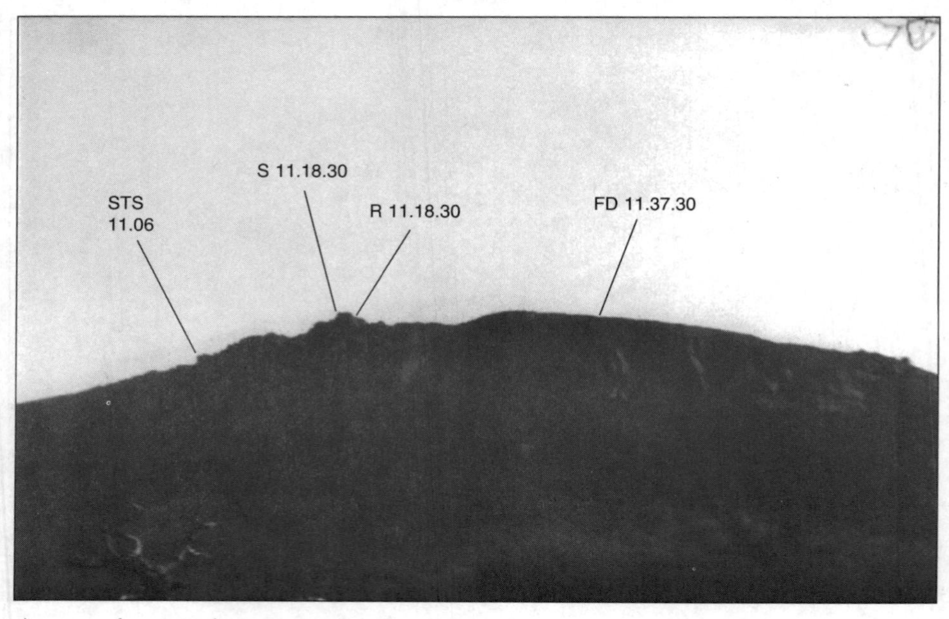

A second sunrise!

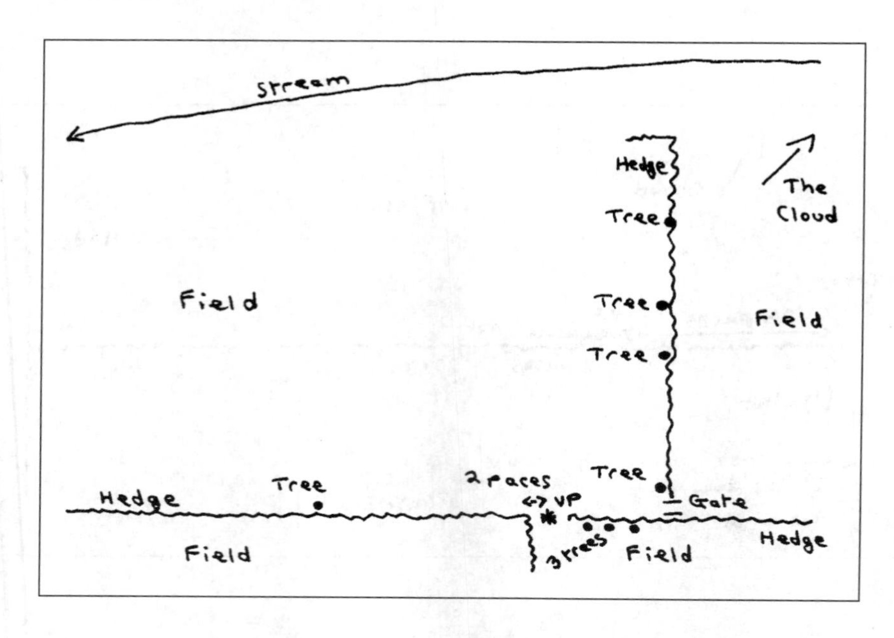

CLOUD SIDE LINE: No. 1, 9 FEBRUARY 1999

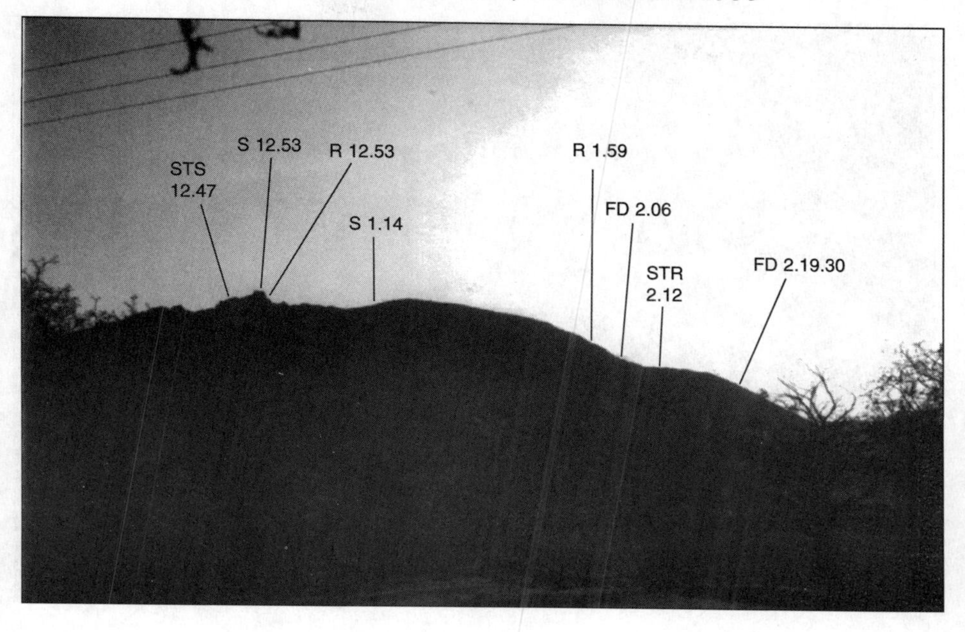

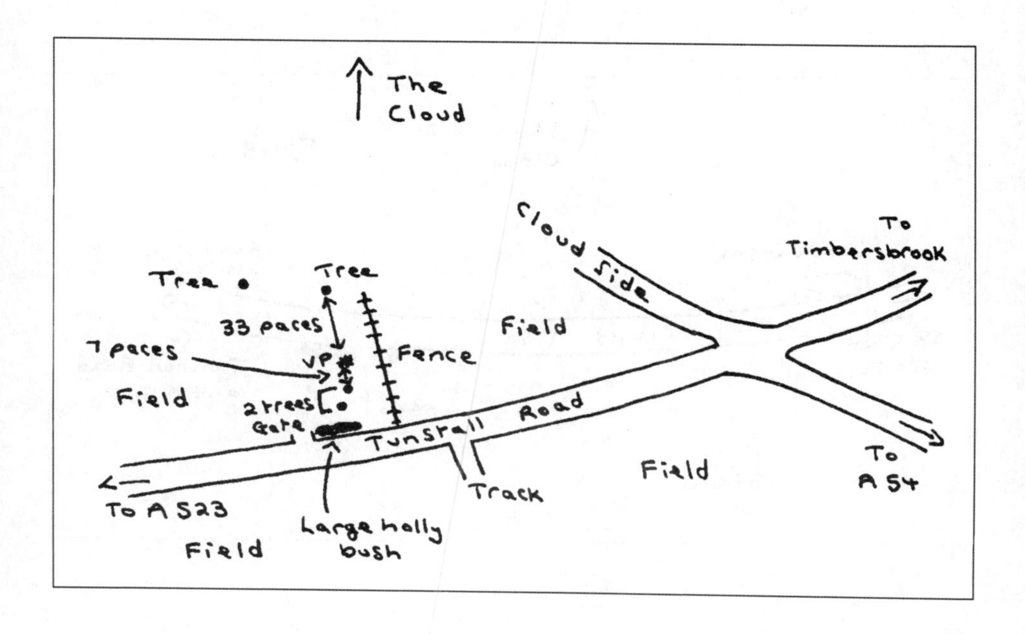

CLOUD SIDE LINE: No. 2, 23 FEBRUARY 1999

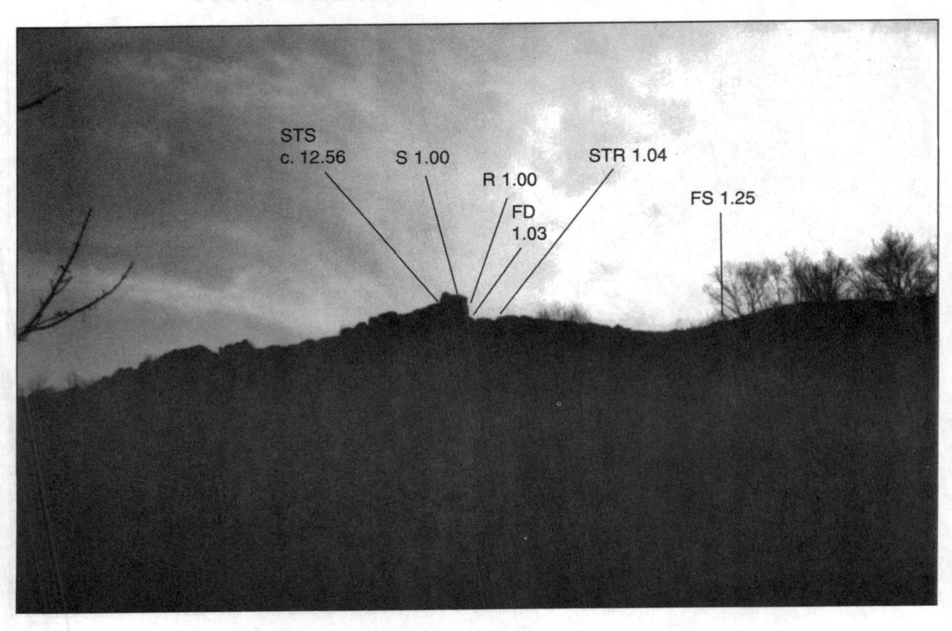

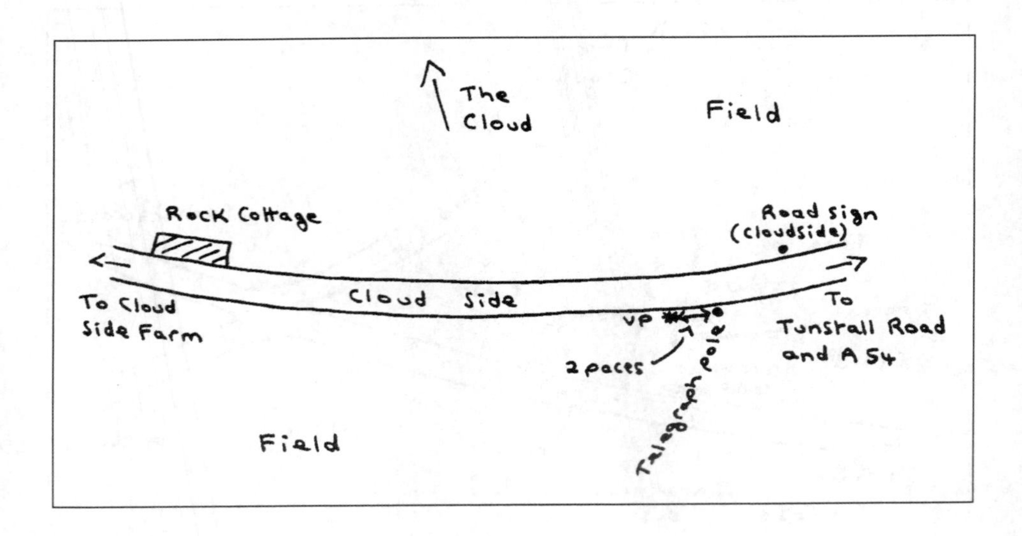

CLOUD SIDE LINE: No. 3, 8 MARCH 1997

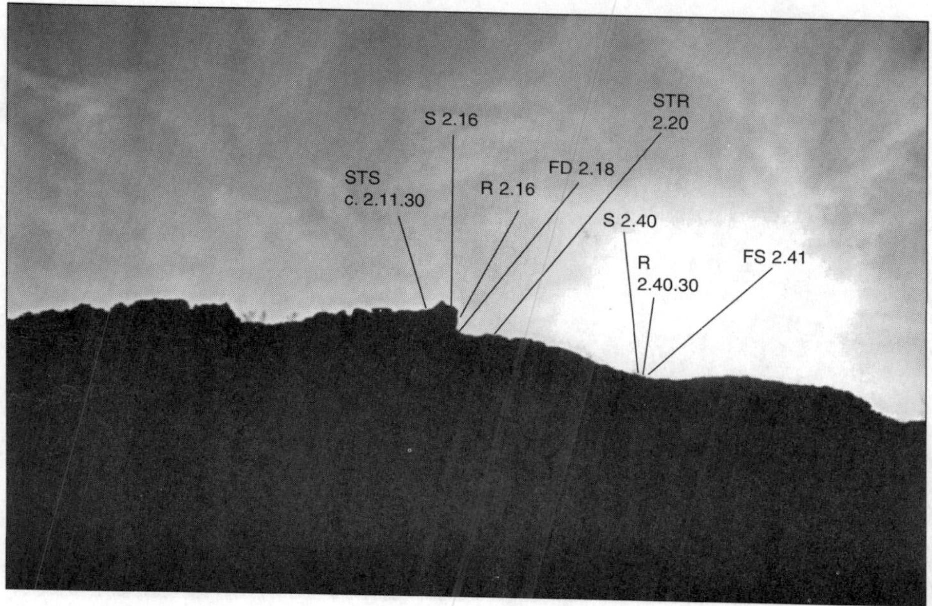

A triple sunset!

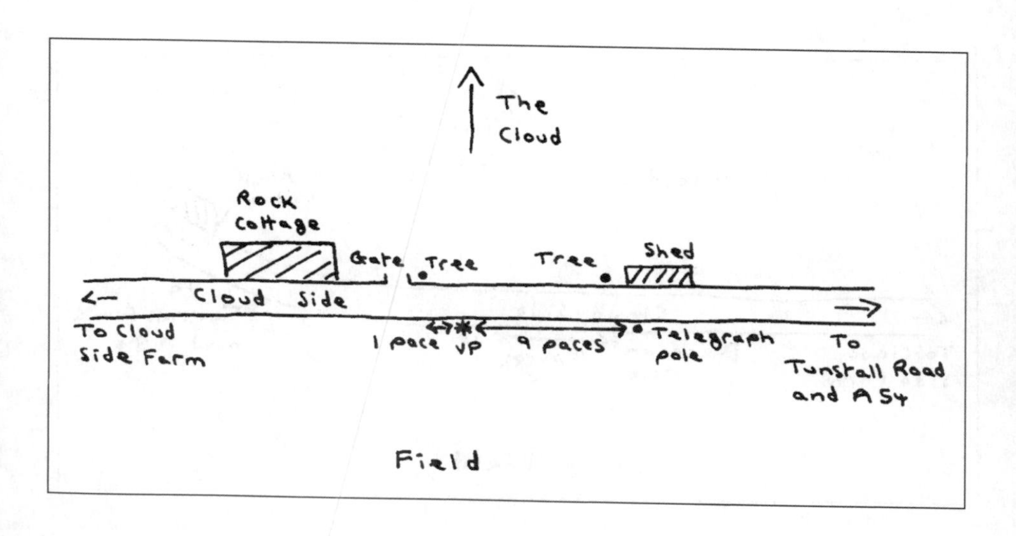

CLOUD SIDE LINE: No. 4, 18 MARCH 2000

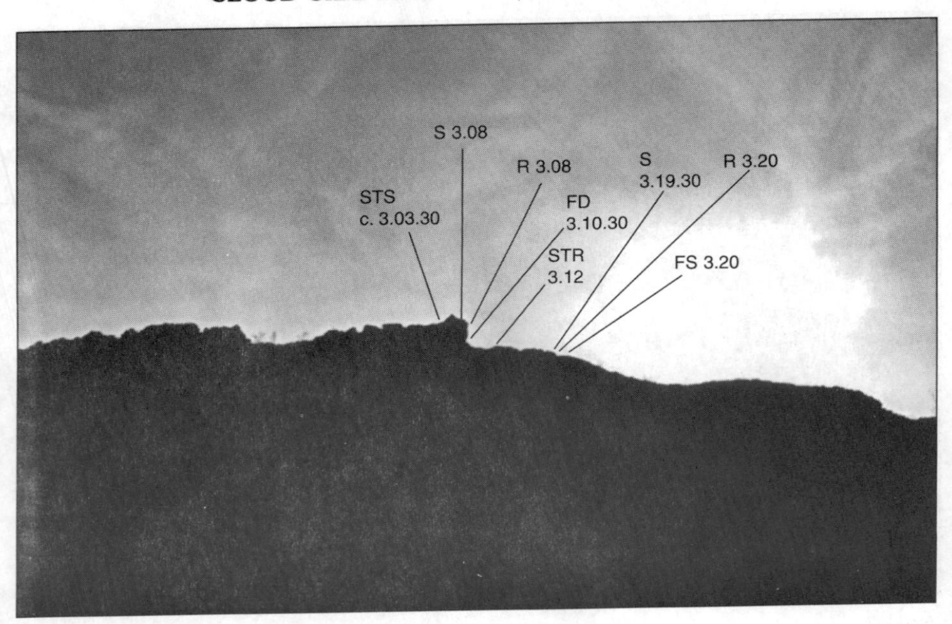

A triple sunset!

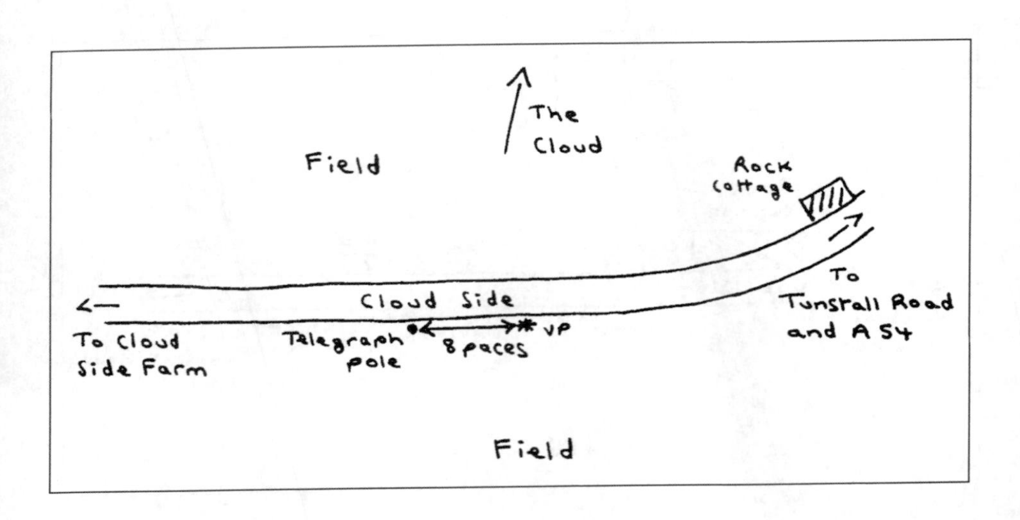

CLOUD SIDE LINE: No. 5, 9 APRIL 1992

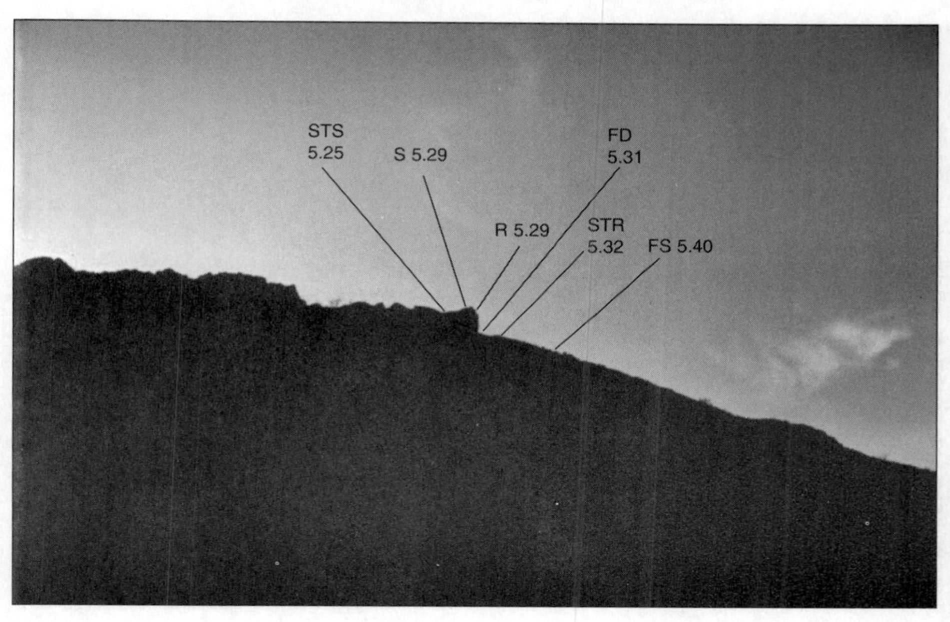

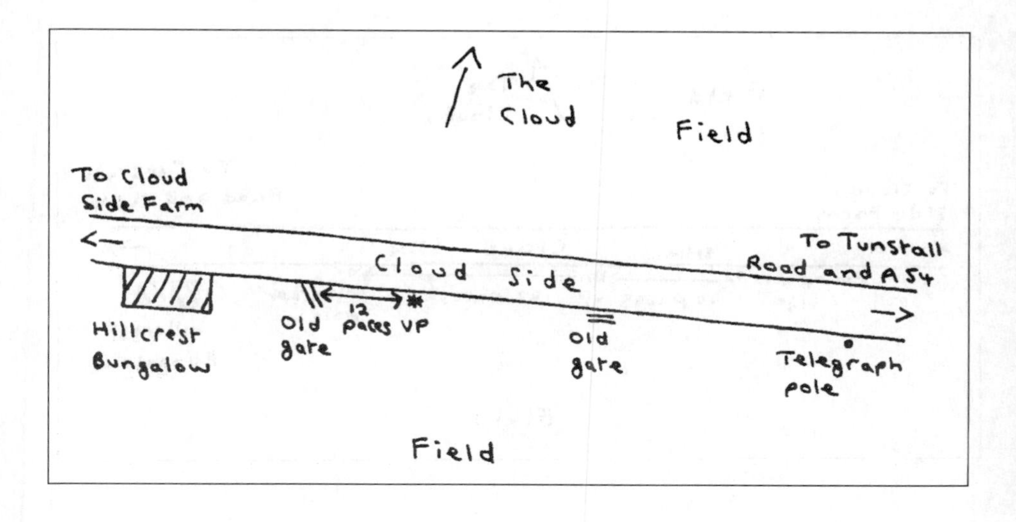

CLOUD SIDE LINE: No. 6, 21 APRIL 1996

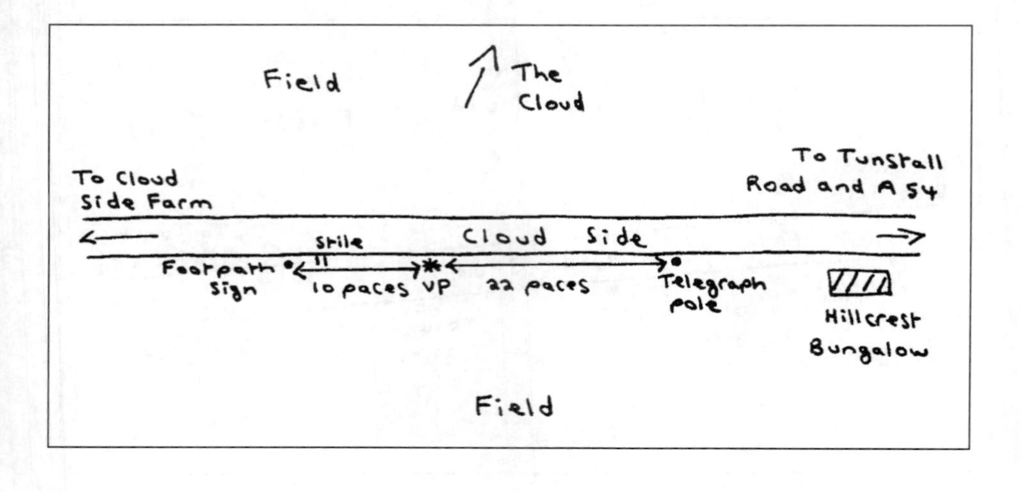

CLOUD SIDE LINE: No. 7, 3 MAY 1999

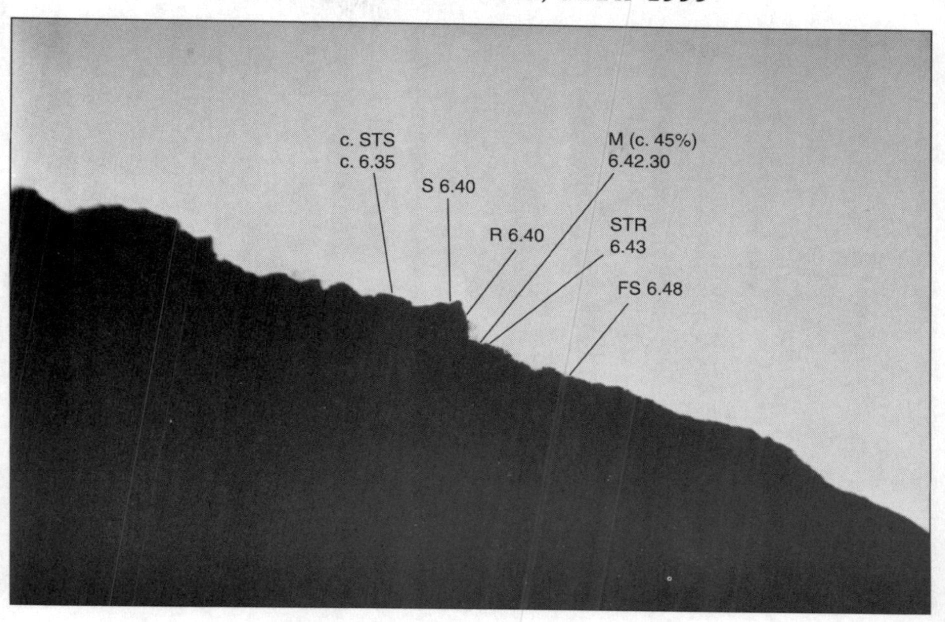

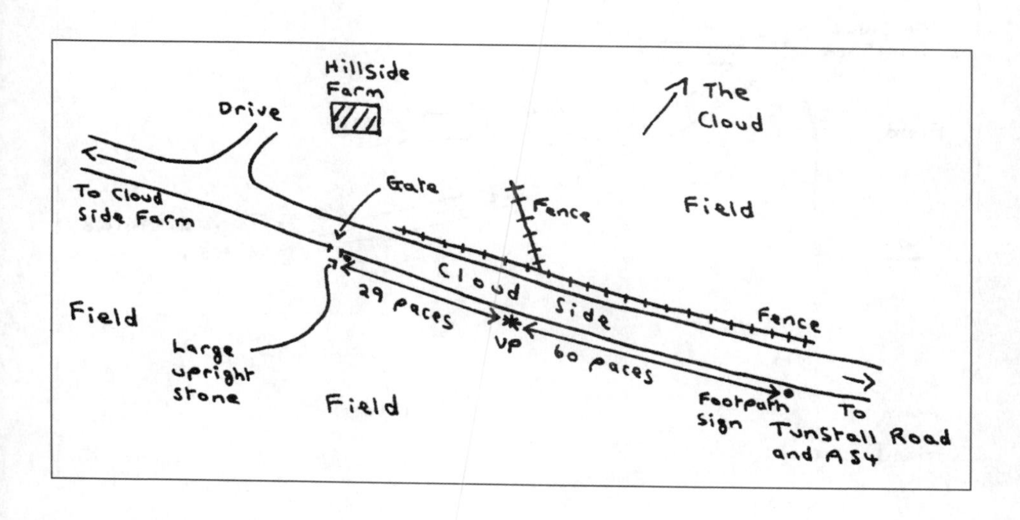

CLOUD SIDE LINE: No. 8, 24 MAY 1997

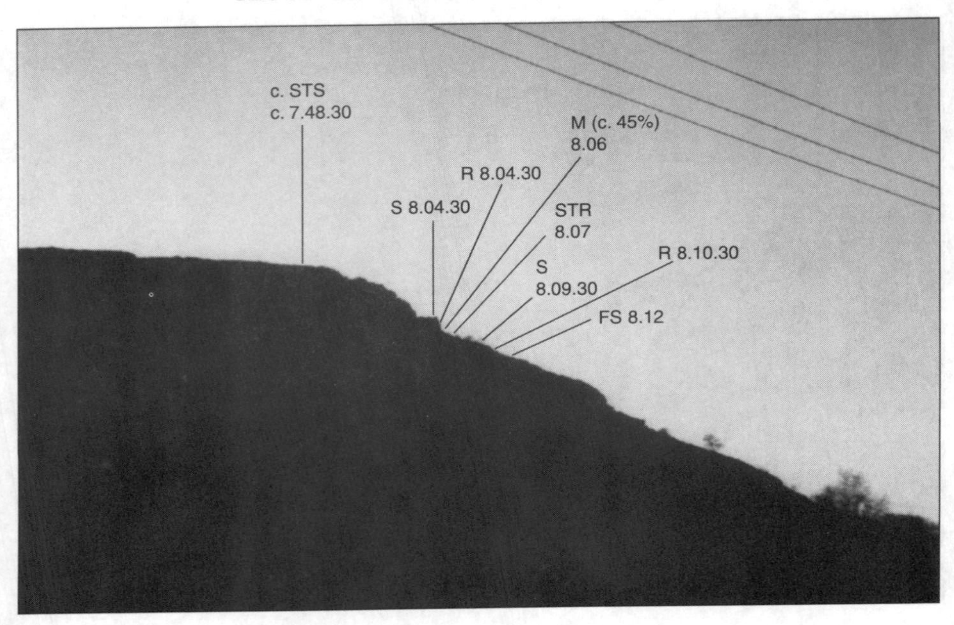

A triple sunset!

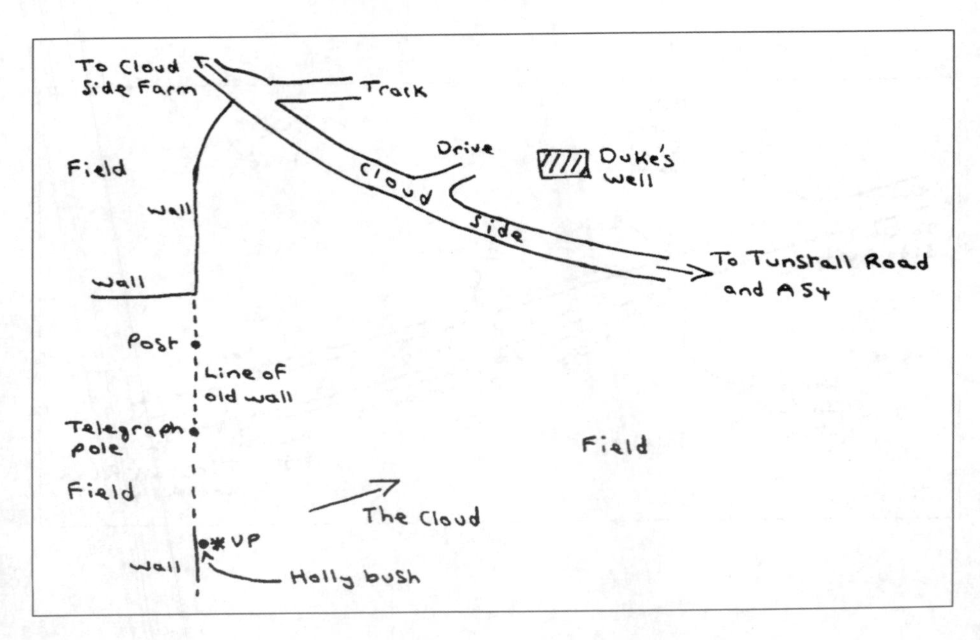

CLOUD SIDE LINE: No. 9, 8 JUNE 1999

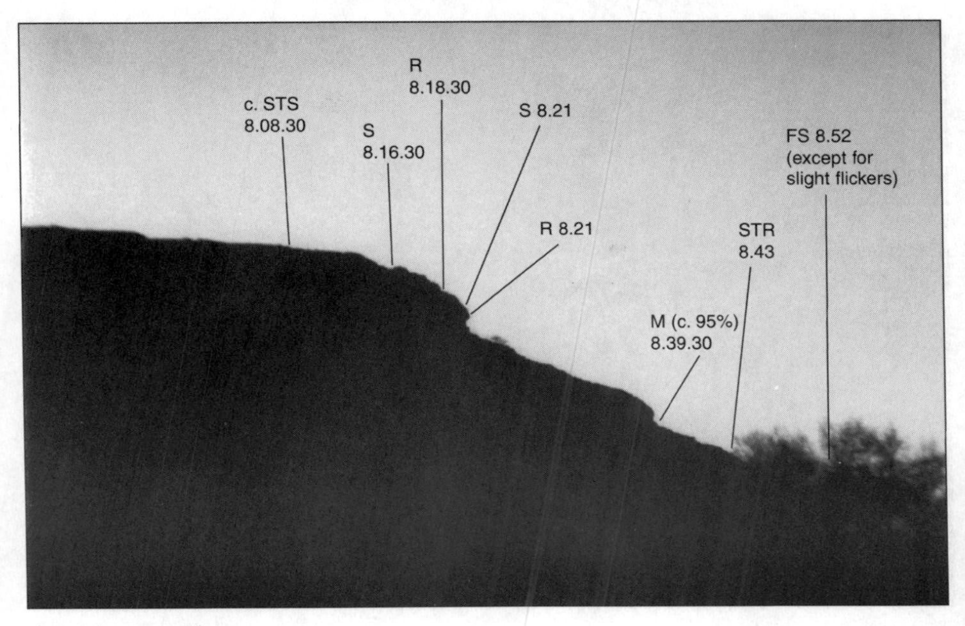

A triple sunset!

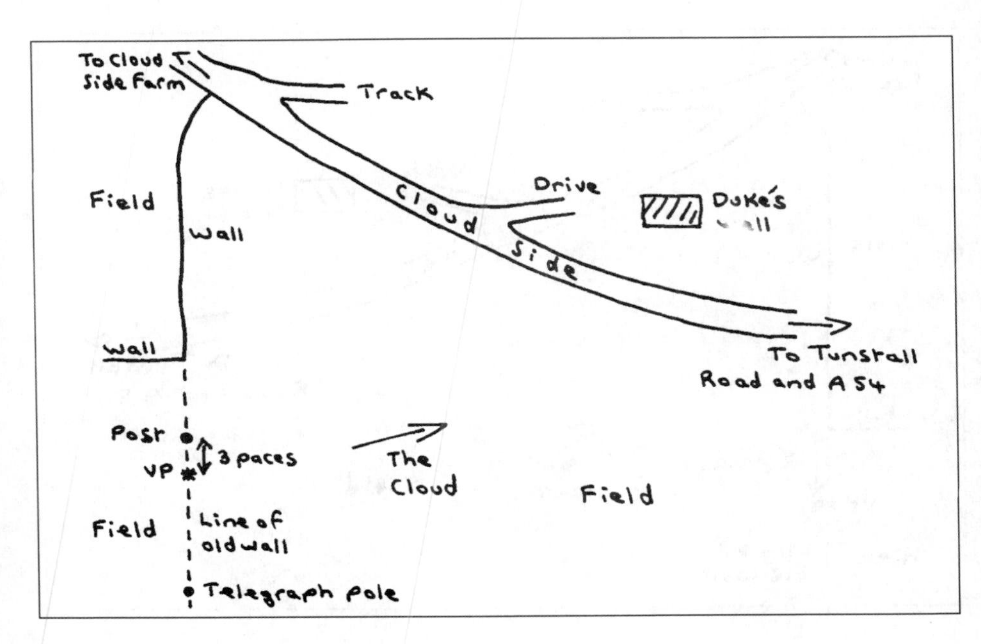

CLOUD SIDE LINE: No. 10, 21 JUNE 1998

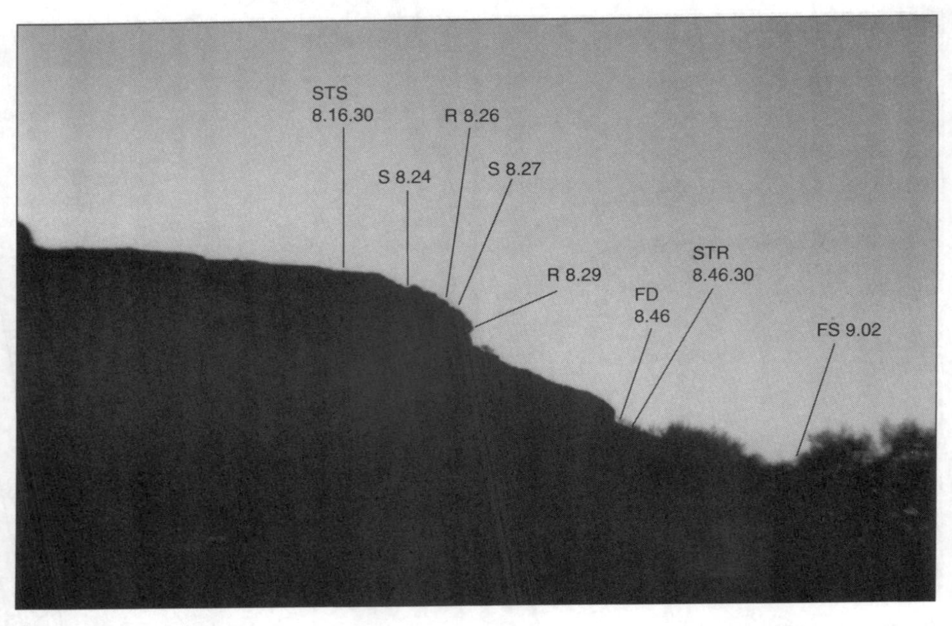

A triple sunset!

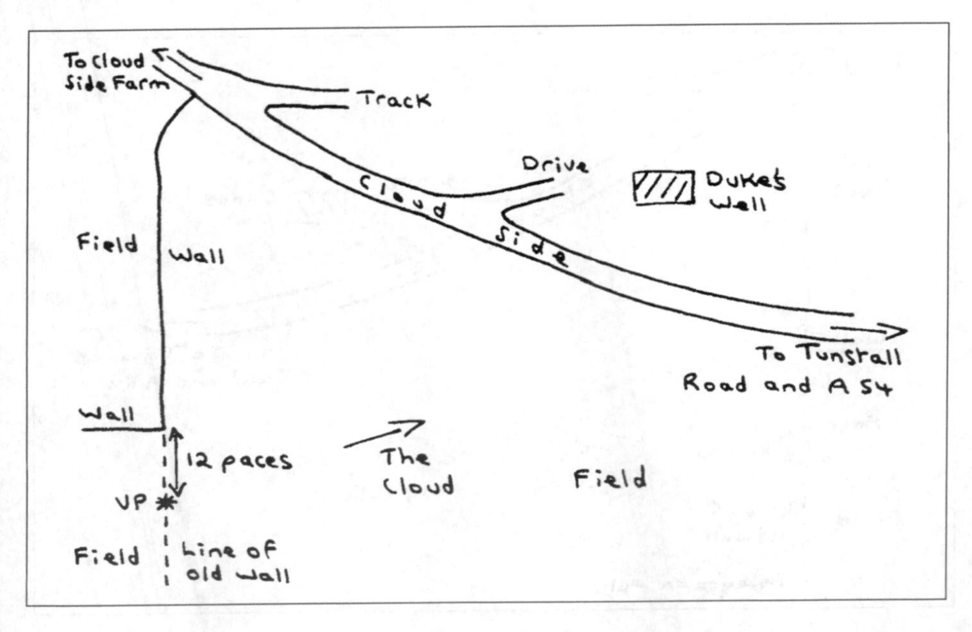

CLOUD SIDE LINE: No. 11, 6 JULY 1997

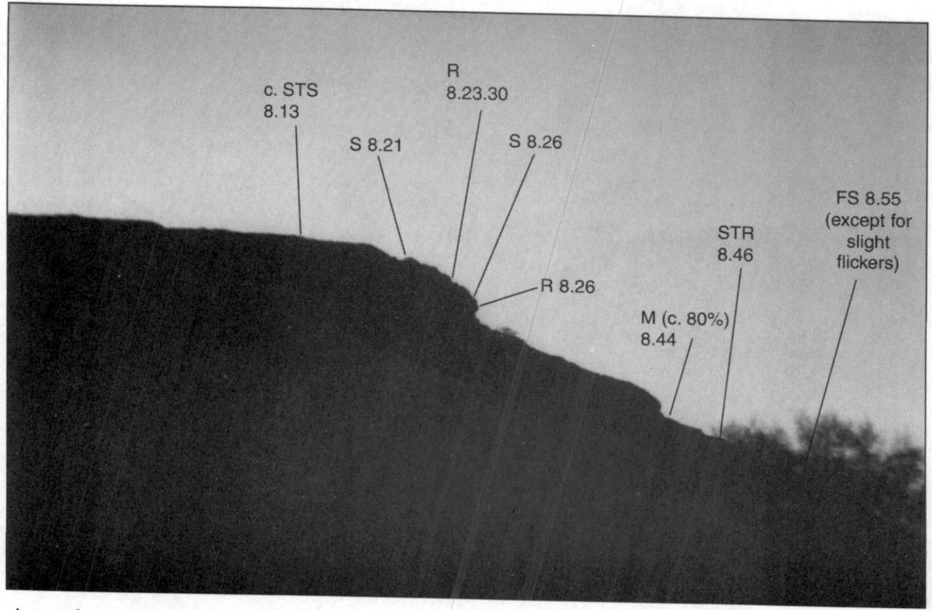

A triple sunset!

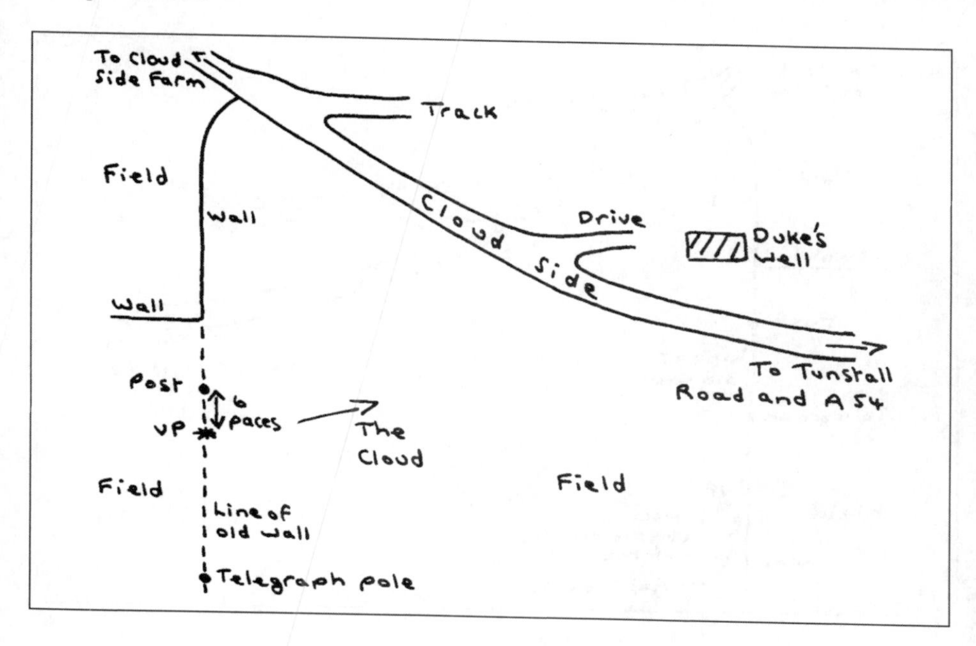

CLOUD SIDE LINE: No. 12, 18 JULY 1997

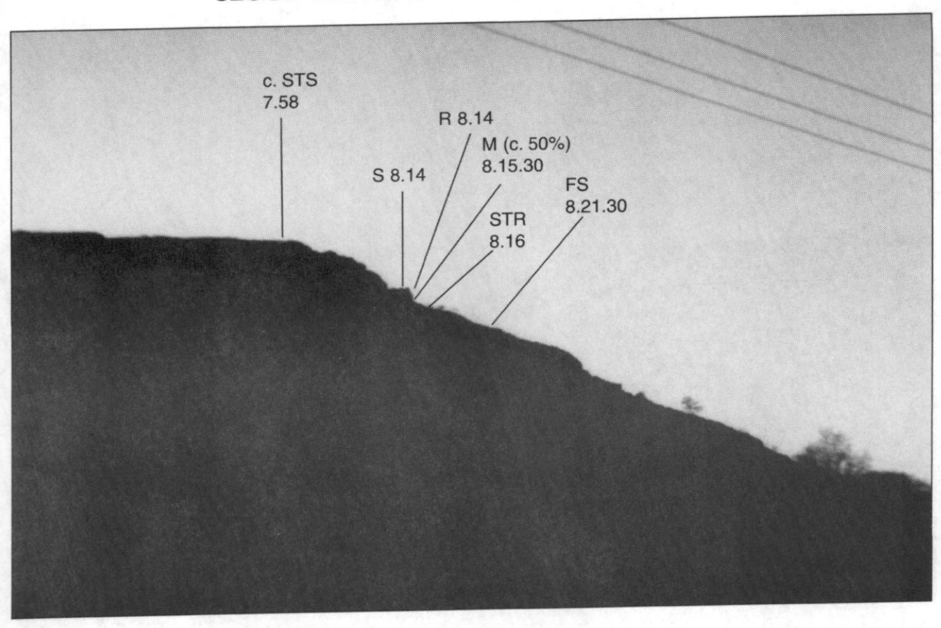

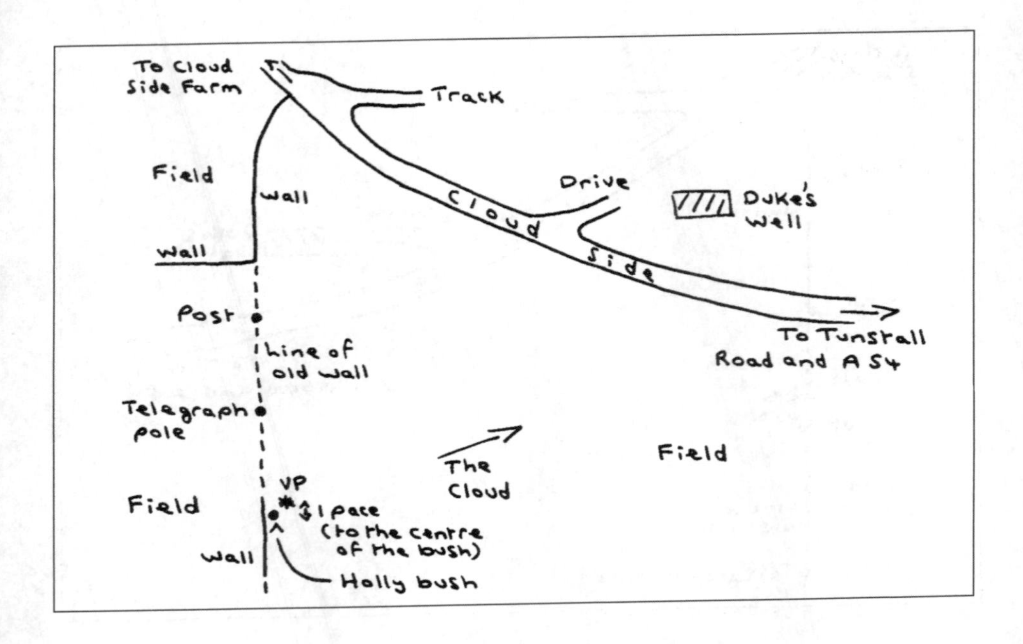

CLOUD SIDE LINE: No. 13, 6 AUGUST 1992

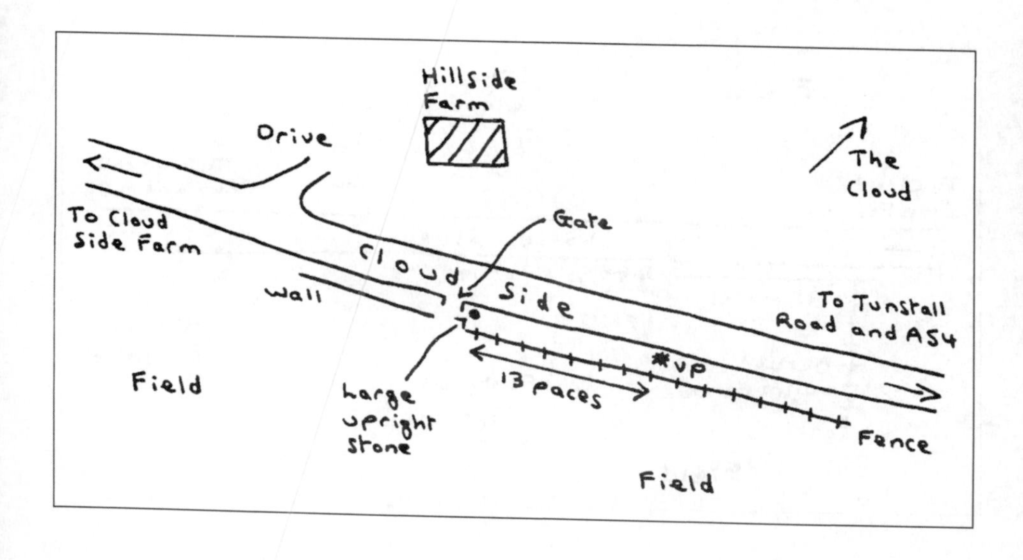

CLOUD SIDE LINE: No. 14, 19 AUGUST 1999

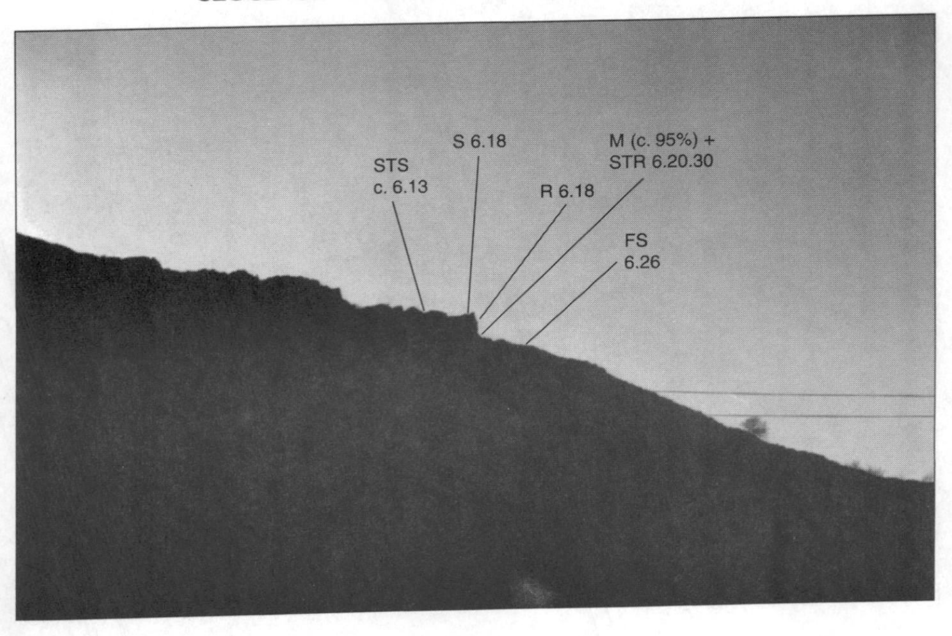

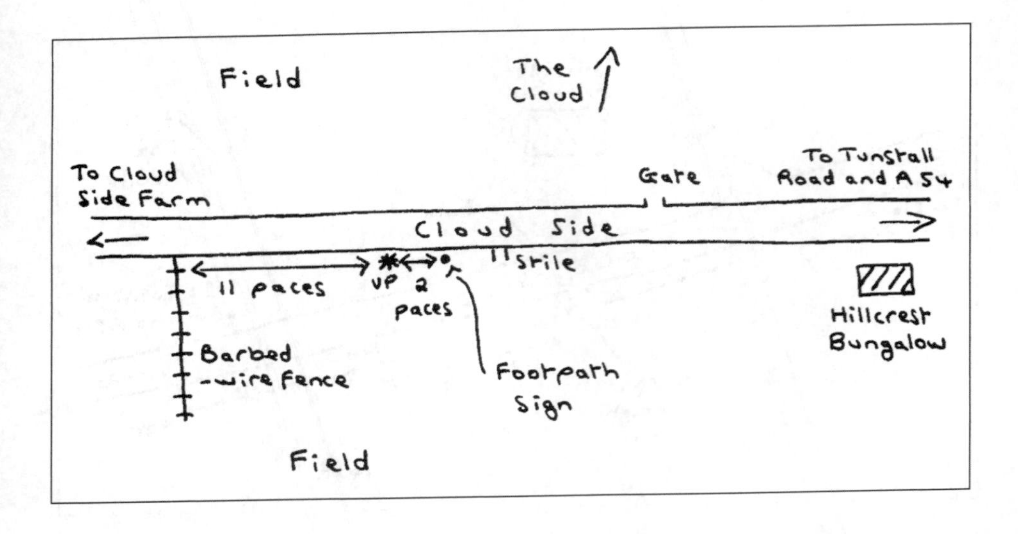

CLOUD SIDE LINE: No. 15, 3 SEPTEMBER 1999

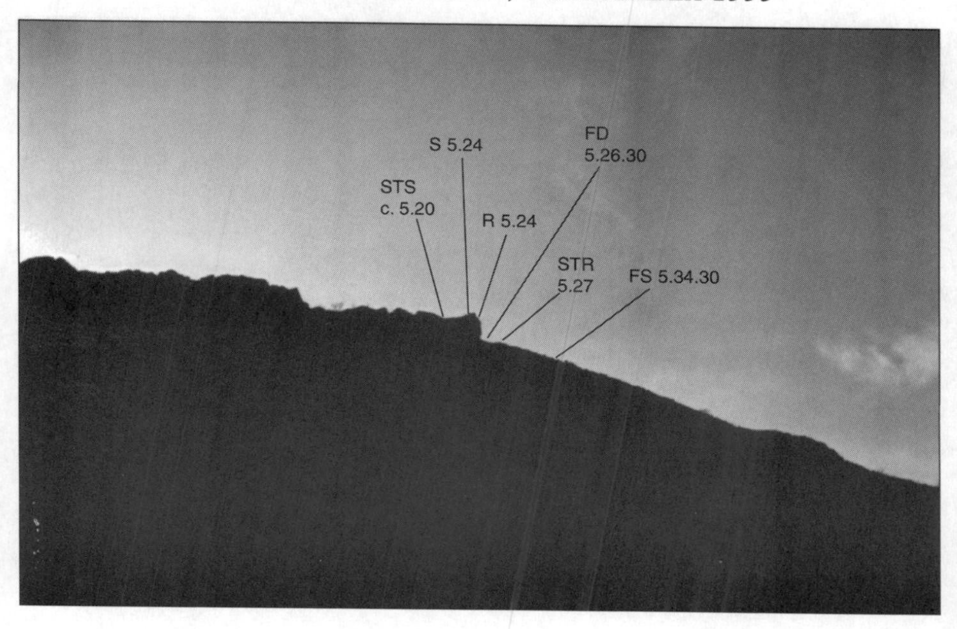

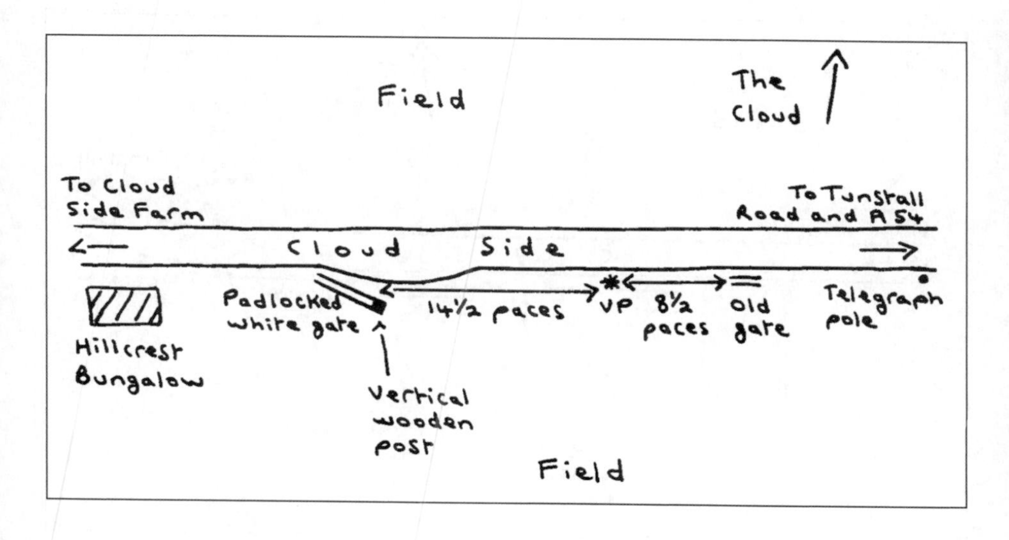

CLOUD SIDE LINE: No. 16, 21 SEPTEMBER 1999

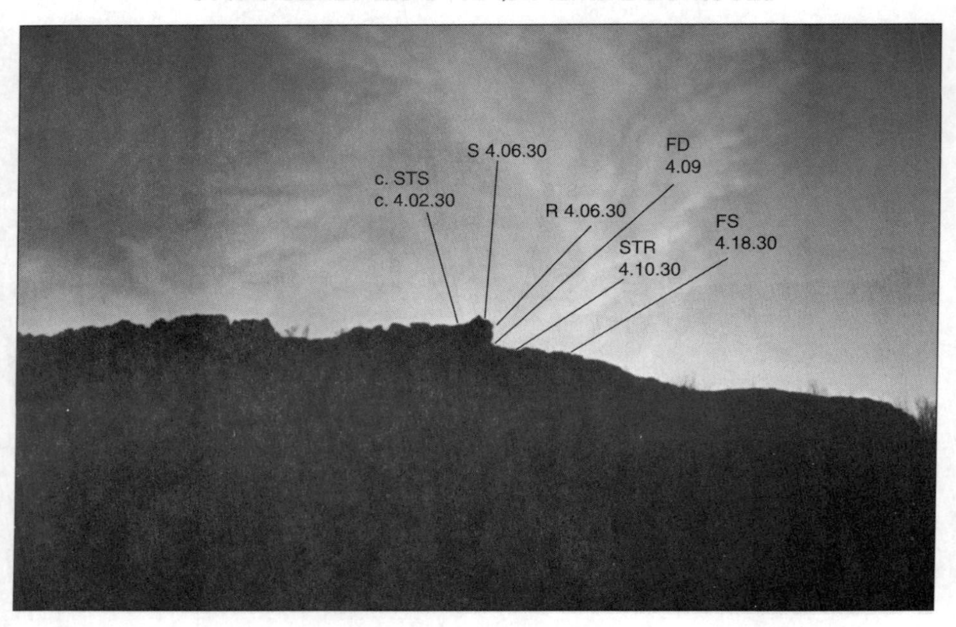

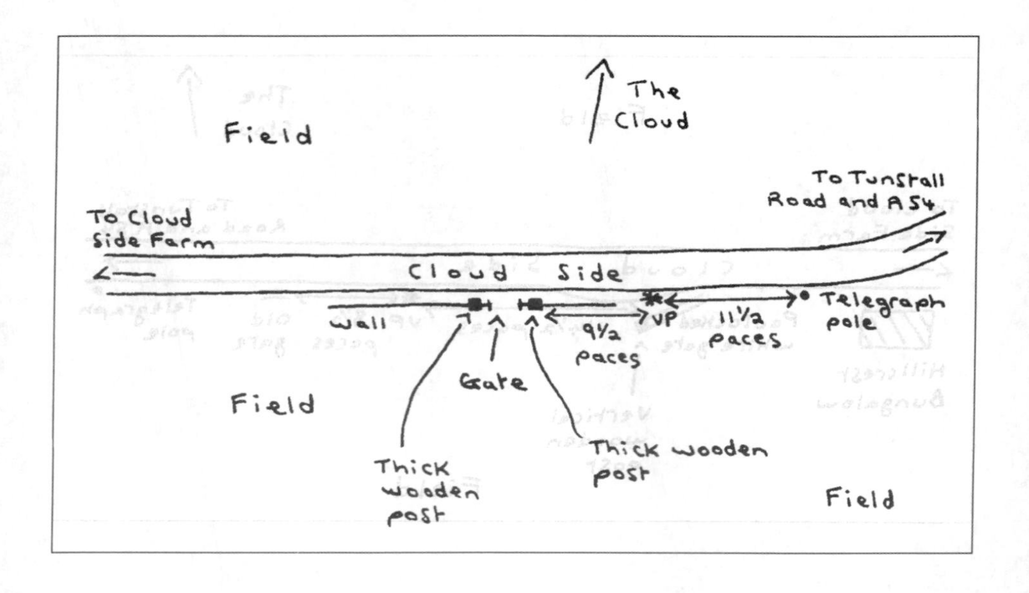

CLOUD SIDE LINE: No. 17, 5 0CTOBER 1995

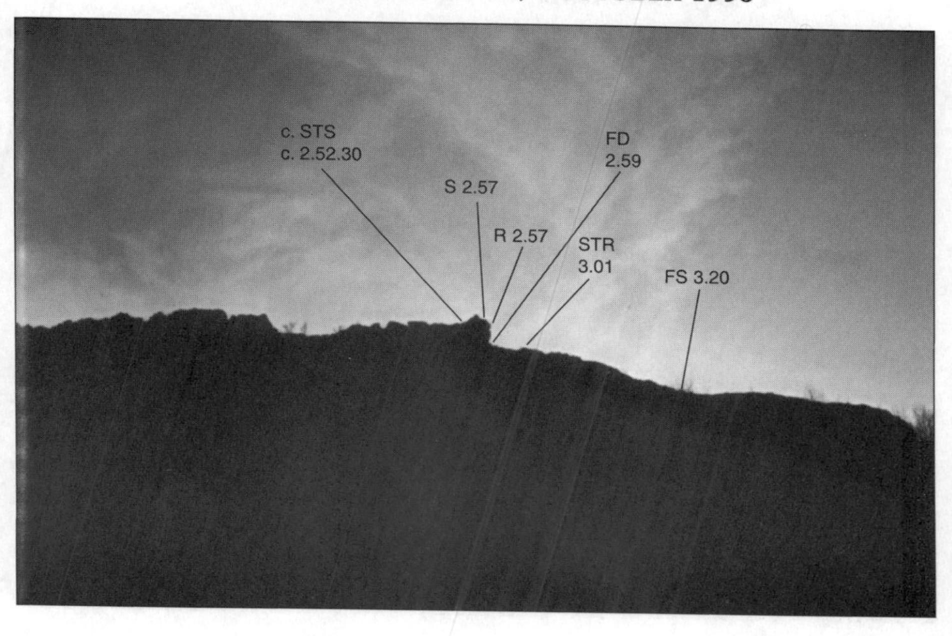

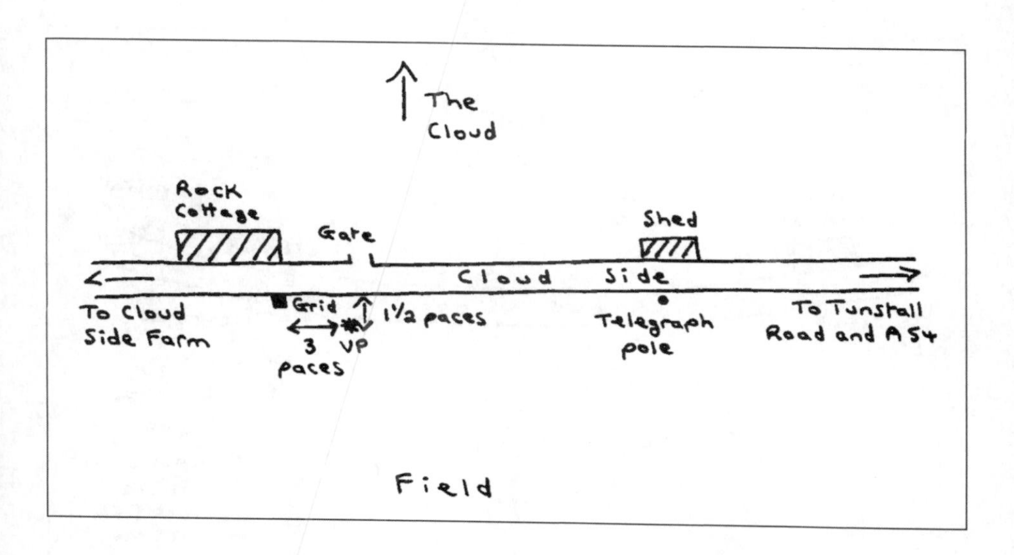

CLOUD SIDE LINE: No. 18, 22 OCTOBER 1995

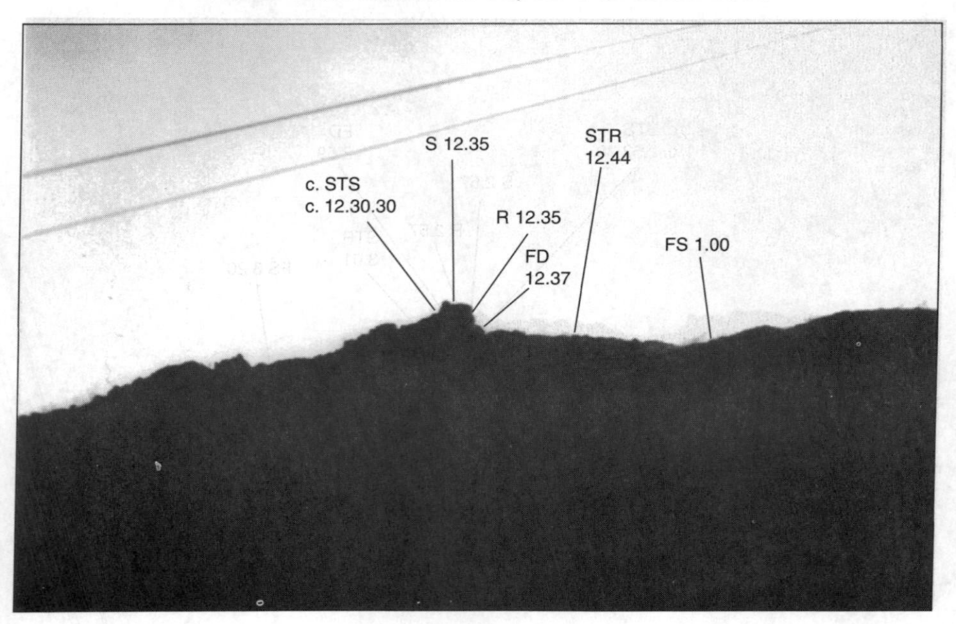

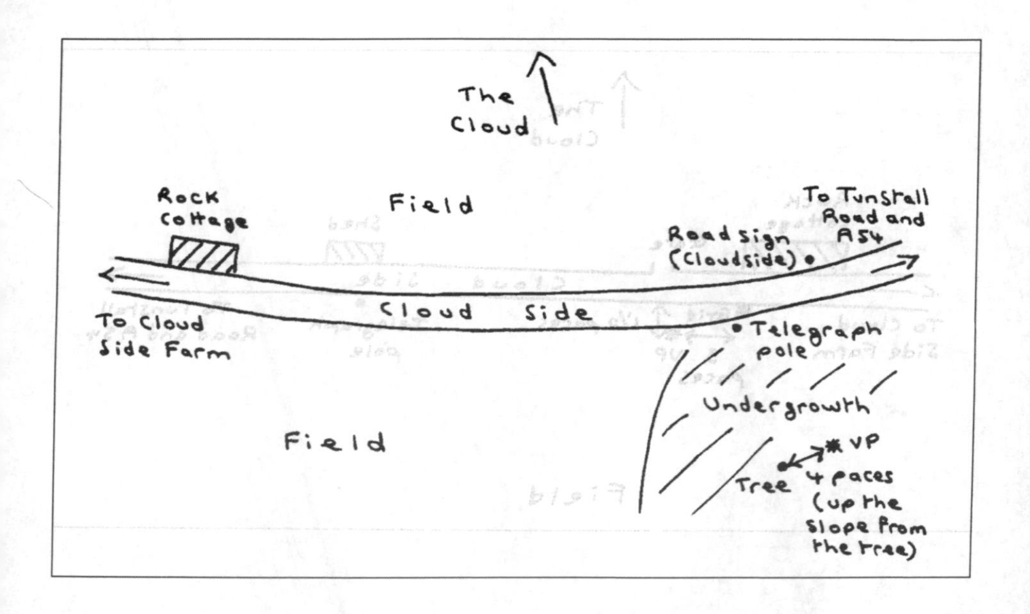

CLOUD SIDE LINE: No. 19, 6 NOVEMBER 1999

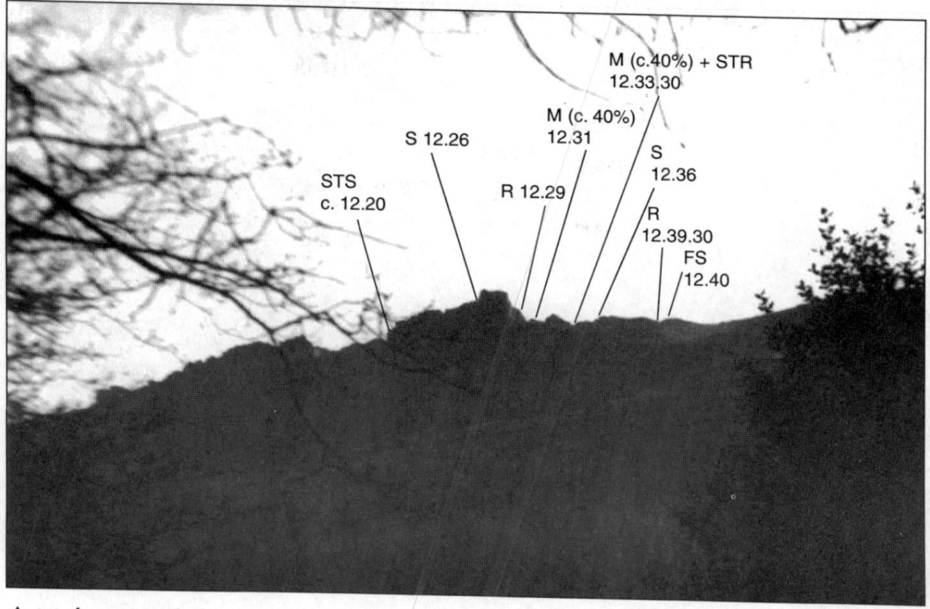

A triple sunset!

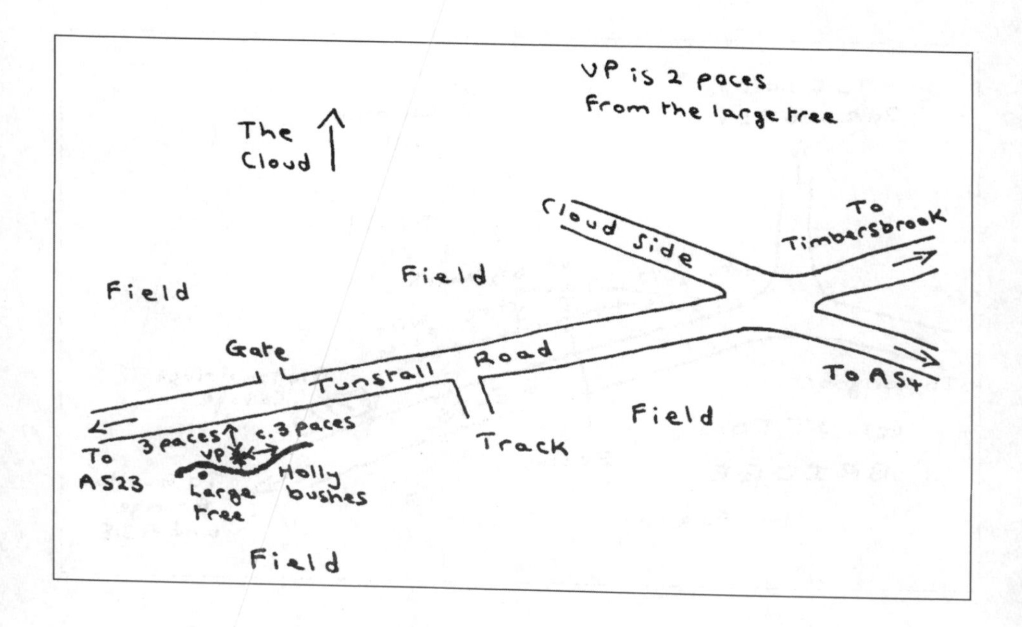

CHROME HILL: 22 JUNE 2001

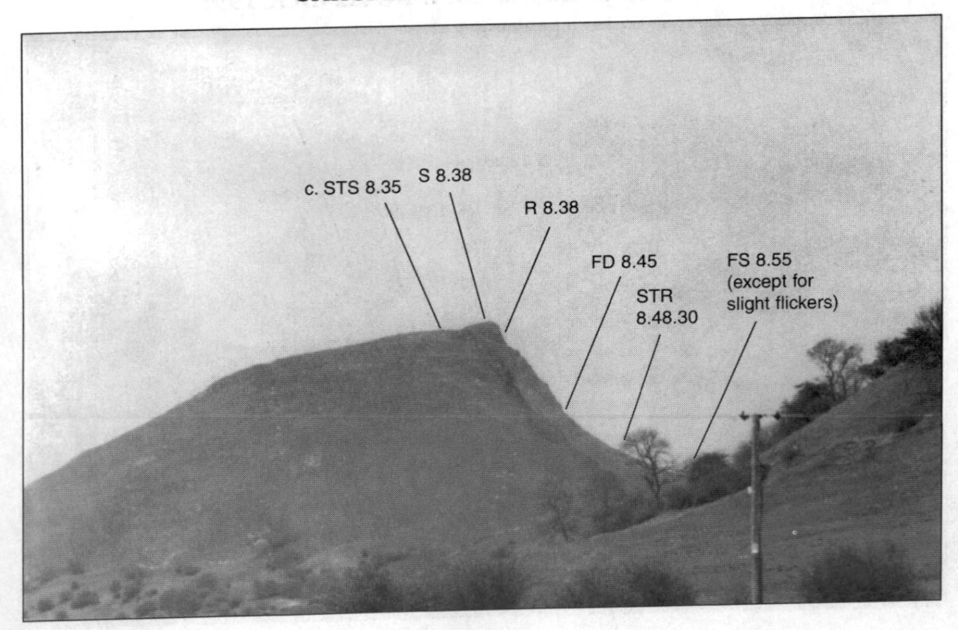

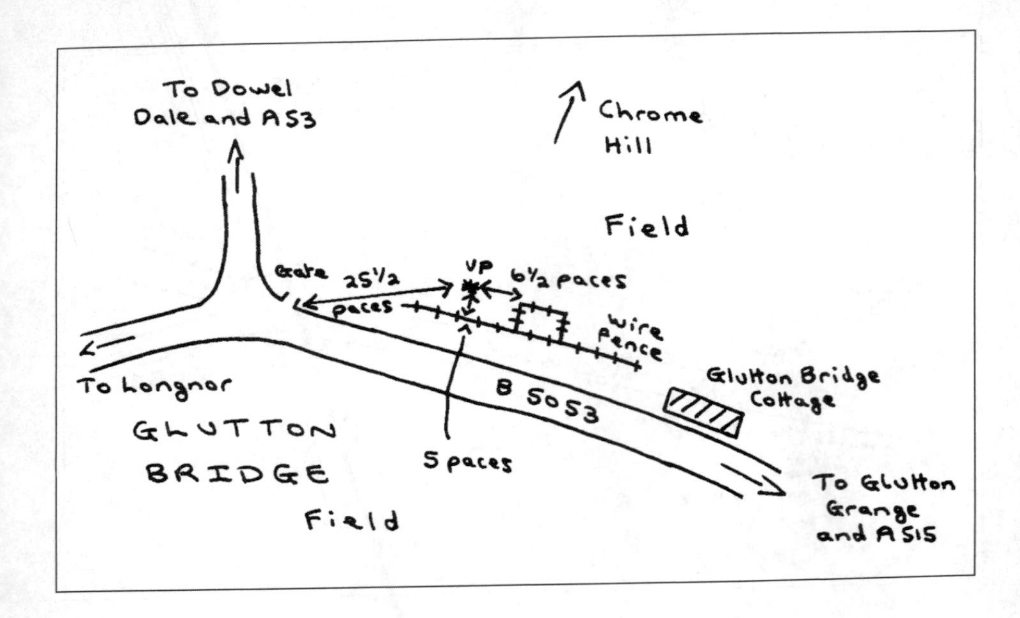

PARKHOUSE HILL: No. 1, 3 APRIL 1999

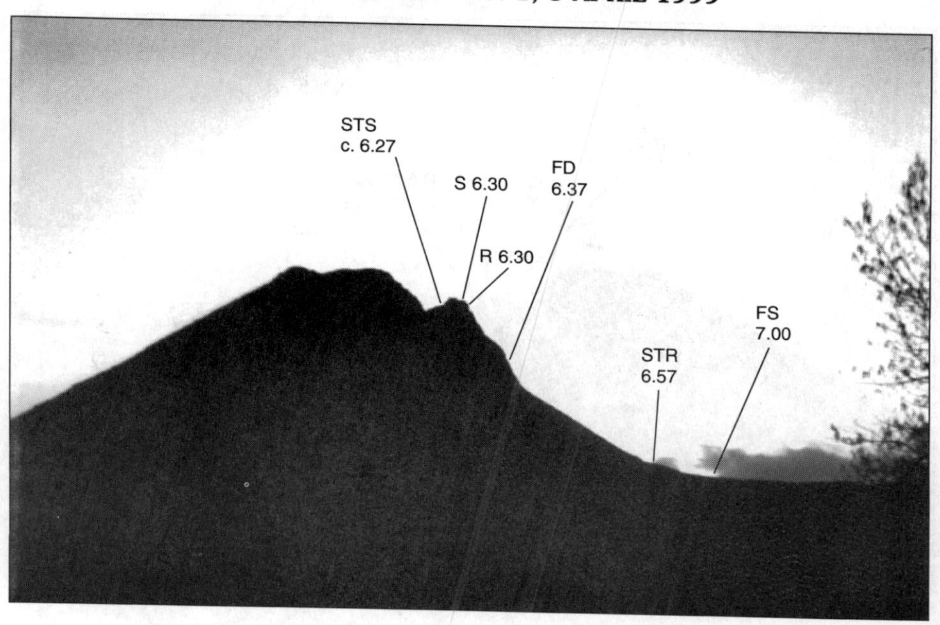

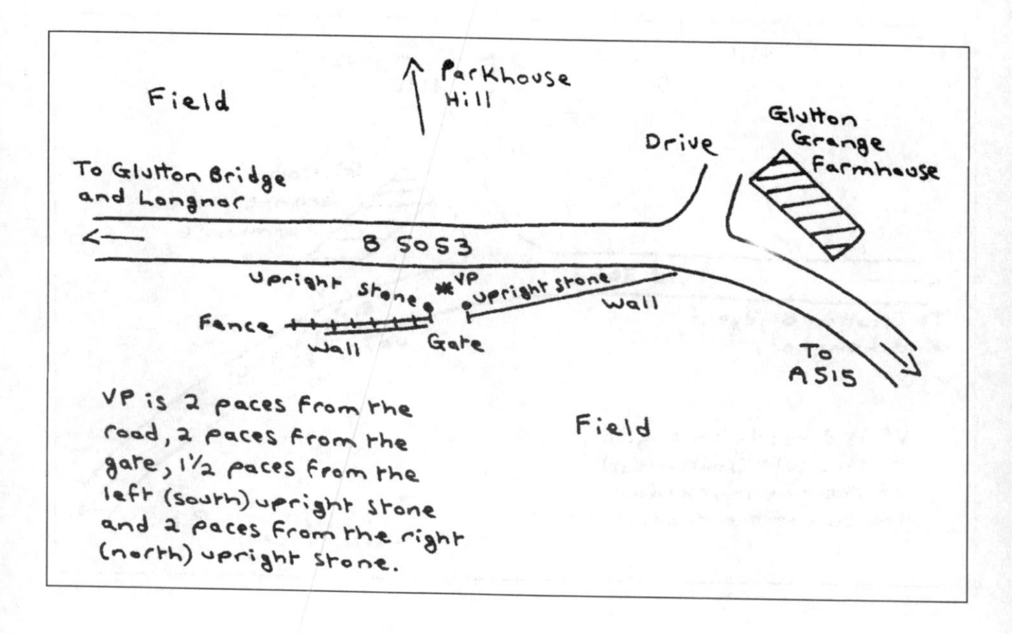

PARKHOUSE HILL: No. 2, 16 SEPTEMBER 1999

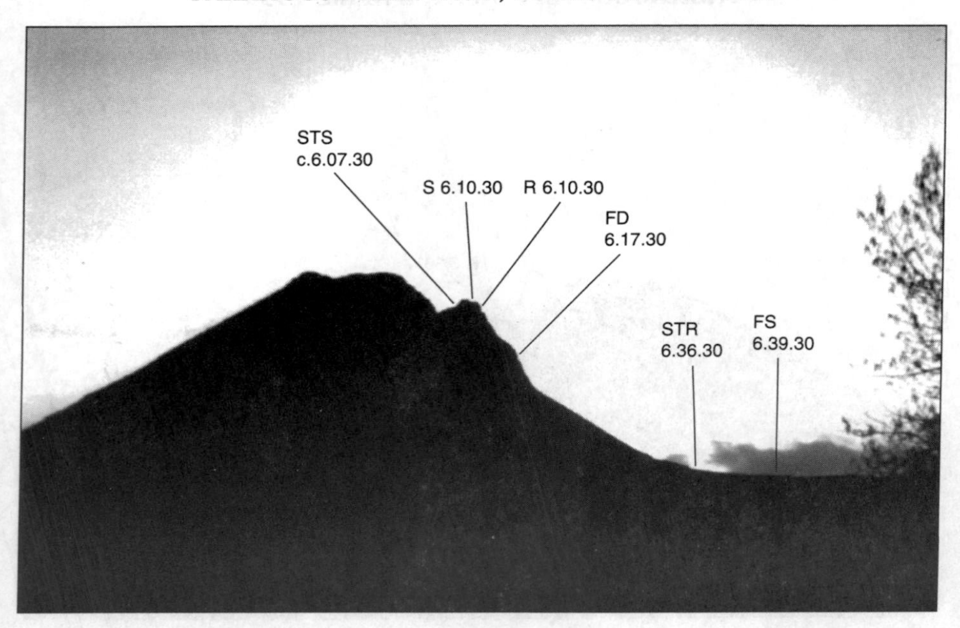

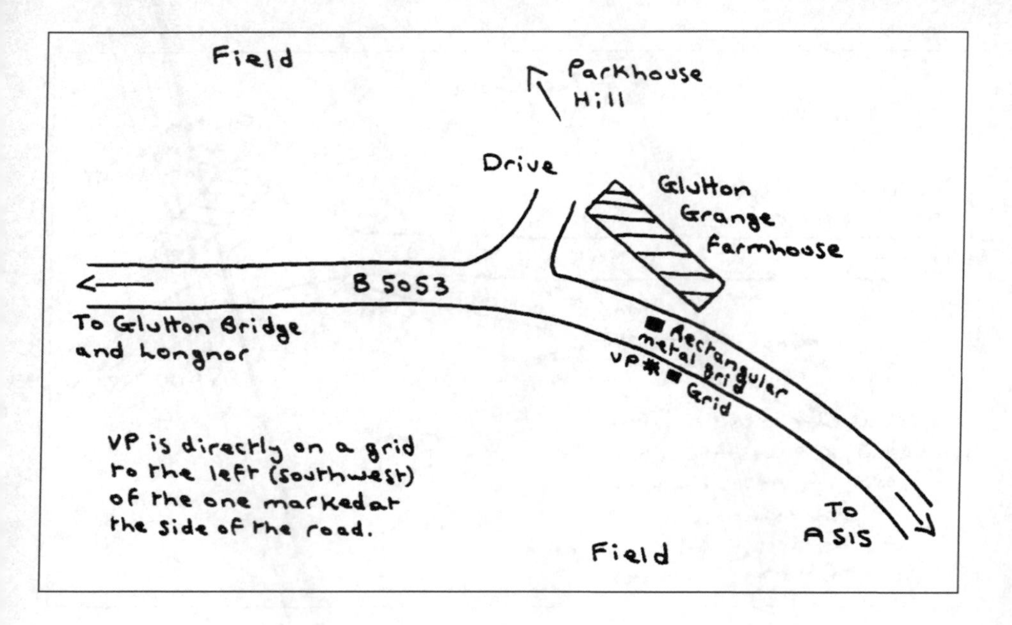

THORPE CLOUD: 17 JUNE 2000

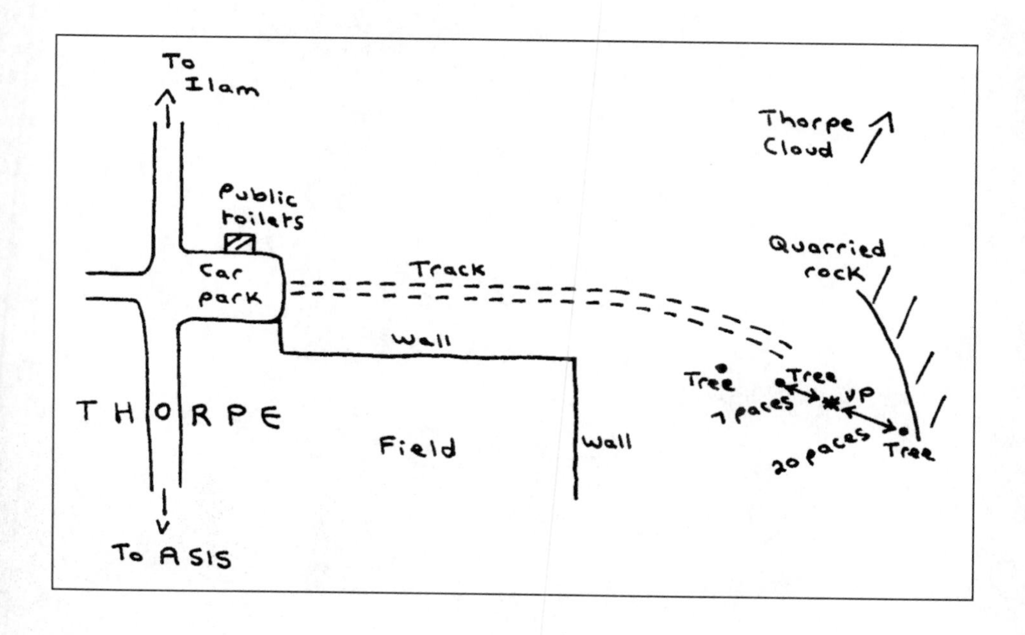